Hesperornis,—a wingless, toothed, diving bird, about five feet in length, which inhabited the great seas during the Cretaceous period, some four millions of years ago.

THE BIRD

ITS FORM AND FUNCTION

by C. WILLIAM BEEBE

WITH A NEW INTRODUCTION BY
DEAN AMADON
Lamont Curator of Birds
The American Museum of Natural History

DOVER PUBLICATIONS, INC., NEW YORK

Published in Canada by General Publishing Company, Ltd., 30 Lesmill Road, Don Mills, Toronto, Ontario.

.

This Dover edition, first published in 1965, is an unabridged and unaltered republication of the work first published by Henry Holt and Company in 1906.

A new Preface has been written by Dean Amadon, Lamont Curator of Birds, The American Museum of Natural History, specially for this Dover edition.

The frontispiece was reproduced in color in the original edition, but appears in black-and-white in this Dover reprint.

Library of Congress Catalog Card Number: 65-26074

Manufactured in the United States of America

Dover Publications, Inc.
180 Varick Street
New York, N. Y. 10014

PREFACE TO THE DOVER EDITION

Charles William Beebe died in 1962 at his tropical research station, Simla, in Trinidad. Like Ernest Thompson Seton, he was an impresario among naturalists, not as fully valued sometimes by his colleagues as by the general public, which avidly read the succession of fluently written volumes that flowed from his pen. But again like Seton, William Beebe found time for works of major importance. His four-volume folio *Monograph of the Pheasants* perhaps outshines any other ornithological work produced by an American, save only Audubon's great elephant folio tomes.

The Bird: Its Form and Function, published as long ago as 1906, was, I believe, only the second of Beebe's twenty-three books. The approach is perfectly straightforward with chapters on The Skull, The Senses, Heads and Necks, and so forth. The abundant illustrations are in large part from the files of the New York Zoological Park, of whose staff Beebe was a lifelong member. In other hands, the plan of the book might have led to a static or old-fashioned anatomical approach, but Beebe was nothing if not imaginative, and his point of view is always comparative and evolutionary.

The extensive, detailed information that Beebe packed into this book is for the most part of the kind that does not change or lose its importance. The amateur naturalist will find *The Bird* to be a mine of information. The professional biologist, too, will profit by reading it.

DEAN AMADON

New York
May, 1965

DEDICATED
IN GRATITUDE AND ESTEEM
TO
Professor Henry Fairfield Osborn
BY HIS FORMER PUPIL
THE AUTHOR

PREFACE

WE find to-day some thirteen or fourteen thousand different forms, or species, of birds upon the earth. For many years ornithologists have laboured to name, and to arrange in some rational order, these multitudinous forms of bird life. Some such arrangement is, of course, a necessity—without a handle we should indeed be handicapped in studying a bird; but let us not forget that classification is but a means to an end.

Far too many students of birds follow some such mode of procedure as this: When a new bird is found, it is shot, labelled, preserved in a collection and forgotten; or, if studying the bird with a glass, all effort is centred in finding some characteristic by which it can be named, and, succeeding in this, search is at once made for still another species, whose name can in turn be added to a list. Observing the habits, the courtship and nest-building, and memorizing the song, is a third phase of bird-study— the best of all three methods; but few indeed have ever given a moment's thought to the bird *itself*.

I have lectured to an audience of teachers, every one of whom was able to identify fifty birds or more, but not one among them knew the significance of the scales on a bird's foot. It is to bridge this gap that this book is intended—an untechnical study of the bird in the abstract. This, it seems to me, is the logical phase of bird life, which, with an earnest nature-lover, should follow the handbook of identification—the study of the physical life of the bird itself preceding the consequent phase of the mental life, with its ever-varying outward expression.

Far from considering this treatment exhaustive, one must remember that any chapter subject could easily be elaborated into one or more volumes. I have intended the book more as an invitation than aught else: for each to observe for himself the marvellously fascinating drama of evolution; to pass on from the nature stories of idealized composite animals and birds to the consideration of the evolution of all life; to the tales of time and truth which have been patiently gleaned by the life-long labours of thousands of students.

Whenever possible I have illustrated a fact with a photograph from a preparation or from a living bird, believing that, where verbal exposition fails, pictorial interest will often fix a fact in the memory. First of all we must consider a few of the more important and significant of the bird-forms of past ages; because no one who is interested in living birds from any standpoint should be entirely ignorant of a few facts concerning the ancestors of these creatures. Otherwise it is as if one, entirely ignoring the rest of the plant, studied certain leaves and flowers, knowing not whether they came from tree or vine.

In my treatment of the various phases of the bird's physical life I have been considerably influenced by the many questions which I have heard asked by visitors to the New York Zoological Park. The short list of books in the Appendix will indicate the sources whence much more detailed information may be obtained by those who desire it.

Some two dozen of the illustrations are from outside sources, and for permission to use these I am indebted to Dr. William T. Hornaday, the American Museum of Natural History, Prof. A. Smith-Woodward, Prof. R. S. Lull, A. E. Brown, Esq., Mr. R. H. Beebe, Mr. T. H. Jackson, Mr. Harold Whealton, and Mr. E. H. Baynes; and for the use of specimens to Dr. F. A. Lucas, Dr. Robert Ridgway, and Dr. Jonathan Dwight, Jr. Unless otherwise indicated, the illustrations were taken by the author.

The work of Mr. Walter King Stone in the painting for the frontispiece and a number of text cuts is gratefully acknowledged; and for the skilful printing of many of the photographs my thanks are due to Mr. E. R. Sanborn.

To my wife, for constant and valuable help, criticism, and suggestion in all departments of the book, I render my sincere appreciation.

To take a few dead facts and clothe them with the living interest which will make them memorable and full of meaning to any lover of birds, and at the same time to keep them acceptable in tenor and truth to the most critical scientist—this has been my aim.

A few chapters of this volume have already appeared in print in "Outing," "Bird-Lore," and the "New York Evening Post."

C. W. B.

New York Zoological Park, May, 1906.

CONTENTS

THE BIRD

CHAPTER I

ANCESTORS

WITH the exception of Astronomy, the science which most powerfully dominates our imagination is Palæontology, or the study of the life of bygone ages. Of all things in Nature, the stars symbolize absolute immensity, their distances stretching out beyond our utmost calculation. So the revelations of Palæontology take us far beyond the sciences of life on the earth to-day, and open vistas of time reaching back more than five-hundred-fold the duration of the sway of mankind. Fossil bones—philosophically more precious than any jewels which Mother Earth has yielded—are the only certain clews to the restoration of the life of past ages, millions of years before the first being awakened into human consciousness from the sleep of the animal mind.

Until recently, Palæontology has been popularly considered one of the dryest and most uninteresting of the 'ologies, but now that the fossil collections in our museums are being arranged so logically and so interestingly, the most casual lover of Nature can read as he runs some of the "poems hidden in the bones." As Professor Huxley once said, "Palæontology is simply the biology of the past, and a fossil animal differs only in this regard from a stuffed one, that the one has been dead longer than the other, for ages instead of for days."

A great many more fossil mammals and reptiles have been discovered than birds, and the reason may perhaps be conjectured. The bones and bodies of birds were in former times as now very light, and if death occurred on the water, the body would float and probably be devoured by some aquatic reptile. Then, again, when some cataclysm of nature or change of climate obliterated whole herds and even races of terrestrial creatures, the birds would escape by flight, and when death eventually came, they would be stricken, not in flocks, but singly and in widely scattered places as to-day.

For perhaps a million years in the past, birds have changed scarcely at all,—the bones of this period belonging to the species or at least genera of living birds. But in the period known as the Cretaceous, when the gigantic *Dinosaurs* flourished and those flying reptile-dragons— the *Pterodactyls*—flapped through the air, a few remains of birds have been found. Some of these are so complete that almost perfect skeletons have been set up, enabling us vividly to imagine how the bird looked when swimming through the waters of our globe, or flying through the air, perhaps four millions of years ago.

The most remarkable peculiarity of these birds was the possession of teeth. Two of the most well-known examples are called *Ichthyornis* and *Hesperornis*. The bones of these birds were discovered by Professor Marsh imbedded in the rocks of western Kansas, and they are now preserved in the museum of Yale University. Professor Marsh tells us that *Hesperornis*, the Bird of the

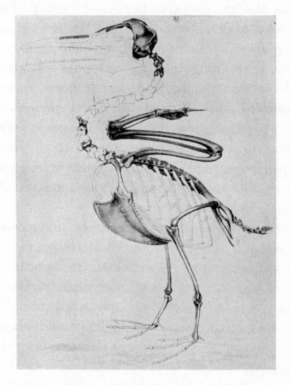

Fig. 1.—Restored skeleton of *Ichthyornis* (after Marsh). 1/2 natural size.

West, "was a typical aquatic bird, and in habit was doubtless very similar to the loon, although, flight being impossible, its life was probably passed entirely upon the water, except when visiting the shore for the purpose of breeding. The nearest land at that time was the suc-

cession of low islands which marked the position of the
present Rocky Mountains. In the shallow tropical sea,
extending from this land five hundred miles or more to
the eastward, and to unknown limits north and south,
there was the greatest abundance and variety of fishes,
and these doubtless constituted the main food of the
present species. *Hesperornis*, as we have seen, was an
admirable diver; while the long neck, with its capabilities
of rapid flexure, and the long slender jaws armed with
sharp recurved teeth, formed together a perfect instrument for the capture and retention of the most agile fish.
The lower jaws were united in front only by cartilage,
as in serpents, and had on each side a joint which admitted
of some motion, so the power of swallowing was doubtless equal to almost any emergency."

Hesperornis had numerous teeth set in grooves like
those of serpents and crocodiles, but in *Ichthyornis* ('Fish-
bird,' so called because its vertebræ are biconcave like
those of a fish) the teeth were in separate sockets as in
alligators. The latter bird was not large, being about
the size of a pigeon, and it had well-developed wings.

It is interesting to compare *Hesperornis* with the
group of penguins, both being highly specialized, although
i.i ways so different, for an almost wholly aquatic life.
Hesperornis swam by strong strokes of its great webbed,
or lobed, toes, its wings dangling uselessly for generation after generation, until all trace, save a vestigial
humerus, of their bony support disappeared. Penguins,
however, make but little use of their feet in swimming,
only occasionally aiding the tail in steering; but they

literally fly through the water by means of their flipper-like wings.

The large size of the leg and toe bones of *Hesperornis* shows that great speed was attainable in the water,

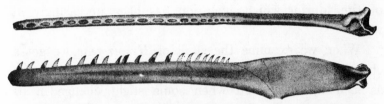

Fig. 2.—Lower jaw of *Ichthyornis* (after Marsh).   4/5 natural size.

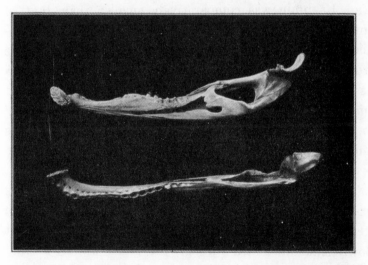

Fig. 3.—Lower jaw of Alligator.   1/6 natural size.   The teeth are set in distinct sockets both in the extinct bird and in the living reptile.

while only a single bone remained to show where the wings of its ancestors were situated.   It is doubtful if it could stand erect upon land, being in this respect more helpless even than a grebe.   Its nest, if it made one, must have been at the very edge of the shore, from which it could wriggle or push itself with its powerful toes into the water. The thought of the untold generations of birds which must have preceded this toothed, wingless, feathered being, makes the mind falter at the vast stretches of time during which evolution has been unceasingly at work.

When we examine the skull of *Hesperornis* we get a clew to the reason why this great creature, nearly as large as a man, succumbed when some slight change in its environment called for new adjustments in its habits of life. Its brain was comparatively smaller than that of any existing bird; and this absence of brain power implied a total lack of that ingenuity, so prominent in the crow, which, when man alters the face of the land, changes its habits, and with increasing wit holds its own against guns and traps.

When *Hesperornis* passed, it was succeeded by birds much smaller in size but of greater wit—loons and grebes —which hold their own even to the present day.

When in the depth of the winter, a full hundred miles from the nearest land, one sees a loon in the path of the steamer, listens to its weird, maniacal laughter, and sees it slowly sink downward through the green waters, it truly seems a hint of the bird-life of long-past ages.

We must now pass back, as nearly as can be estimated, over two millions of years, through the ages when the *Iguanodonts* and *Megalosaurs* lived, long before the first serpents had evolved and about the time when the first timid forerunners of the mammals made their appearance,—tiny insect-eating creatures which were fated to remain so long subordinate to the masterful giant reptiles. This was about the middle of the Jurassic period, and in deposits of this epoch have been found remains of the very first birds of which we know anything.

Two specimens have been discovered and named *Archæopteryx* (ancient-winged-creature). From these two little stone slabs, one in the British Museum and the other at Berlin, we know that these birds were about the size of a crow. Instead of the broad, fan-shaped tail of modern birds, the tail of the *Archæopteryx* was a long, jointed affair like that of a lizard, and was fringed with large feathers—a pair growing from each of the twenty joints. The wings were not large, and instead of the fingers being concealed by feathers, there were three entirely free digits, each armed with a claw, in front of each wing. The skin-covered jaws were furnished with teeth, but the feet and legs were much like those of an ordinary crow.

Taken all in all, this was a most wonderful discovery, linking birds and reptiles together, and proving beyond all dispute the fact of their common origin. Perhaps the most surprising fact was the remarkable development of the plumage of the wings and tail, showing that perfect feathers were in existence at least six millions of years ago.

In the rocks deposited in very ancient epochs are found many footprints which were supposed to be those of huge birds, but it is more probable that they were made by certain three-toed reptiles which, like birds, walked or hopped on two feet. Indeed Nature seems to have made several abortive attempts to produce bird-like creatures before she struck the right adjustments. *Pterodactyls* failed to become birds because they depended on a broad web of skin, like the wing of a bat, thus missing the all-necessary feather-ideal; *Dinosaurs* began at the wrong end, learning to stand on their hind feet and to hop, but never the delights of flight. These offshoots sooner or later were forced to the wall, but *Archæopteryx* seems to have been very near the true line of descent.

But after all, what a meagre record we have of the untold myriads of generations of birds which have succeeded each other through ages past! It is to be hoped that many more fossils may be discovered, for the hints given us in the anatomy of birds, and the glimpses of past history which flash out from the development of the chick within the egg,—all this evidence is becoming ever more and more clouded and illegible.

Having learned that birds are descended from a reptile-like ancestor, it is interesting to search among living reptiles for the one which most resembles birds, and we have no choice but to select the alligator—cold-blooded, scaly, bound to the earth though he is. A second near relation is to be found in the group of long-extinct *Dinosaurs*. A complete record of past ages would show the ancestral stems of alligators, *Dinosaurs*, and birds gradually approaching each other until somewhere, at some time, they were united in a common stock. But we must guard against the notion that birds are descended from any group of living reptiles; which is as fallacious an idea as that we Americans trace our direct descent from

FIG. 4.—*Archæopteryx* preserved in the British Museum. The pelvic girdle, leg and tail show best in this specimen. 1/5 natural size.

9

the Chinese, or that mankind is descended from the chimpanzee or gorilla.

For the purpose of making more clear and interesting the ways in which birds have become especially adapted to their surroundings and needs, we may consider *Archæopteryx* as resembling closely the typical original bird-type from which all others have at least indirectly evolved; and thus having obtained a definitely fixed starting-point, we may consider how some of the more representative birds of the present day came to acquire their widely differing structure and characteristics.*

The tree of evolution of reptiles may be compared to a growth where several great trunks spring from the ground close together, towering up separately but equally high; the topmost twigs of which are represented by the living species of serpents, turtles, lizards, and crocodiles respectively. A very different arboreal structure is presented in the genealogical tree of the Class of birds. Here, from a short trunk, we have many radiating branches, widely spreading and with thickly massed twigs, confusedly intermingled; so slight are the divergences between adjoining groups and so equally do almost all share between them various reptilian characteristics.

It is not necessary to concern ourselves now with the processes of evolution, especially as scientists are still in doubt as to the exact methods. Let us read our Darwin, and hope for another, philosophically as great, to com-

* There are one or two reasons for regarding *Archæopteryx* as merely the tip of a parallel branch, but one sprouting close to the base of the avian tree.

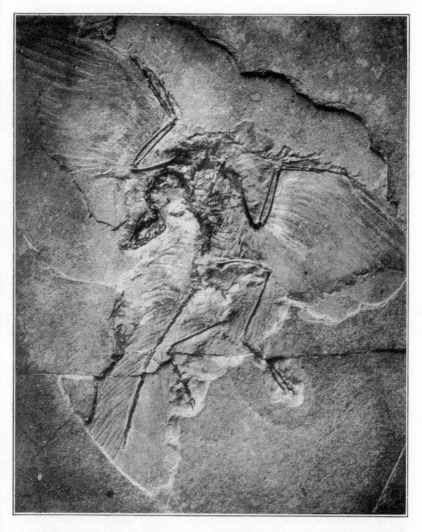

FIG. 5.—*Archæopteryx* preserved in the Berlin Museum. The skull, vertebræ, forelimbs and flight-feathers are remarkably distinct. 1/3 natural size.

plete the work, meanwhile adding our own mite of truthful observation to swell the whole, and help prepare the way for this other. For even Darwin's theory of evolution was but the consummation of theories of former years and centuries,—beginning with Thales and Anaximander, in the days of early Grecian civilization: indeed Aristotle, coming but two hundred years later, is the only name in the history of zoology worthy of a place with that of Darwin.

From the fragmentary evidence afforded by *Archæopteryx* we may conclude that this Bird of Old had a short, blunt, skinny bill of moderate size, furnished with teeth which would enable the owner to feed upon Jurassic berries and fruit, or more probably a carnivorous diet of lizards and insects. Its wings were weak, hinting that it was a flutterer rather than a true flyer, perhaps only scaling like a flying squirrel from the summit of one tree to the base of the next. Even this would give it an immense advantage over its terrestrial and arboreal non-flying enemies. The three free fingers on each wing would allow it to climb easily, to pry into crevices for insects, or to draw a berry-laden branch close to its bill.

Doubtless it frequently walked or ran on all fours, the more probably from its weak-loined condition,—the bones of the thigh-girdle not being fused together as in modern birds. Its tail has already been mentioned—a long double-feathered appendage, composed of a score of little vertebræ jointed together,—as we will later see the true forerunner of the modern fan-like tails. Its

FIG. 6.—Restoration of *Archæopteryx* (adapted from Smit). Notice the teeth, three fingers, and lizard-like tail.

13

feet and legs were little different from those of perching birds of to-day, with strong toes well adapted to cling to a branch. Finally, from a cast of the brain, which fortunately was found with one of the fossils, we know that, although small, it was that of a true quick-witted bird. As yet science has no more to tell us.

Our fancy may add an archaic attempt at song—a lizard's croak touched with the first harmony, which was to echo through all the ages to follow; we may also imagine, if we will, leathery eggs deposited in a rotten knot-hole of a Jurassic conifer.

In both islands of New Zealand well-preserved remains of giant birds have been discovered, to which has been given the name of moas. One species must have reached a height of ten or eleven feet, which would make it tower above the largest living ostrich. They were, in fact, not unrelated to these latter birds and, like them, were flightless (in some cases absolutely wingless), and they had great massive feet and legs. Native legends among the Maoris hint that these birds were in existence during the last few centuries before the coming of the white men.

In South America also, giant birds lived in ages past. One, the *Phororhacos*, stood seven to twelve feet in height, with a head and beak like that of a gigantic eagle. Unlike all eagles, however, this bird could not fly and doubtless ran down its prey, as a chicken runs down a grasshopper.

It is an interesting fact that in South America there lives to-day a bird known as the Seriema, which is prob-

ably at least an indirect descendant of the *Phororhacos*.
The Seriema defies exact classification, sharing characters
of cranes, bustards, and eagles. Its beak and inner
claw are like those of a bird of prey, while in form of
body, and in the other claws of the toes, and in the legs
it is crane-like. One of these birds which I have observed for years in captivity is as gentle and as fearless
as a bird can be. It will chase insects and field-mice
outdoors in the Zoological Park, and will occasionally
stalk solemnly into my office and, coming close to my
desk, watch me closely. It has most beautiful gray-
blue eyes, with long eyelashes (Fig. 199), and if the
birds of past ages were as comely and as lovable as this
interesting species, I regret that only their fossil bones
are left to us. As the Seriema runs down and kills a
mouse, so the giant *Phororhacos*, doubtless, overtook
and slew creatures as large as a deer. Its skull (Fig. 7)
is drawn to the same scale as that of the living Seriema
(Fig. 8).

The evolution which has gone on since these epochs
of old, bringing into being the wonderfully varied forms
of penguin, ostrich, albatross, peacock, and hummingbird, may be summed up in two words which it is well
to know and remember,—Adaptive Radiation. This is
the spreading out or radiating of bird-forms descended
from the ancient stem, into all parts of the earth, each
coming into contact with a particular environment, to
adjust itself to which, its various organs and parts exer-
cise different functions, until the friction of the "struggle
for existence" has moulded each to its particular niche.

If its lines lie in happy places, its race is established, and it pursues and flees, it fights and plays, it sings with joy or pants with fear, and Evolution marks another success in its inexorable movement onward and upward, —a new species is born!

Earth has few secrets from the birds. With wings and legs there is hardly a spot to which they cannot and indeed have not penetrated. Some find food and contentment in the desolate wastes of the far North; others spend almost all of their life on or above the sea far from

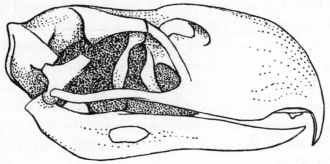

Fig. 7.—Skull of *Phororhacos*, drawn to scale with Fig. 8. 1/6 natural size.

land; thousands revel in the luxuriance of reeking tropical jungles; a lesser number are as perfectly suited to the blazing dust of the desert; and there are birds which burrow deep into the very earth itself. Day and night; heat and cold; water, earth, and air, have all been conquered by the thirteen or fourteen thousand species of birds which share the earth with us at the present day.

These brethren of ours, whose clans have so bravely conquered the dangers of millions of years, and at last have gained a foremost rank in the scale of living crea-

tures, now find themselves face to face with the culmi-
nating effort of Nature,—Mankind. They cannot escape

FIG. 8.—Seriema, a living descendant of *Phororachos*, with characters of Cranes,
Bustards, and Eagles. 1/6 natural size.

from us, though the least among them laughs to scorn
our efforts at following through the air. Yet all must

return sooner or later to earth for rest and food, and thus all are at our mercy.

Let us beware of needlessly destroying even one of the lives—so sublimely crowning the ages upon ages of evolving; and let us put forth all our efforts to save a threatened species from extinction; to give hearty aid to the last few individuals pitifully struggling to avoid absolute annihilation.

The beauty and genius of a work of art may be reconceived, though its first material expression be destroyed; a vanished harmony may yet again inspire the composer; but when the last individual of a race of living beings breathes no more, another heaven and another earth must pass before such a one can be again.

A list of all the structures of animals which are products of the outer layer alone would be a long and surprising one, and we would be very ready to grant the importance of skin. Such an enumeration would include all claws and talons, nails and teeth, the rattles of a snake, spurs, hairs, the scales of fishes and reptiles,

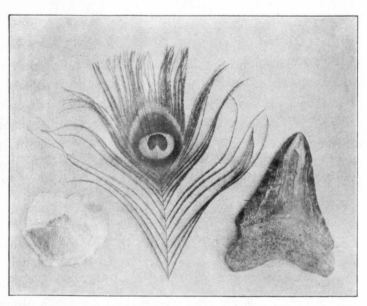

Fig. 9.—Tarpon-scale, shark-tooth, and peacock-feather; showing diversity of structure derived from the skin alone. 1/2 natural size.

spines, whalebone, beaks and feathers. Even the horn of a rhinocerus is only a solid mass of agglutinated hairs, while as the antithesis to this may be mentioned all down and feathers: the tiniest fluff from a humming-bird to the great pinion of a condor.

If we examine a newly hatched dove or sparrow, the little, ugly, sprawling creature, at first glance, seems

CHAPTER II

FEATHERS

ANY definitions of the Class of birds h[ave]
given, but all fall short in some parti[cular or]
are weak in having exceptions. FEAT[HERS is]
the one word which always holds true. All bi[rds have]
feathers, and nowhere else in the world are simil[ar struc]tures found. A feather, like an egg, is perfe[ct in its]
adaptation to the bird's requirements, and also, [like an]
egg, its structure is rather complicated.

Structure and Development

First let us look at the skin itself in which the [feathers]
grow. To skin a bird is an easy matter, for t[he skin]
or integument as it is called, is very slightly [attached]
to the muscles underneath. The skin of a dove i[s just]
like tissue-paper, and tears so easily that it is a [wonder]
how the hundreds of feathers find a sufficiently [firm]
attachment. Thin as is this skin, it is made up [of many]
separate layers, but in order to make our feath[er study]
enjoyable by not overburdening it with too many [terms,]
we will consider only the two more important la[yers of]
the skin—a deeper one, the dermis, and an oute[r, more]
horny covering, the epidermis.

to be entirely naked; but a closer inspection shows
scanty tufts of down scattered irregularly over the body.
This, like the set of milk-teeth in mammals, is useful
only for a time, and is later pushed out by the second
or true plumage. Even more numerous than the down-

Fig. 10.—Brown Pelican nestlings, showing feather papillæ on body and wings.
About 1/4 natural size.

tufts are little pimples or dots, many hundreds of which
cover certain parts of the skin. Each of these will eventually give rise to a perfect feather—quill, vane, barbs,
and all.

The under layer of skin, or dermis, is very thin in
birds, much more so than in reptiles and other animals.

The first intimation of the appearance of a feather, or of down, is shown by a thickened group, or pimple, of cells in this under layer of skin, which grows and presses upward toward the outer layer—the epidermis. This is exactly the way in which the scales of fishes and reptiles begin to form; and if, at this stage, the tiny projection should flatten out, the shining scale of a carp, the armor

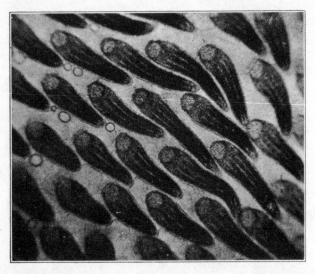

Fig. 11.—Sprouting feathers of a 12-day embryo chick. Magnified 25 diameters.

of an alligator, or the cobble-scale of an iguana lizard might result. Indeed, in the feathers of a penguin we find transition stages of flat, almost unsplit feather-scales; while on the legs and feet of birds are reptile-like scales.

The evolution of scales, hair, and feathers is a most interesting problem, most of the details of which are beyond the scope of this work. Suffice it to say that

in sharks, which are among the most primitive forms of
fishes, the skin is covered with tiny denticles or spines,
which consist of enamel and dentine, and which rest on
small bony plates. This form of scale is the most ancient
known, and the hint of teeth which the description con-
veys is not misleading; for we find that in some of these
voracious fishes the spines in the skin become enlarged
near the edge of the mouth, merging imperceptibly into
the rows of cruel teeth which, to a certain extent, are
homologous with the teeth of all higher animals. In
other fishes the denticles become flattened scales, and
many of these fish have teeth of corresponding plate-
like form. So it is interesting to know that the scales of
fishes and reptiles, the feathers of birds, and the teeth
of animals have all evolved from skin structures which
at an early stage of growth bear considerable resemblance
to each other.

But, in our young bird, the slender finger of cells
which reaches upward, and whose base at the same time
sinks deeply into the dermis, does not broaden out, but
splits longitudinally into a number of folds, which gradually dry apart and harden into the slender, silky fila-
ments which we know collectively as down.

At the base of, and in fact attached to, the little projection which gives rise to the nestling down is a small
circular body of cells, which grows but little while the
down plumage is serving its use; but when the bird is
ready for a coat of true feathers this lower cellular mass
begins to grow upward into a second finger, or column,
of cells, pushing the base of the down feather out of its

socket. This growth continuing, the down is lifted clear
of the skin, being supported on the new structure, and

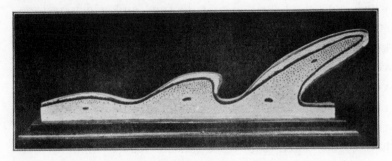

Fig. 12.—Early stages in the development of a down feather, showing close
resemblance to scale of fish or reptile.

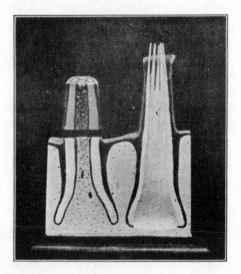

Fig. 12a.—Later stages of Fig. 12, showing the first splitting up of the
feather pulp.

soon brushed off and lost. Thus, little by little, in
shreds and tatters, the baby plumage is shed and replaced

by true feathers, which overlap, protecting the body from heat and cold, dust and rain.

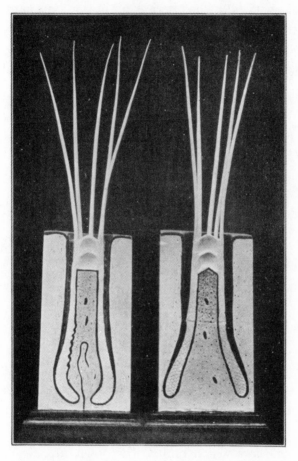

FIG. 12b.—Last stages in the formation of a down feather, showing the plumes well above the surface of the skin, as in a newly hatched chick. All greatly enlarged.

At the time of the first moult, this succession of feathers can be observed in almost any young bird, being more noticeable in large species, which have very thick or lengthened down, as gulls and ducks. A Red-winged Blackbird, or for that matter almost any passerine nestling, looks very odd when it rises up in the nest, gaping for food; the long gray streamers of down waving like an aureole around its head. In some water-birds this nestling down retains its usefulness for nearly two months.

Fig. 13.—Feather from the head of a young Bobolink, with down still attached to its tip. Twice natural size.

The feathers which replace the down are, when they first appear above the skin, rolled tightly and bound up in the thin tissue of the horny sheaths, so that they resemble a bundle of withes wrapped together in a cloth. In many young birds the feathers remain in this condition until they are nearly full grown, and a young cuckoo or kingfisher is a curious-looking object, most of the bird's body seeming to be tiled with small, bluish sticks.

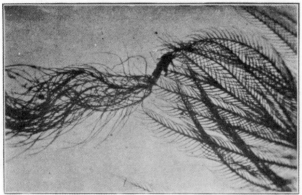

FIG. 14.—Tip of feather from the crown of a young Song Sparrow, showing connection with down. Magnified 25 diameters.

FIG. 15.—Duck Hawk moulting into juvenal plumage, with the natal down coming away in shreds and tatters. 1/4 natural size.

When the folds of the developing feathers are sufficiently dry, they burst their sheaths and rapidly spread out.

The appearance of a young kingfisher or heron may be completely changed within a few hours time, so quickly and simultaneously does the first suit of feathers unroll.

The condition of young birds when hatched varies greatly in birds of different groups. Nestlings are, in many ways, like human babies, and there are as many differences in the one class as there are in the other,

FIG. 16.—Growth of an Ostrich feather from sheath to plume. 1/5 natural size.

between those from different countries, only Nature does for the little birds what parents do for the babies.

We see American babies wrapped in furs and blankets, wheeled in carriages, and rocked to sleep; while a tiny savage is strapped tightly to its mother's back, and as soon as possible allowed to run where it pleases, find its own toys and develop its little muscles, gaining a degree of health and strength which many a civilized child would envy. So with birds, the highest—such as crows and thrushes—are hatched almost naked and must be warmed

and cuddled and fed for many weeks, before they learn
to take care of themselves; while birds lower in the
scale—as our quail—are born covered thickly with
down and with wings nearly feathered, and in a few days
can fly and find their own food.

So a bird naked at birth is very helpless, one covered
with down is more capable of taking care of itself, while

FIG. 17.—Nestling Kingfisher with feathers still in their sheaths.
2/3 natural size.

the few which are completely feathered when hatched
may be said to have no chickhood except in the egg.

In the Crested Screamer (Fig. 264) the down-like
character of the body-feathers of the adult birds may be
a hint of the plumage of very ancient types of birds such
as *Archæopteryx*.

Now we are ready to begin our study of the perfect
feather itself, and we will, for once, have to disregard
our rule of starting with the simpler form—the scale of

a reptile—and working up to a feather; for, if we except
the down, there seems to be no connecting link left.

Fig. 18.—Young Brown Pelicans; hatched naked and helpless (altricial).
1/4 natural size.

Fig. 19.—Young Red Jungle Fowl one day old; hatched covered with down and
able within a few hours to help itself (precocial).   Almost natural size.

Although that old, old fossil bird *Archæopteryx*
still retained reptile-like teeth, fingers and tail, it had

feathers which were apparently as perfect as any we may examine to-day. When some form of scale had once changed so that it was of use in flight, the hollow elastic vane took first place at once, and all intermediate stages, which perhaps had been acquired merely for warmth, went to the wall. A creature could have flight if provided with perfect feathers, or it could retain its scales and find existence possible along the old reptilian planes of life, but no awkward scale-flutterer could long be tolerated. All through the evidences of evolution we find instances like this,—a change for the better beginning slowly, through many channels, then the one best suited forging ahead with inconceivable swiftness, and crushing out all other less adapted structures. Hence the rarity of "missing links."

Feathers are certainly among the most beautiful objects in Nature; and when we learn a little about their structure, they will be still more interesting. No matter how closely we may examine them, with hand-lens or microscope, their beauty and perfection of structure only increase. If we study a feather, say from the wing of a pigeon, we see that its whole structure is subservient to two characteristics—lightness and strength. What wonderful elasticity it has! We can bend the tip so that it touches the base and it will spring back into shape without breaking.

If we look closely, we will see that each feather is composite—feathers within feathers. The quill gives off two rows of what are called barbs which together form the vane of the feather; each of these barbs has two rows of barbules, and these give rise to a series of curved hooks, known as barbicels, which work into opposite series of grooves, so tightly that air cannot force its way through the feather. When the wings are pressed downward, the phenomenon flight is made possible by the accumulated resistance which the flight-feathers offer to the air. At the lower end of our pigeon's feather, barbicels are present only near the quill. Therefore the

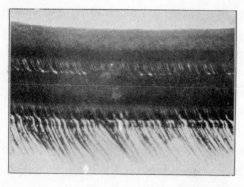

FIG. 20.—Two interlocked barbs from the vane of a Condor's wing-feather, showing barbules and barbicels. Magnified 25 diameters.

tips of the barbs are loose and fluffy, unconnected and useless for flight. This is the condition in all down and in the feathers of the ostrich and cassowary. We might naturally think that feathers stiffened by so many close rows of interlocking barbicels would be useful in many ways beside flight. But fluffy feathers are evidently just as efficient in keeping warmth in and rain out as the other kind; so Nature, economical to the most microscopic degree, has lessened the number of, or has never provided, barbules and barbicels wherever a feather is not needed for flight or steering.

The two lines of barbs which grow out on each side of the quill are very elastic and so intimately hooked to each other that they will bend some distance before separating. If we ever tried to force our way through a

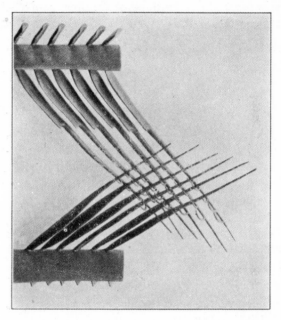

Fig. 21.—Model showing interlocking barbules and barbicels of feather, greatly enlarged.

bramble of sweet-brier or blackberry-vines, we can more readily appreciate how these barbs and the interlocking barbules clutch each other. The thorns in the bramble catch our clothes and, when we move, the elasticity of the long stems tends to make them hold the tighter.

We notice that one line of barbs—that along the inner curve of the quill—is much longer than that on the outer curve and we might think the air would force this upward and escape beyond the edge. So it would, if it were not for the arrangement of the feathers on the wing, which overlap like the tiles on a roof, each vane over-lying and holding down the long barbs of the feather in front, while, above and below, other shorter feathers help to bind the whole tightly, thus enabling the bird at every stroke to whip a wingful of air downward and backward.

A feather and its parts, like all the rest of the bird, is composed of cells—empty and hollow ones in this in-stance, as we can easily see for ourselves by placing a barb from a pigeon's feather in a drop of water and looking at it under a low-power magnifying-lens. The network of horny cells is very plain.

It is a simple matter to say that a feather consists of quill, barb, barbules, etc., but to appreciate the wonder-ful complexity of this structure let us make a little cal-culation. Suppose we have a wing-feather from a com-mon pigeon with a vane about six inches long. If we have patience enough to count the barbs on one side of the quill, we will find there are about six hundred of them. So the vane of the entire feather has twelve hundred of these little side featherlets. One of these, from a narrow part of the vane, will show under the micro-scope about two hundred and seventy-five pairs of bar-bules, which multiplied by the number of barbs on that side amounts to three hundred and thirty thousand. Making a very low estimate of the whole vane, we have nine hundred and ninety thousand separate barbules on this one feather, and when we think of the innumerable

FIG. 22.—Feathers illustrating conditions where barbicels are unnecessary and are hence reduced or entirely lost, causing downiness. 3/5 natural size.

(a) Primary of Pigeon—an important flight-feather; hence possessing a stiff vane. (b) Under wing-covert of a Great Blue Heron; downy portion was overlapped by the adjoining feather. (c) Wing-covert of Owl; the downy edge makes possible the all-important noiseless flight of this bird. (d) Feather of Ostrich; the power of flight being lost, the feathers are downy throughout the entire vane.

finer hooklets, and then the number of feathers on the pigeon's body, we can echo the exclamation of Solomon: "The way of an eagle in the air" is "too wonderful for me!"

Another beautiful adaptation to flight is seen in our

FIG. 23.—Feathers of Condor and Emeu. The aftershaft in the former is reduced to a downy filament at the base of the vane; in the latter it equals the feather itself in size.

feather. The upper part of the wing must of course be perfectly level, with no projections to catch the air and retard motion. So, on the upper side of the feather, we notice that the lines of barbs spring out flush with the flattened quill-top, while below, the shaft projects prominently from the vane. The obliquely forward direction in which the barbs grow, the change in shape of the quill—round where the body or body-feathers conceal it, square where it supports the vane,—and many other niceties which we can each detect for ourselves, show how exquisitely exact is the adaptation of a feather to its uses.

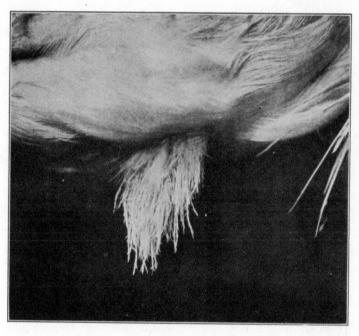

Fig. 24.—Powder-down patch on the breast of a live Great White Heron. 2/3 natural size.

Growing from the under side of the quill, at the beginning of the vane, is a tiny feather known as the aftershaft. In an ordinary down-feather of a young bird this is of considerable size, but it is either small or entirely absent in an ordinary feather. It reaches its greatest development in the emeu and the cassowary, where it is as long and as perfect as the main feather. The origin and use of this feather-double is not known.

Parrots, herons, and some other birds have a most convenient arrangement—a kind of automatic clothes-cleaner and valet combined. Concealed by the long body-plumage are several dense patches of down-feathers which grow quite rapildy, but instead of constantly increasing in length, the tips break up into a fine, white, greasy powder. This works its way through the entire plumage, and is doubtless of use in keeping the feathers in good condition and the body dry. Most of the birds possessing this convenience are comparatively free from lice, so this natural dressing may be as unpleasant to these vermin as camphor-balls are to clothes-moths.

The forms and textures of feathers are innumerable, and the uses to which they are put, more than we would ever imagine, but these will be spoken of under the chapters treating of the different parts of the body where they are found.

Arrangement

In examining a nestling we will notice that the feather-dots are not scattered at random over the surface of the skin, but grow in lines and tracts, whose limits are very sharply defined. In an adult bird, say an English Sparrow, this is even more noticeable. If we part the feathers on the centre of the breast, a broad, bare area is seen, with only a thin scattering of soft downy feathers. Under the wings are other naked spaces, and several more are on other parts of the body. The most ancient birds were probably covered uniformly with scale-feathers, but as these increased in length there was less need for an unbroken covering, the feathers of one portion overlapping and protecting the surrounding parts, and besides, for ease in active motions, bare patches of skin were required.

It has been found that the arrangement of the feathers on a bird's body varies in different groups, and, such variation being rather characteristic of these larger divi-

FIG. 25.—Nestling Crow, showing feathered and infeathered portions of the body (pterylæ and apteria). 1/2 natural size.

sions, pterylosis—as it is called—is of some importance in classification. Penguins only, of existing birds, have feathers growing uniformly on all parts of the body. In the ostrich, which has given up flight and taken to running, the body feathers have grown over almost all the bare spaces which existed in its flying ancestors. There are two marked exceptions due to the present habits of these birds. Like the camel, when resting, these giant birds lean upon their breasts. This portion of the body is provided with a thick, callous pad, which, by constant use, is thus kept bare of feathers. In addition, the under sides of the degenerate wings are also free of plumage, owing no doubt to the continual close application of these organs to the sides of the body. The other bare areas are almost obliterated, but the legs are bare, thus allowing perfect freedom in action.

Some birds, such as vultures and cassowaries, have lost all feathers on the head and neck, or other portions of the body, from various causes, as for cleanliness, or, in some cases, probably for ornament. This will be spoken of more in detail in a later chapter.

Moult

The waste of internal tissues and organs in animals is repaired by means of the blood which brings them fresh material and carries away worn-out cells, as it traverses arteries and veins. Entire parts, as the tails of tadpoles, may even be absorbed; but, in general, skin structures when old and worn out are cast off and renewed from the lower, or derm, layer. This takes place in various ways. The skin, even to the covering of the eyeballs, may come off entire, as is the case among snakes, or portions peel off and tear away, as in lizards. Warm-blooded animals also shed, or cast, their outside covering; mammals shedding their coats of hair, and birds their feathers. In the latter class this process is called moulting.

The nestling down and the feather which replaces it can hardly be considered as separate structures, as the

same channel perforates both and the nutriment pith
which supplies the down traverses the hollow quill of
the succeeding feather. A bird's swaddling-clothes and
his first full dress are cut from the same piece. But when
these perfect feathers reach full size, the aperture at the
base closes, all blood-supply is cut off, and the feather at
the commencement of its usefulness becomes a dead
thing. There is no vital connection between the feathers
of all the following moults. Each is separate, the papilla
or feather-cells reawakening to new activity every time
the process occurs. So when a bird's wing is clipped, no
pain is felt, any more than when a person's hair is cut.
Such feathers are of course not renewed until the succeeding moult. If a feather in a living bird be *pulled out*,
it will be replaced immediately by another, and this will
be repeated as often as the feather is removed.

In cassowaries, each moult is advertised by dangling
streamers of the old plumage still attached to the tips
of the incoming feathers, but this connection is not a
living one, the adult feathers being as lifeless as those of
other birds. As powerful savages often exhibit very
childlike traits, so these great birds are absurdly marked
with what, in other species, are sure signs of recent chickhood.

The changing of plumage of the Brown Pelican is well
shown by the illustrations. The naked young (Fig. 18)
become covered with papillæ (Fig. 10) which soon burst
into a coating of the softest white down (Fig. 36); this
in turn gives place to the juvenile plumage of gray, the
features of the wings and shoulders appearing first (Fig.

37). This is also the winter plumage of the adult birds, both sexes moulting alike into the rich-hued breeding plumage (Fig. 38) of yellow, chocolate, and silver-gray.

The feathers of the entire bird are moulted or fall out naturally at least once a year, and in some cases twice or even three times. If we were asked at what season the

FIG. 26.—Flight-feathers of Chimney Swift clogged with soot, showing necessity for moulting.

principal annual moult would be most likely to occur, the fall of the year would suggest itself, and such is the case, for a number of good reasons.

First, the hardest work which birds have to do, hatching and caring for their young, has, at this season of the year, just been accomplished, and has doubtless told heavily on their plumage. Breast-feathers are worn thin, tails are badly frayed, and wing-pinions are broken and ragged. Two alternatives confront birds at this period. Those species which are to take their migratory flight over hundreds of miles of land and water must have perfect wings and rudders to carry them safely, against contrary winds and sudden accidents. Others which are contented with the food found near their homes, and elect (by the laws of their kind) to remain, must be prepared to withstand the blasts of winter. Their plumage must be abundant and thick to keep out the cold and snow, and to enable them to bury their tender eyes and feet in its warm mass. Otherwise the tiny round fluffs huddled close to the trunks in the evergreens would drop stiffened to the ground during some long winter night. So a renewal of plumage in the fall is most necessary to the life of birds.

A baby robin, secure from most enemies in his nest, with parents to supply his every want, acquires his wing-quills only when his nestling down is shed. He is carefully watched and tended during his first flights, and takes such good care of these flight-feathers that they serve to carry him to his winter home far to the southward. But a brood of a dozen or more little Bob-whites whose wing-feathers sprout with the most marvellous rapidity, from the moment the birds tumble out of their white shells, would fare ill indeed if they had to trust to these nursery quills all the first winter, with hungry foxes sniffing for their scent, and more-to-be-dreaded owls shadowing their trembling covey. Nature has come to their aid, and when they have fairly worn out their wings in the first awkward attempts at flight, new feathers come in, and this succession of quills keeps them in fine flying condition until full grown. Indeed so solicitous is

Mother Nature about the ground-nesters that she puts strength and vigor into the coverts, or upper feathers on the little wings; so that these shoot forth with an energy far beyond what is usual, for a time lending their aid in flight, although they are not true primaries. Later they

Fig. 27.—Iridescent feather from the breast of a Rufous Humming-bird, showing wearing off of the tips of the barbs, caused perhaps by rubbing against the petals of flowers. Magnified 25 diameters.

are far outgrown by the flight primaries, and then function only as protectors of these more important feathers.

The extreme in this precocious development of chicks is found in those strange Australian birds, the mound-builders, which are left from the first to shift for themselves; even the duties of incubation being shirked by the parents. This necessitates a perfect ability on the part of the young birds to take care of themselves as soon as hatched. They pass the entire first moult within the egg itself, and are covered with perfect feathers and fully developed flight-quills when they emerge from the shell. A wild duckling, although provided with a thick waterproof coat of down, has, like the robin, to wait a long time for his flight-feathers; but his aquatic habits and powers of diving make the dangers to which he is exposed far less than is the case with the young Bobwhite.

The causes of wear and disablement to feathers would make a long list if we but knew them all. As one instance take the wings of a Chimney Swift after she has reared her brood in the depths of some blackened chimney, or even a lightning-struck hollow tree. Her primaries are so matted and clogged with balls of soot that she would often find the migratory flight difficult indeed, were the feathers not replaced by new ones.

When birds return from the South, and when a hint of spring warns winter residents to cease their roving, they prepare to develop all the advantages which may in any way aid them in securing a mate. Some industriously practise dance-steps, others flight-evolutions, a larger number rehearse their songs under their breath, while still others passively await the development of plumes, gorgets, spots and splashes of colour which, if the feathers come out large and brilliant, may stand them in as good stead in their wooing as any song or antic. Thus we find a class of birds which have a partial or complete moult in the spring. These feathers may last all summer, or may drop out as soon as begins the hard work of building the nest or feeding the young, with which labor they might interfere.

To return for a moment to the fall moult. If a sparrow or lark should shed all of its large wing-feathers simultaneously, it would have slight hope of ever living long enough for new ones to grow out again. If such defenceless birds were compelled to hop helplessly along

FIG. 28.—Wings of English Sparrow, showing two feathers of each wing being moulted simultaneously.

the ground, weasels and cats would be able to catch hundreds of them without effort. This is avoided in all land birds by the moulting of only a pair of primaries, as the large flight-feathers are called, at a time, one from each wing. This process usually starts with the pair farthest from the front of the wing, and the second pair does not fall out until the first pair of new feathers is nearly of full size. Thus all danger of a crippled flight is avoided.

One of the most interesting phases of Nature is the way she provides for exceptions to what we are pleased to call her laws. Some birds, unlike those mentioned above, shed every primary in their wings at once, so that their angular stump-feathered wings are perfectly useless for flight. In this class are many water birds—ducks, geese, flamingoes, snake-birds and others. Just before this wholesale moulting occurs, a flock of wild ducks will

FIG. 29.—Wing of adult Mallard Duck, with the new set of flight-feathers just appearing.

make their way, by an unfailing instinct, to some large body of water where they can swim and dive in safety and, if need be, never come within reach of enemies on the shore until the new feathers are strong enough to bear them up.

Associated with this temporary disablement is another provision for the safety of certain birds of this class. Our common Mallard Duck, for example, is sometimes compelled to undergo the fall moult in a rather small body of water, where danger menaces on all sides. Although when flightless he swims low among the thick water-reeds, yet his brilliant colours—iridescent green and white—would too frequently mark him out. So the invisible cloak of his brooding mate is dropped over him for a while—his colours vanish, and by a partial moult thus sandwiched in, the hues of his plumage change to an inconspicuous mottling of brown, hardly distinguishable from the female. Then when the splitting of his quill-sheaths hints of coming power to take care of himself again, the dusky mantle is lifted, and, triumphantly treading water, he stands upright and shakes his glistening wings, daring his enemies to catch him if they can. This has been happily termed the "eclipse" plumage. In certain portions of the Old World where foxes are scarce and the ducks have been persistently pursued by men in boats, the knowing birds have changed their habits and, when their wing-quills fall, they make their home in deep woods, finding greater safety there than on ponds or lakes.

A somewhat similar condition occurs in the Black Grouse of Europe, which loses the conspicuous black feathers of the head and neck during the helpless period caused by the moult of its tail-feathers.

This additional moult brings us to the consideration of the birds which have no less than three changes of plumage, and here we find the cause intimately connected with the colour of the birds' surroundings. Ptarmigans, which are species of grouse living in the far North, moult

Fig. 30.—Eclipse plumage of Mallard Duck. Male in full breeding plumage (the brilliant green of the head and neck is lost in the photograph).

Fig. 31.—Male in eclipse plumage during moult of wing-feathers.

Fig. 32.—Female Mallard.

after the breeding season into a special gray or dark plumage, harmonizing well with the autumnal shades of the grass and lichened rocks. In the late fall a second plumage of immaculate white is assumed, affording these birds great protection on the snowy wastes where they

Fig. 33.—Willow Ptarmigan in early spring, with brown feathers beginning to replace the white. 1/4 natural size.

live. In spring a third suit is donned—brown and parti-coloured like the environment, which late in the year is still covered with patches of snow here and there. This too is the nuptial plumage, and lasts until the gray garb completes the cycle of the year's changes. The wing-feathers are white all the year, but when the wings are

closed they telescope so neatly beneath the feathers of
the shoulder that they are not noticeable while the bird
is in either the autumnal or vernal plumage.

As the feathers on the flipper-like wings of a penguin
resemble the scales of reptiles in appearance, so this

FIG. 33a.—Ptarmigan in the fall, showing the gray autumnal plumage (which
has replaced the brown of summer on the upper parts of the body and wings),
gradually giving place to the white of the coming winter feathers. Wild
birds in Alaska. (Harold Whealton, photographer.)

homology is carried out in the method of shedding them.
Unlike the dropping out of feathers one by one, as in
other birds, these come off in flakes, like the skin of a
lizard. The feathers of the back loosen, shrivel up, and
fade to a brownish hue before they peel away.

We have seen how birds, by moulting their feathers, change the colour of their plumage; in some cases several times each year. There is, however, still another way in which the appearance of new colour is brought about. Not by increase of pigment, for the feather when once full grown is dead; but by the mere breaking or fraying

Fig. 34.—The three moults of the Ptarmigan, shown in three individuals.
(Courtesy of American Museum.)

of the edges of each feather. It is thus that the Snow-flake brushes off the rusty trimmings of his winter's suit and returns to his home in the far North, dressed in spick-and-span black and white. A much more familiar example is to be seen at our very doorstep. The cock English Sparrow in midwinter is even more sombrely clad than usual; but as spring approaches, although he can attain to no elaborate song or flowing plume, yet even this commoner feels the call of love for beauty, and day by day the dusty brown tips of his throat-feathers wear away one by one, and leave exposed the clear black centres; and behold, the vulgar frequenter of our streets

FIG. 35.—Two male English Sparrows, showing the difference in colour caused by wear of the feather-tips between October and April.

and alleys, flaunts a jet cravat before the eyes of his lady-love!

Colour.

The very interesting uses which the colours of birds serve, the part they take in courtship, in evading danger, or in enabling birds to find each other, are many. These uses have been much written about, but of the nature and formation of colour less is known. Few of us have

probably ever given a thought to the colours themselves
Why is that feather blue?   Why—because it *is* blue!

There are two principal ways in which colours are
produced in feathers: first, when a real colour-pigment
is present, and again when the structure of the feather is
more or less like miniature prisms in shape, breaking up

Fig. 36.—Young Brown Pelicans in the downy plumage.   1/6 natural size.

the rays—rainbow-like—into the iridescence of the spectrum.   In the case of almost all the beauties of Nature,
the more closely we examine them, the more beautiful
they become.   But this is not true of the iridescent
colours of birds such as hummingbirds, unless we consider the structure.   The colour itself disappears under
the microscope, and only gray or black tints are seen.

The black, red, brown, and yellow colours of feathers

are almost always due to pigment or colouring-matter in
the shaft or vane. If we take a black feather and hold
it to the light, it will still look black; if we pound it with
a hammer, it will not change.

Green is never found as a pigment except in the
feathers of a small family of birds called plantain-eaters
or turacous, which inhabit West Africa. For some time
it was thought that the natives dyed the birds artificially,
as when these birds were kept captive, the magnificent
scarlet patch on the wing would gradually fade and
become a dull gray. It is a fact that this colouring-
matter washes out when the feather is washed in alkaline
water. Even ordinary water will be slightly tinged if the
feather is soaked in it. The pigment contains about ten
per cent of copper, and this can be extracted chemically
in the form of a metallic powder. The plumage of almost
all brightly coloured birds will fade in the course of years,
if the feathers are left exposed to direct sunlight; but, like
photographic plates, the hues of some birds are more sensitive than others to the light. The delicate reds and
yellows on the lower parts of Mexican Trogons are particularly evanescent, and the rose-pink of the African
Fairy Warbler disappears a short time after death.

We might speak of a third class of colours, which are
due to both pigment and structure. For instance, no
blue pigment is known to exist in the feathers of birds,
but blue feathers contain a brown or yellowish pigment
which is encased in the horny coating of the feather.
Between this outer sheath and the underlying pigment
is a layer of many-sided cones or small projections which

have numerous little ridges extending down the sides, and in some way, by reflection, these change the yellow or black to blue. If we take a parrot's feather and pound the blue portion, that colour will disappear and the vane will become black.

It is surprising to see how the colours of many beautiful feathers will vanish when we hold them between our eye and the light. When we look at feathers under the microscope, and see their horny rays, we forget, for a time, the delicacy and fluffiness which the bird's plumage as a whole exhibits, and we are constantly reminded of the scales of reptiles. And in colour we have another similarity between the two: lizards have both pigment and prisms, and the scales of large snakes glow like opals when the sunlight falls on them.

White never exists as a pigment in the feathers of birds, but is always due to innumerable air-spaces in the substance of the feather, by which the rays of light are reflected and deflected until, as in snow or foam, all colour is lost and white results.

In any one Order of birds there may often be found a series of species with colour patterns grading into each other and connecting two extremes, perhaps very diverse in appearance. But it is seldom that we can examine such a series at once, and, except in a large collection of birds' skins in a museum, these wonderful life-chains, or twig-tips of the tree of evolution seldom appeal to us very forcibly. But in a feather it is different. We may find on one bird a most delicately graduated series, showing every step in the process by which simple unicoloured

Fig. 37.—Half-grown Brown Pelicans, with the gray plumage of the first winter beginning to show on wings and shoulders. 1/8 natural size.

or spotted feathers assume most intricate and complex colour masses and patterns.

Darwin illustrates this very plainly in the case of the Argus Pheasant, and pays a fitting tribute to the evolution of the marvellous colour patterns among birds. "The ocelli on the wing-feathers of the Argus Pheasant are shaded in so wonderful a manner as to resemble balls lying loose within sockets. That these ornaments should have been formed through the selection of many successive variations, not one of which was originally intended to produce the ball-and-socket effect, seems as incredible as that one of Raphael's Madonnas should have been formed by the selection of chance daubs of paint made by a long succession of young artists, not one of whom intended at first to draw the human figure. In order to discover how the ocelli have been developed we cannot look to a long line of progenitors, nor to many closely allied forms, for such do not now exist. But fortunately the several feathers on the wing suffice to give us a clue to the problem, and they prove to demonstration that a graduation is at least possible from a mere spot to a finished ball-and-socket ocellus."

Two feathers from the wing of a Vulturine Guinea-fowl have been chosen to illustrate a more simple but no less beautiful colour evolution. On the less exposed side of one of the feathers are three or four series of irregular white spots which tend in places to form transverse bands. On the opposite side of the shaft near the tip these spots are still distinct, but as our glance passes gradually toward the base of the feather, the spots con-

FIG. 38.—Adult Brown Pelicans in full breeding plumage. 1/8 natural size.

59

verge more and more, until two distinct longitudinal lines are formed, with traces of a third near the quill. A smaller feather from the same wing is marked with spots which are nearly circular and which show faint traces of encircling bands of white pointing toward a still more elaborate system of decoration.

FIG. 39.—Evolution of a colour pattern upon two feathers of a ulturine Guinea-fowl; a stripe breaking up into dots, these forming cross-vars, and on the second feather a regular series of dots encircled with white.

It is interesting to conjecture in which direction the decoration of feathers is proceeding. In the case of the guinea-fowl, are the spots converging into lines or are the lines the more ancient, and for some reason gradually splitting up into smaller divisions? This is hard to decipher, and if we look at the rest of the guinea-fowl's body, the matter becomes only the more complicated.

For, higher up on the wings, and on the shoulders, we find that the fine specks which were barely noticeable on the tips of some of the wing-feathers, are in the ascendant, and absorb or replace the white spots over the whole feather. The faint trace of the third line near the shaft of which I spoke, has suddenly assumed an unexpected importance and has spread out into a broad central band. The young or the female might give us a clew; for in many birds the coloration of these shows a more ancient arrangement of colour pattern than the feathers of the male.

The Indian Wood Ibis—what an imbecile it looks to our eyes when we observe it in a zoological garden; what a fishy smell it generally diffuses, how unpleasant are its feeding habits, and what a dull black and white coloration it has! Surely here is a bird with nothing which could possibly appeal to our æsthetic sense. But we are mistaken. Some of the innermost feathers of its wings, seldom visible, except when the bird partly spreads them, are of the most beautiful rose hue, shading at the tip into a deeper pink. Seldom, even in Nature, will we find tints comparable to the delicacy and bloom of these hidden feathers.

We have gone into these details only to show the possibilities of a little feather-study. Even our common Plymouth Rock chickens and hundreds of other birds will show us unthought-of beauties, and in the fields or in a zoological park we have only to use our eyes more carefully to realize how much we usually pass by unnoticed.

CHAPTER III

THE FRAMEWORK OF THE BIRD

HEN we look at a living bird, we see only feathers, horn, and skin, and we sometimes forget that hidden beneath all these are many bones,—the framework of the body. If we wish to alter the style of architecture of a house, we need only to change the exterior, columns, arches and windows, while the stone foundation and brick walls may remain as they are. So in fashioning new forms of life, Nature has often altered the covering, and even the muscles and organs, of animals to such an extent that we would have little clew as to the relations of these creatures, were it not for the underlying bones, which are so deeply seated that they react less slowly to changes in the outside life. If a fish, a lizard, a bird, a whale, and a man should be presented to us for classification, we might well hesitate until we had seen their bones, when there would flash upon us the same moulded type running through all.

The study of the skeleton, or Osteology, is like all other 'ologies; it can be made as dry as the bones themselves; or the very opposite, by leaving the minor details and less important particulars to text-books, choosing only the most significant facts. One may smile at the

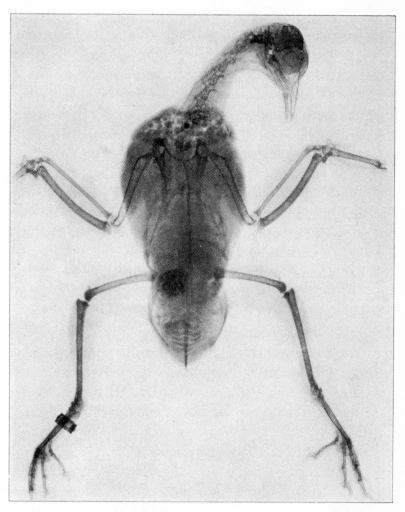

Fig. 40.—X-ray photograph of the front view of a homing Pigeon, showing the bones clearly through the surrounding flesh. Observe the light, spongy character of the skull and the bones of the limbs, the latter appearing almost hollow. The crop filled with corn is visible spread out at the base of the neck, and low down in the body, near the right thigh, the grit and pebbles within the gizzard are very distinct. About the tarsus of the right leg is seen the metal tag which was used for the identification of the living bird. (Photographed by Dr. Henry G. Piffard.)

63

thought of bestowing an encomium on a jaw-bone, and yet the history of the lower part of a sparrow's beak opens a vista so far-reaching that the mind of man falters at the thought; it shows the last roll of an evolving which, could we follow it back, would merge the man, the whale, the bird, the lizard, the fish, into one.

Let us look at some of the bones of a sparrow or dove or chicken. One way to do this is to place a dead bird in a box pierced with numerous holes, leave it near an ant-hill, and wait for the industrious insects to do their work. Another way is to clean as much flesh as possible from the skeleton and deposit the bones in a pail of water. In a few days they can be washed white and clean. Perhaps the easiest way of all is to save what bones you can of a boiled chicken. These are of large size and will show us all we wish to know.

The framework of a bird consists of a long jointed string of bones called vertebræ, with the brain-box or skull at one end and a blunt tail at the other. Near the middle, the outcurving ribs extend around the organs of the body, and, with the breast-bone, form an encircling protective sheath. Two short series of bones project in front of the ribs—the bones of the wings,—and two more behind the ribs—those of the legs and feet; while at the point of attachment of each of these four limbs there radiates a trio of bones.

The back-bone is the fundamental and oldest part of the skeleton, and though we cannot follow its evolution directly backward through the long ages, yet there is sufficient gradation among living creatures to give us

Fig. 41.—Common Fowl, showing relation of the bony framework or skeleton to the contour of the body. Notice large eye, long and mobile neck, the knee wholly within the body plumage, and the well-developed keel hinting of ancestors with strong powers of flight. 1/4 natural size.

hints of the way it originated. In the lowest of fish-like
creatures—the Amphioxus, a tiny animal, an inch or two
in length, living in the sand along our shores—there is
a thread-like cord of a gelatinous substance (not cartilage, however) extending down the back, known as the
notochord. He looks like some kind of worm, but this
little gristle is his badge of nobility and lifts him clear

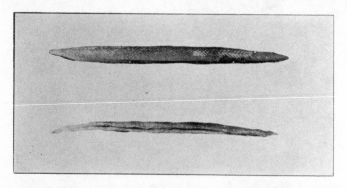

Fig. 42.—Amphioxus, one of the lowest vertebrates, with a mere thread of
gristle foreshadowing the back-bone of higher animals. This creature burrows in the sand along the Atlantic coast.

of corals, snails, insects, and worms, into the realm of
back-boned animals. This notochord lies underneath a
thin white line which is all the spinal chord he has, and,
at the front end of this, a tiny dot of pigment stands
for brain, eye, and ear. Indeed Amphioxus has neither
skull, brain, nor limbs.

The history of the back-bone, like human history, is
not altogether a majestic upward evolution; it has its
tragedies and set-backs, its hopes and failures. In the
waters along our Northern seashores are creatures, some
sponge- or lichen-like, others with strange bulb-like bodies

growing on the end of long stalks.   We call them almost
plants.   But they hold a secret from the crabs and snails
which crawl about, and when the fishes brush against

Fig. 43.—A colony of living Boltenia, photographed by the author in the Bay
of Fundy. The Boltenia is one of Nature's failures to make a vertebrate.
The larva is active and has a notochord; the adult is degenerate and fixed
on a stem. Found in five fathoms and deeper off rocky coasts north of Cape
Cod.

them—if their poor dull senses only knew it—they
might claim a blood-brotherhood.   When they were
young, for a little while, a gelatinous notochord was
theirs also, but this, with all the hopes that such a be-

ginning brings, of fish, of bird, of man even, soon melted away and there they nod and sway in the watery currents, never to know of the opportunity Nature has snatched from them—why, who can tell?

In adult sharks, the back-bone has become jointed and flexible, and a crude kind of skull is present, but still more important is the presence of four fins which correspond to the four legs of lizards and to the wings and legs of birds. A curious basket-like skeleton protects the delicate gills, and it is probable that this existed

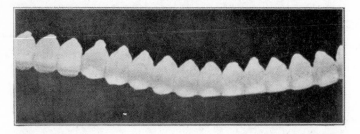

FIG. 44.—Back-bone of Dogfish, with simple cartilaginous vertebræ.

long before the limbs appeared. All of this is composed of gristly cartilage. In the higher fishes, bone replaces the cartilage, and when the lowly tadpole—fish-like at first, swimming about by means of the fin around his tail—pushes forth his legs and climbs upon the land, our skeleton is well on its way birdwards.* Reptiles of old took to trees; their back-bones grew less flexible, so that they might safely sail through the air; feathers replaced

* The actual evolution of birds was of course not through fish, tadpoles, and reptiles as we know them, but by some line of creatures unknown to us forever, and resembling some of these other living Classes at least in the possession of gills, scales, etc.

scales, two fingers of each hand were lost, and one from each foot; teeth disappeared; a beak of horn proved best; intelligence increased and the forehead rose high, and behold,—a bird! Can we then despise even an English Sparrow?

All these things we have learned from a comparison with creatures other than birds, and we may, without trouble, take one more glimpse into the dim past. Let us go to the hencoop, where for three days the patient biddy has been sitting on her precious eggs. We will

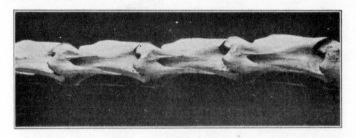

Fig. 45.—Neck vertebræ of an Ostrich, highly complex and bony in structure.

rob her of one—she will not miss it—while from it we may learn many wonderful things. Rest the warm egg in a dish of sand, carefully picking away the shell from the upper part. A glance at the tiny embryo lying on the yolk within will show a double series of tiny squares extending down the long diameter of the body. These are the first hints of the spinal column, and if we could follow its further development we would see something of great interest. The squares are now divided up like beads, just as are the bones of our bird's vertebræ; but in reality this first segmentation is a false one. It is simply a copy of the primitive flakes or joints of the tiny muscle-beginnings, and is comparable to the joints or rings in the body of a beetle, butterfly, or earthworm. In a short time all the squares will fuse together, and not until later will they separate again into divisions which will ultimately form the real bones of the spinal column. Every little chick, before it hatches, goes through the same strange changes,—living reminders of the evolution which has gone on in past ages of the earth. It is inter-

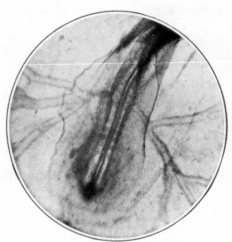

FIG. 46.—Muscle-plates, or false vertebræ, of third-day embryo chick. Magnified 25 diameters.

esting to note that the vertebræ of the embryo chick pass through a stage when they are biconcave,—a condition found both in Amphioxus and Archæopteryx.

This digression upon the back-bone history may seem out of place, but in reality such a bird's-eye survey of the past, imperfect as it is, will add a new interest to our handful of chicken-bones.

Let us suppose that we have strung a wire through the hollow centre of the back-bone of our chicken, to which the ribs are still attached, and that we have besides the skull and the bones of one wing and one leg. Compare them with those in the illustrations and we will see if they can tell us aught of interest.

The bones of the neck are all separate, and slide back and forth on the wire, like beads on a string. How unlike

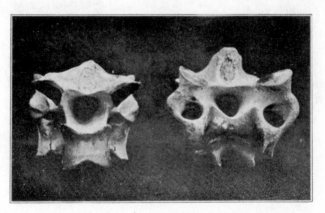

Fig. 47.—Front and rear views of seventeenth and eighteenth cervical vertebræ of Ostrich, showing complicated saddles and sliding surfaces, giving great freedom of motion.

the long smooth ribs are these vertebræ, bristling with spines and projections! How is it that a bird can be comfortable with a string of such irregular-looking objects run through its body? But fit two of these bones together and see how beautifully they saddle end to end, every convexity or projecting knob exactly adjusted to a corresponding concave portion of the neighbouring bone. These saddles are characteristic of birds alone. Every one of the sixteen bones of the neck is different from its

fellows and exactly suited to the requirements of its
position, but the first two following just behind the skull
are so radically unlike the others that we know at once
that they must serve some particular purpose. The first
is little more than a simple ring * of bone, and is called
the atlas, after the mythological giant who held up the
heavens upon his shoulders; named very aptly too, for

FIG. 48.—Atlas and axis of Jabiru, separated.   FIG. 49.—Atlas and axis of
                                                        Jabiru, joined.

this tiny collar of bone supports the skull itself. The
next vertebra is ring-like too, but has a curious knob in
front, which projects forward through the atlas and forms
a pivot on which the head turns, hence its name,—the
axis.†

Let us compare the neck-bones with those of a reptile
and a man. Although, as a whole, the bones of the

* This bone is formed chiefly of two intercentra, which are small bones,
very characteristic of reptiles (chevron-bones of the tail) and are not uncommon among the lower Orders of birds.

† In Hornbills the atlas and axis are fused together.

skeleton of a bird are more or less soldered together,
yet the neck is far more flexible than in either of the
other examples. Indeed the neck of a bird has greater
freedom of motion than that of a snake. A lizard can
turn his head only a little way around, and we ourselves
can look only across our shoulder, but with a bird it is

FIG. 50.—American Egret, showing curves into which the neck naturally falls
when the bird is at rest. When striking at a fish the vertebræ straighten
out.

very different. Watch a heron or, better still, a flamingo and see its neck describe figures of eight as he
arranges the feathers on its back. Few people would
ever imagine that there are exactly twice as many neck-
bones in a sparrow as in a giraffe, but such is the case,
there being fourteen in the former and seven in the latter.
In the neck of a swan there are twenty-three of these
bones.

The remaining vertebræ, those of the upper and lower back, are very different from those of the neck. The flexible neck enables the bird to reach all parts of its plumage with its beak, and to pick up food from the ground or from twigs overhead, but the all-important function of flight must be provided for by means of a

Fig. 51.—White-throated Sparrow, three inches tall, with fourteen neck vertebræ. (Compare with Fig. 52.)

rigid body-frame. In reptiles and in the embryos of birds only two pelvic vertebræ are fused together, but in adult birds many dorsal and caudal vertebræ (as many as 23 in some cases) are fused into a single bone. Thus the rib-bearing upper back vertebræ are partially fused together, and below them those of the lower back have merged until it is difficult to realize that this portion of the skeleton was not originally one bone. Passing on for a moment to the bones of the tail, we find a number of separate pieces, ending in a curious-shaped bone, called the ploughshare. This is at the tip of the tail, or "pope's

Fig. 52.—Giraffe, reaching with tongue for leaves perhaps eighteen feet above the ground, with but 7 neck bones.

nose," of the chicken and really consists of many vertebræ fused together. It is necessary for this to be large and strong: for it supports all the feathers of the tail. But to be of efficient aid in steering, the tail, like the rudder of a ship, must have freedom of motion, and

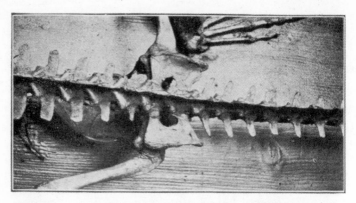

FIG. 53.—Pelvic vertebræ of young Alligator.

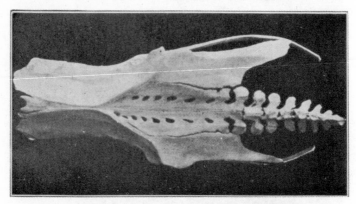

FIG. 54.—Pelvic vertebræ of American Flamingo.

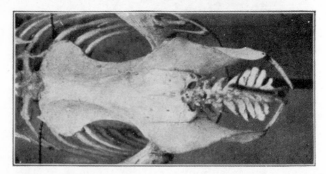

FIG. 55.—Pelvic vertebræ of Bald Eagle. In the reptile, where there is no need
for rigidity, only two typical pelvic vertebræ are joined together; in the birds
many dorsal and caudal vertebræ are joined with these to make a rigid frame
for flight and for bipedal locomotion.   76

hence the separate bones which unite it to the vertebræ of the lower back. The evolution of the tail will be treated of in another chapter.

Ribs

The ribs are the long, narrow, double-headed bones which curve out from the vertebræ of the upper back and, uniting with the breast-bone, form a barred protection for the heart, lungs, liver, and other organs. These are the ribs proper, but there are other smaller ones, called false or floating ribs, which reach only part of the way around the body. Look at the largest ribs of the chicken and an added provision for making this box of bone more solid will be seen. From near the centre of the upper part

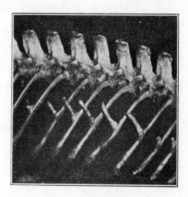

Fig. 56.—Ribs of Hatteria Lizard, with uncinate processes.

of each rib a small bony projection laps across the rib next behind and thus forms a kind of lattice-work, movable but of great strength. A further interest attaches to these cross-rib pieces when we learn that every bird except the Screamer possesses them, while elsewhere they are found only in crocodile-like reptiles and in the Hatteria Lizard of New Zealand.

The similarity of the ribs—slanting one after another

around toward the breast-bone—hints of something which perhaps has never occurred to us. We spoke of the worm-like appearance of the lowly Amphioxus— the sand-fish with the shadow of a back-bone. When we think of a worm we think of a creature very much alike from head to tail, one in which a section across the neck is not very unlike one across the centre of the body or near the tail; indeed that is exactly what the word Amphioxus means,—like head, like tail. This repetition of segments or similar parts is a sign of low degree in the scale of life, as it harks back to the time when the very highest form of life was worm-like.

The flesh of a salmon or of a trout shows such a condition very well, the body consisting of flake after flake of flesh. Now in birds and the higher animals this division into successive segments is hardly noticeable, and almost every inch of a man or bird, from head to toe, seems very distinct and individual. But ribs bring back the old ancestral condition very vividly, and when a peacock, strutting proudly before us, resplendent from beak to tail, picks up and swallows an unfortunate angleworm, we may remember that, no matter what geological eras or inexplicable physical gulfs separate the two, the bird carries within his body indelible imprints which insolubly link his past with that of the lowly creature of the dust.

As in various other cases throughout nature, when the many ribs of the bird's ancestors began to be reduced in number, some attained to other uses beside that of arching around the whole body and protecting the heart, the

lungs, and other organs.   Look at the two neck-bones of
the ostrich in Fig. 47, where in addition to the central
aperture, through which the spinal nerve-cord passes, two
other openings will be seen, one on each side.   Through
these the vertebral arteries carry their burden of pure
blood.   The outer wall of this bony canal, extending up
the whole length of the neck, is formed principally by
what is left of the ribs which were once long and free,
like their fellows farther down the back.   Though reduced to a tiny fragmentary arc of bone, yet they still
perform a protecting function.

In *Archæopteryx* (Fig. 5) there existed well-developed
abdominal ribs, exactly like those found in crocodiles
and other reptiles.   In no living bird, however, are these
found.

Breast-bone

The lower portions of the true ribs of our chicken
are separate pieces of bone, slanting in a forward direction and attached by a movable joint to the upper parts.
These end close together along the sides of the large
breast-bone, or sternum as it is called.   In fact the origin
of the sternum can be traced to the fused ends of these
ribs, and in the sternum of an immature ostrich (Fig.
58) the line of juncture between the two lateral halves is
still distinct or even open.   To the edge of this bone,
nearest the head, two column-like shoulder-bones are
attached, and in some birds the wish-bone is also joined
to it (Fig. 103).

The sternum is one of the largest single bones in

the body of the chicken, and is very different from our own breast-bone, which is long and narrow. The posterior edge of the sternum is of many shapes, varying in birds of different species. Deep channels may extend into each side, leaving long slender splinters or spines

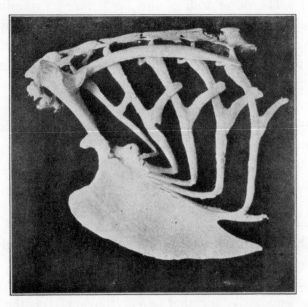

FIG. 57.—Ribs and sternum of Flamingo; notice what a complex box of bone is formed by the vertebræ, scapula, ribs with their uncinate processes, and the sternum; notice large keel for the attachment of flight-muscles.

of projecting bone, or this channel may be partly closed, forming a round hole quite through the bone. The sternum and its various processes are of considerable value in classification, the same configuration being found throughout allied groups, in consequence, doubtless, of the slight chance of modification resulting directly from any specialized habits in the life of the bird. The portion of this bone which is most characteristic of birds is the central ridge or keel which projects straight out from the surface of the sternum. This is of the utmost importance in giving firm anchorage for the great flight-muscles of the breast.

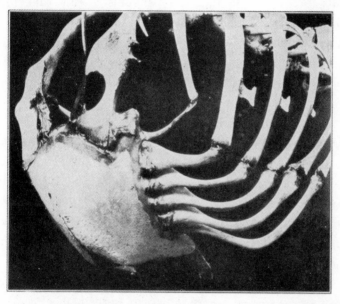

Fig. 58.—Ribs and sternum of Ostrich; notice absence of keel correlated with loss of power of flight. The suture through the centre of the sternum reveals its paired origin.

The keel is of many shapes, but when well developed is generally very high at the upper end of the breast-bone and becomes lower as it slopes gradually backward. In birds which have lost the use of their wings the keel has disappeared completely, the sternum being flat, as in ourselves. This is its condition in the ostrich and cassowary, and it is the character which has given a

name to two great divisions of birds: *Rati'tœ* (those with
flat breast-bones, raft-like), including the ostrich, rhea,
emeu, cassowary, and apteryx; and *Carina'tœ* (birds
with keeled breast-bones, boat-like), including all other
living birds, whether flyers, as the thrushes, storks, and
gulls, or swimmers like the penguins. But this difference in breast-bones is far from being as profound as
other differences existing between certain birds which
are alike in having keels to their sternums. The presence or absence of a keel is not of great taxonomic importance.

The size of the keel is a pretty sure criterion of the
flying powers of a bird, that is, judging not the actual
duration of flight, but the actual muscular power and
amount of energy used in flying (Fig. 59). The albatross, and other birds which, trusting to the air-currents
to bear them upward, flap seldom and soar much, have
comparatively smaller keels than do those birds which
flap their wings more frequently. Thus the pigeon has
a very good-sized keel; while in the humming-bird this
bone is enormous, compared to its spread of wings. Dr.
Frederick A. Lucas has expressed this very graphically
in a diagram, where it is supposed that the albatross,
pigeon, and humming-bird have an equal spread of wings.
On comparison, the keel of the first is seen to occupy but
a small fraction of the surface of the same bone in a
humming-bird. To account for this we must realize
that the wings of the humming-bird execute from six
hundred to a thousand strokes a minute; while the albatross may soar for miles with wings held outstretched

and all but motionless. It is said that, comparatively, the muscular energy is greater and the wing-bones more powerful in a hummingbird than in any other animal.

Nature has a puzzling way of achieving similar results in a very similar manner in creatures wholly unrelated. We have a good example of this in bats and birds, both

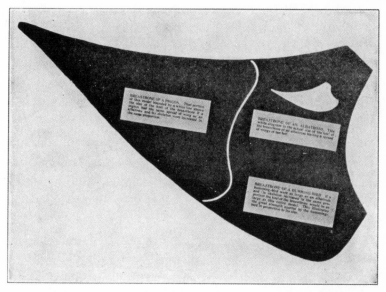

FIG. 59.—Comparison of the size of the keel of the Albatross, Pigeon, and Hummingbird, supposing all to have an equal spread of wing. (Courtesy of Dr. F. A. Lucas.)

of which have independently learned to propel themselves through the air by means of their front limbs. If we take the breast-bone of a common bat and that of a small bird and place them together, few persons unacquainted with the bones of the two types could tell which was that of the bat,—different as that little creature is in external appearance from a bird. Their keels and sternums are very much alike. This is called parallelism, and sometimes it gives a great deal of trouble to naturalists when they are trying to find the right relationships between living animals.

Shoulder-girdle

It will be remembered that mention was made of the trios of bones which radiate near the juncture with the body, of each wing and each leg,—girdles or arches they are called. The pectoral, or shoulder, girdle meets the upper arm-bone of each wing at the shoulder-joint. If we run our hand along the back of our shoulders, we will feel a prominent bone, called the shoulder-blade, and in almost the same place in our chicken we notice a very long and thin bone. This is the scapula, and is one of the pectoral-girdle trio, the other two being known as coracoid and clavicle.

The coracoid is a short, but stout, column of bone joined to the shoulder-blade and extending down and backward to the breast-bone. This coracoid bone is especially developed in birds as compared with other creatures. When their forefathers began to scale through the air, thus putting a great strain on the muscles of the breast, Nature seized on these coracoid bones, giving them such strength and thickness that they have become the pivots upon which, at each swift vibration through the air, turn the marvellous wings of a modern bird. In reptiles, this bone is divided into two weak, thin plates which would hardly afford strength for a single wing-flutter. Since mammals in their high evolution have found no use for this bone, it has become reduced to a small projection on the shoulder-blade.

The clavicle we will recognize instantly, when we give it another name—the wish-bone or merry-thought.

FIG. 60.—Pectoral girdle of bird (scapulas, coracoids, and clavicles); compared with the scapula and coracoid of a young Leopard, the latter bone in the Leopard being reduced to a tiny process.

In birds the wish-bone is generally V-shaped, the two clavicles usually meeting and fusing at their tips. Through this V-shaped opening in the neck, the œsophagus and the windpipe pass from the throat into the body cavity.

We too have wish-bones, although they are not placed exactly as are those of a chicken. We call them collar-bones, but by whatever name we know them they are of importance, both in ourselves and in birds, in serving to brace out the shoulders. In creatures which, unlike mankind and most birds, have less varied movements of the fore limbs, the clavicles have fallen into disuse, as in the lion and the horse. But in climbing, burrowing, and flying animals, such as the squirrel, mole, and bat, these bones have been of active use and are well developed. But to keep its wish-bone a bird must continue to fly: for Nature is opposed to useless parts. So, in the flightless cassowary and ostrich, the wish-bone is very small or altogether absent. Parrots are almost alone in appearing to suffer no inconvenience in flight by the lack of clavicles,—these being greatly reduced in some species.

In that anomalous bird the Hoatzin, the clavicles are fused not only at their base, but the tips are ossified firmly to a projecting spine of bone from the upper part of the breast-bone.

In glancing back over the lower back-boned animals we realize that a shoulder-girdle of bones is of no use without a limb. Therefore we find the first hint of the shoulder-girdle in sharks, in which we also find the first limbs, or fins. In these fishes it is nothing but a single bar of soft cartilage. In the girdle supporting the pectoral fin of such a fish as the trout or other bony fish, we find the adumbration of some of our bird's bones. When we remember how very wing-like is the movement of a fin in the water, we will not be surprised to learn that the girdle is almost all epiclavicle; these bones being the forerunners of clavicles, and giving place, in the higher forms, to the real wish-bones which steadily increase in size and importance. We would hardly

recognize in these primitive types the wish-bone of our
Christmas turkey.

In terrestrial quadrupeds and birds we usually find
the front limbs near the front part of the body and the
hind limbs much farther back, but it is interesting to

Fig. 61.—Girdle of a bony fish.

notice that in the fish, Fig. 61, all four limbs or fins are
very far forward, almost or quite in the head region
itself. This is a result of the function of balance which
these structures almost wholly perform, the fin of the
tail furnishing the locomotive power.

It is very interesting to notice how many bones have
kept to their respective places in the evolution of animals,

no matter how much change has occurred in their shape and size. Take, for instance, the shoulder-blades. When a tiger crouches they are very conspicuous, and whether we take a frog, a turtle, a lizard, an armadillo, a mouse, or a horse, we may always be sure of finding a scapula in the region where we have observed it in the bird. This is an important fact, and one which makes the identification of many bones an easy matter.

Thigh-girdle

The shoulder-girdle which we have just examined was not joined to the back-bone, but only saddled on the ribs, the scapula extending backward, just clearing them. What kept it in place in the chicken's skeleton was the fact that it was strongly attached to the sternum, and this in turn joined to the back-bone by means of the ribs. But the pelvic arch or thigh-girdle is very different. If the entire framework of the bird is to be supported on two legs, the point of attachment of these limbs must be solidly fixed to the back-bone of the body.

Although there are as many bones supporting the leg or thigh as there are bracing the shoulder, we would never know this from examining our chicken. As in other places in a bird's skeleton, the bones—six in this case—have fused together in one solid piece, and only in very young birds are they separate.*

The names of the bones composing the pelvic girdle, or arch, are the ilium, ischium, and pubis. The easiest

* They were separate also in *Archæopteryx*.

way to locate these is first to find the socket in which
fits the head of the thigh-bone. This is the deep cup-
shaped depression on each side, and all three bones join
in making the socket. The ilium lies along the back
and forms a sort of roof over the portion of the back-
bone in this region. If we look at the under side of this
bone, we may see the fused vertebræ more distinctly—
fourteen or fifteen of them. The two deep depressions
in which the kidneys of the bird were located are also

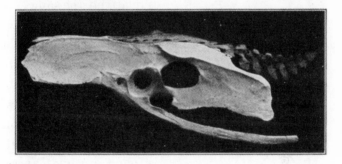

Fig. 62.—Pelvic girdle of a bird.

now visible. As the coracoid is the great pivot of the
wing, so the ilium helps most to bear the strain of hopping and running. In the frog, which progresses by
hops or great leaps, the ilium is also largely developed;
indeed we can see it through the skin, thus giving the
broken-back appearance to that creature.

Each side of the thigh-bone box is formed by the ischium,
which is closely fused with the ilium except in most of
the ostrich-like birds, the tinamous, and in reptiles,
where these bones are free throughout their entire length.
We can readily make out the pubis as a slender bar of

bone extending backward from the thigh-socket, sepa-

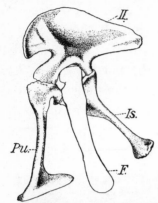

FIG. 63 — Pelvic arch of a Dinosaur

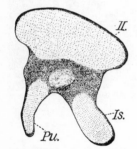

FIG. 64.—Pelvic arch of an embryo bird, to show similarity of the two as contrasted with Fig. 65.

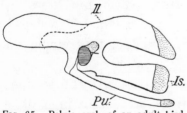

FIG. 65.—Pelvic arch of an adult bird. (The three figures by courtesy of Prof. H. F. Osborn.)

rated from the ischium (except at the extreme end) by a long open slit. In other animals these bones are as different in shape as can be imagined, but, almost without exception, the position of each is relatively the same. The extreme extension, forward and back, of the ilium above the back-bone, thus joining with more vertebræ, is directly connected with two-legged erect locomotion. A parallel condition is found in some *Dinosaurs* —those extinct giant reptiles — certain of which walked more or less on their hind legs.

Another fundamental resemblance is found between the thigh-girdles of *Dinosaurs* and other reptiles and that of a bird in the egg. As is shown in Figs. 63–65, the pubis slants slightly forward in both reptile and embryo bird; but in

the adult bird the shifting backward of this bone until it
is parallel with the ischium is wholly an avian feature.

Fig. 66.—Bullfrog.   The bend in the back shows the great development of the
ilium for bipedal locomotion in the sense of leaping ability.

Wings

We will now consider the framework of the fore limb,
or wing, of a bird, and a glance at the illustration showing the arm of a man and the wing of a bird will at once
make plain the relation between the two.   Here we again
find a great help in the fact that many of the bones keep
to their respective places in frogs, lizards, birds, and man.

We know but little of the direct change from a fin to
a hand or foot, although there are some fishes living at
the present day with large finger-like bones in their pec-

toral fins. Even among fossil forms there have as yet
been found no "missing links" in this respect. But however it came about, it is certain that when the fish-
amphibians of olden time, venturing into shallow water,
felt more or less solid mud under them, and tried to
move about upon it, their fins must have become pressed
downward, and before they could safely push themselves
about on dry land or lift their bodies clear of the ground,
the stiff fin-rays must have become split up into a few,
thick, bony rays or toes. We know that these were
originally five in number on all four limbs, and whenever, among living creatures, we find a lesser number, the
reduction has been brought about by some subsequent
change in the life of the animal. As yet, however, we
know of no direct transitions from fins to feet.

The requirements of flight demanded a fin-like stiffness in the wings of birds, and therefore many of the
smaller bones of lizards, counterparts of which we find
in our own wrists and hands, are in the bird fused together.

The upper arm-bone, or humerus, corresponds exactly
to our bone of that name, and when we feel the two long
bones of our forearm and look for them in the bird, we
find both very plainly represented, the large one with
notches, where the great wing-feathers are fastened, being
called the ulna, and the smaller, straighter bone the
radius. In our wrist there are eight little bones which
are joined to each other so delicately that we can move
and turn our hand in every direction. But when a bird's
wing is extended, if the wrist was at all flexible, the pressure of air on the great wing-feathers would turn the

FIG. 67.—Wing of Pigeon, feathered.

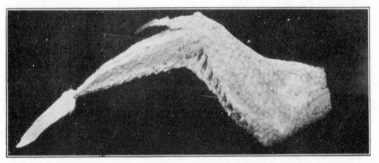

FIG. 68.—Wing of Pigeon, bare, compared with Fig. 69.

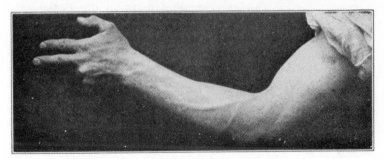

FIG. 69.—Arm and three fingers of a man.

wing-tip around and make flight impossible. So but two of these small bones are free in our chicken's wrist, although in the small chick several more (six in all) are separate.

If we double back our fourth and fifth fingers and imagine that they have disappeared, extend our other three fingers and then suppose that all our wrist-bones, save two, have fused with the three long bones leading to the base of our thumb, index and middle fingers,* we will have an idea of the condition of our chicken's wing, and indeed there is very little difference between this and the wings of all other birds.† We have two separate bones in our thumb, and three in each of the next two fingers, and the bird has the same number, except in its third finger, in which there is but one. The principal value of this comparison is to show us that the bird, even in its most characteristic and specialized organ,— the wing, is not physically so unlike ourselves as we might at first glance suppose. When a bird folds its wing against its body, the joints are bent sharply, and the Z, formed by the elbow and the wrist, almost closes up. We can place our arm and hand in much the same position.

If we move our arms slowly up and down, little by little greatly increasing the speed, we will realize how much greater strength and rigidity the whirring wings

---

* Some morphologists homologize the fingers of a bird's wing with the second, third, and fourth digits of a pentadactyl hand. The question is still a mooted one.

† In the embryos of some birds, traces of a fourth finger have been found.

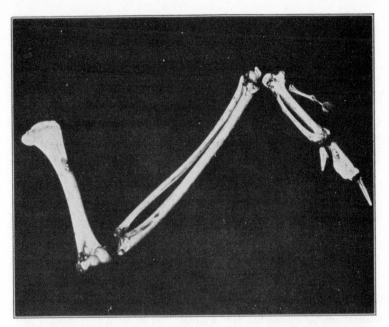

FIG. 70.—Skeleton of wing of Condor, compared with Fig. 71.

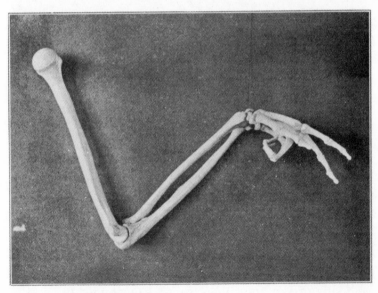

FIG. 71.—Skeleton of a man's arm; notice close correspondence of bones in the two. (The extended thumb of the human hand is not silhouetted against the background, and hence not very distinct.)

95

of a hummingbird or a grouse require than do the slowly
flapping pinions of a gull or an albatross. When we
compare the relative shortness of the upper arm-bone,
or humerus, in the former groups with the long wing-
bones of the sea-birds, we again realize what exquisite
adaptations exist everywhere in Nature.

The proportionate length of the various parts of the
fore limb of a bird forms an interesting corollary to its
habits of life. For example, the hand in penguins and
in hummingbirds is very long indeed; while in the ostrich the humerus is considerably longer than the forearm and hand combined. (Compare Figs. 269 and 272.)

Before we leave the wing-bones, it will be well worth
our time to consider for a moment how limbs first origi-

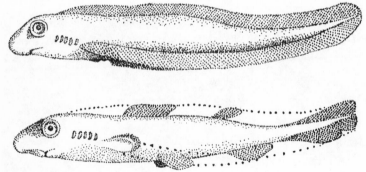

Fig. 72.—Diagram showing the origin of paired fins (limbs) from a continuous
fin-fold. (After Wiederscheim.)

nated. In the lowest of fishes, such as our friend the
Amphioxus and in lampreys, limbs are altogether absent,
but in embryos of sharks we get a hint of what the first
great fish-like forms were like. Along the lower part of
each side of the body there runs a continuous fin, so that

the front view of a section would be something like this,
the dorsal fin being above and the lateral
fins on each side.   Now owing to certain laws
of mechanics, whenever such a creature as this
moved about in the water, the stress of balancing would be thrown most heavily on two points in
these side fins, and gradually at these two nodes the fin
became more strongly developed; while between these
points it degenerated and finally disappeared.   So in
modern fishes we find the quartet of limbs alone left of
this continuous fin or fold of skin.

Look at a little embryo in the egg, taking one which
has been incubated for six or seven days, and see the
curious paddle or fin-like wings and feet—simply four
rounded flaps projecting from the body—as unlike the
limbs of the chick when it emerges from the egg as can
be imagined (see Fig. 367).   The ridge or fin of skin in
the early, soft-backboned creatures could have been of
no use whatever, except in balancing.   In fact if we
watch a trout carefully, we will see that it is the tail-fin
which does almost all the propelling, the front- and hind-
limb fins simply acting as guides and balances.

So in this instance (as indeed in almost every organ
in ourselves as well as in birds) we learn that the original
function was entirely unlike that which the part now
serves.   The idea of miraculous change, which is supposed to be an exclusive prerogative of fairy-tales, is a
common phenomenon of evolution, and the shadows of
these miracles of the past are forever coming and going,
over the growth of the tiny bird hidden in the egg.

Legs

The leg of our chicken, as we have seen, is attached to the great bone of the thigh-girdle. Being used for locomotion on land, the foot is not very different from that of a lizard, but there seems something very strange about the leg. Can it be possible that a chicken's knees bend backward? If so, it must be different from all other two-legged or four-legged creatures. Much of a bird's leg is concealed beneath its feathers, and when we see the bones as far up as the thigh-joint, we understand our mistake at once, and see that a bird has knees which bend in the same way as our own, that is, forward in an opposite direction from the elbow. The knees of a bird are usually concealed within the skin of the body, as in the short-legged ducks, and are never visible outside the plumage. Hence the wide-spread mistake concerning them. For this reason the femur, or thigh-bone, is, in birds, relatively very short, even in the long-shanked herons and flamingos, the extra length of limb resulting from the elongation of the next two lower joints.

The thigh-bone, or femur, alone forms the upper leg, or "second joint," and two bones, as in the forearm, the next portion below. One of these, the tibia, is much the larger and is the "drumstick" of the chicken.* When we cut the dark meat from this portion, our knife sometimes slits off a splinter, which is the second bone of this joint, the fibula.

---

* To the lower end of this are fused, in the bird, the bones which correspond to our heel-bone and the small astragalus.

In · the chicken, we next come to a single long bone called the tarsus, which is, in life, covered with scales.

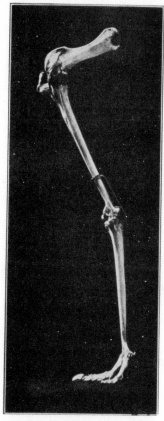

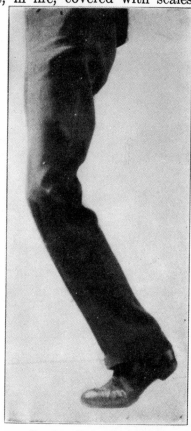

FIG. 73.—Skeleton of an Ostrich leg and foot.

FIG. 74.—Human leg and foot.

In the embryo it is composed of several separate bones.* The simplest interpretation we can give to the foot of

---

* These correspond in ourselves to the bones of the upper foot and the second row of carpals, this joint of the leg coming, therefore, really between the bones of the ankle, instead of, as in ourselves, between the ankle and the lower part of the leg.

the chicken, in comparing it with our own, is to imagine that our small toe has completely disappeared; the great toe (corresponding to the thumb of the forelimb) is turned backward, and the heel is lifted high from the

Fig. 75.—Living Ostrich, showing entire leg; notice the knee almost within the body.

ground, the several bones of the upper foot being greatly lengthened and fused into one. So we, like bears and raccoons, walk with our whole foot, from toe to heel, flat upon the ground, while a bird, like a cat or a horse, walks on its toes alone.

FIG. 76.—Heron, standing naturally upon its eight toes.

FIG. 77.—Jaguar, showing progression upon toes alone (digitigrade). (Sanborn, photo.   Courtesy of N. Y. Zoological Society.)

Fig. 78.—Wood Ibis, resting temporarily upon its whole foot.
(Sanborn, photo. Courtesy of N. Y. Zoological Society.)

Fig. 79.—Bear, walking upon the whole foot (plantigrade). Compare with
Wood Ibis.

CHAPTER IV

THE SKULL

BIRD'S skull has been called a "poem in bone—its architecture is the frozen music of morphology; in its mutely eloquent lines may be traced the rhythmic rhymes of the myriad amœbiform animals which constructed the noble edifice when they sang together." We should all "be able to whistle some bars of the cranial song—the pterygo-palatine bar at least."

We perhaps know that there are twenty-eight bones in our own head, and if we attempt to dissect the skull of a fish we will find many more, but at first glance the skull of our chicken seems to be composed of but one solid bone. Indeed, if we except the lower jaw and a few others, such as the two little bones which unite it to the skull, the entire cranium is soldered together, and the lines of junction obliterated. In young birds these seams are more or less visible, although the soldering process begins very early.

The origin of the skull is wrapped in obscurity, and neither the student of fossil bones, nor of those beneath the skin of living creatures, nor yet the diligent watcher of the mysterious panorama of life in the egg, can tell us very much, although many theories have been sug-

gested. The poet Goethe thought the skull was merely
a continuation of the neck-bones, very much expanded
and changed, and although the division of the skull into
three roughly outlined rings is possible, yet we have no
direct proof of the truth of this theory.

Fortunately, in the skulls of most animals, the bones
are separate, and by keeping in mind the constancy of
their position, the puzzle of the skull of a chicken begins
to clear up.

Just as the first back-bone was a gelatinous or gristly

FIG. 80.—Cranium of Dogfish, cartilaginous, generalized in structure.

one, so the old type of skull was entirely gristly or cartilaginous. Sometimes on the seashore near the huts of
the fishermen, we may pick up a strange-looking object—
translucent and looking as if it were made of hard white
rubber. Clinging to it is perhaps a long string of delicate
beads of the same substance. This is the skull and back-
bone of a dogfish or shark, and although the skull is
very unlike the chicken's cranium, yet many of the parts
in the latter are faintly foreshadowed in the cartilage
skull washed up by the waves.

Through all the long ages of geological epochs, myriads of creatures were changing in form and structure, some growing too bulky and helpless and vanishing, others developing powers of running, burrowing, flying and leaping. But it is a very remarkable and wonderful thing and very fortunate for us poor mortals, striving after knowledge of the past, that in each general class of creatures, certain ones should have found a niche where they were removed from the fierce struggle for

FIG. 81.—Skull of young Alligator. Bones massive and solid, adapting their owner to an active aquatic life but to sluggish terrestrial movements; eye-cavities and brain-case very small, the jaws (organs of prehension) composing by far the major part of the head.

existence, and where for year after year, century upon century, they and their descendants changed but little. We might mention Amphioxus and sharks among fishes, Necturus among amphibians, Sphenodon among reptiles, and the duck-billed mammal and others among hair-covered creatures. These may be meaningless names, but if one will read about them and then examine their skins and skeletons in our museums, many a glance will be given into the ages of the past, compared to which the

few thousand years during which man has reigned seems
but a day.

When we study the early structure of some creature,
say a bird, we find that before it emerges from the egg
the skull is soft and cartilaginous, open and quite different in shape from what it will be eventually, and it is
most startling to find a living creature—a shark—with

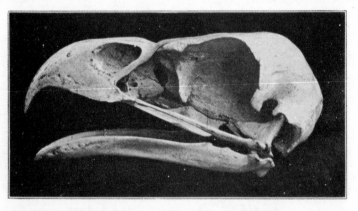

FIG. 82.—Skull of Bald Eagle. Bones light and spongy, fitting for a very active
aerial life; orbit very large and brain-case capacious, showing great advance
beyond reptilian condition.

a skull which never gets beyond this condition. It is
as if the curtain of eternity had been, for a moment, drawn
aside for us, and a glimpse given into the past—a past
so remote and clouded that our keenest searches seem
to reveal but dim, skeletal forms of weird shapes, which
yet we know must have blended and imperceptibly
merged, through millions of years, into the present life
of the earth.

Looking at the chicken's skull as a whole, we notice
a number of uses which the various parts serve. The

large rounded portion taking up most of the skull proper
is, of course, the box of bone which protects the brain.
On each side, a large cavity shows where the eyes are
placed, and if we compare this skull with that of a cat
or dog or with that of a human being, we will see what
great importance eyes must be to a bird; the cavities
for them are so much larger than in other animals. Back

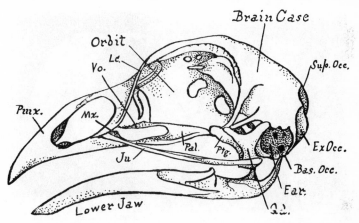

FIG. 83.—Skull of Fowl, showing orbit, brain-case, ear, lower jaw, premaxillary
(*Pmx.*), maxillary (*Mx.*), vomer (*Vo.*), lacrymal (*Lc.*), jugal (*Ju.*), palatine
(*Pal.*), pterygoid (.*Ptg*), quadrate (*Qd.*), and supra (*Sup. occ.*), ex (*Ex.
occ.*), and basioccipital bones. (After Parker.)

of each eye-case we see an irregular opening, the portal
of the ear; and in front of the brain two apertures in the
beak open toward the organ of the nose. The prominent
beak and wide-spreading lower jaw are chiefly concerned
in the procuring of food. We need not bother with the
names of all the bones, but there are some too interesting and with too strange a history to be passed by.

Let us glance at the back of the skull for a moment.
Here we find a large round opening through which the

spinal chord passes into the brain, and below it is a
small knob, which in the living bird fitted into the first
vertebra of the neck. It is a very tiny projection of
bone, but fraught with significance: for if we look at
the skulls of a frog, a mouse, a cat, a horse or a man, we
will see that the head hinges upon *two* bony projections,
but in all birds and reptiles there is but one,—a very

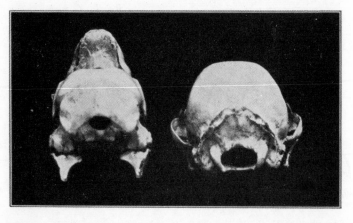

FIG. 84.—Rear views of bird (Hornbill) and mammal (Yaguarondi) skulls. Notice
single facet (occipital condyle) in the bird and two in the mammal, connecting
skull with the neck-bones.

plain hint of the relationship of these two Classes, so different in external appearance. The head thus pivoting
upon a single point, the bird can turn its head much
farther around than if there were two points of attachment. Before we leave this *great opening*, as the scientists call it when they speak of it as the *foramen magnum*,
it may be worth while to mention the remarkably constant position of the bones around it. Whether these
are all separate, or solidly fused into one, we may always

know them by their position relative to the brain opening; the upper edge of the hole is always formed by the supraoccipital, the lower by the basioccipital, the two sides by the exoccipitals.

Although many bones of the skull, such as the supraoccipital, keep their names, whether found in salmon, frog, lizard, bird, or man, others identical in position have had new names given them. For instance, a small bone directly in front of the eye is known as the lacrymal, from its close relation to the tear-duct, but in fishes the bone is called the preorbital, as a suggestion of fish-tears would be rather absurd.

We may find the dried ear-drum, or tympanum, stretched tight across the entrance of the ear-cavities, and if we break this, or even look carefully through the transparent membrane, a long thin bone may be seen beneath, extending backwards from the under surface of the drum. This is the columella, or little column of bone, and will have an interest for us later on.

If we examine the way in which the upper and lower mandibles or jaws are joined to the skull, we will find a very ingenious arrangement; one very different from that in ourselves. If the beak of a bird is to serve as hand, lips, and mouth, it must be as free and movable as possible, and instead of the upper jaw being fixed immovably to the skull, and the lower jaw swinging up and down from it, we find that the upper jaw is attached very loosely, while each side of the lower mandible hinges upon a loose irregular-shaped bone, known as the quadrate. A long slender bone connects the quadrate with the upper mandible, which bone we may call the jugal. Indeed when we come to look closely at the quadrates we find that they are very important, and in addition to supporting the bar of bone from the upper jaw, and pivoting the lower jaw, they bear another pair of bones

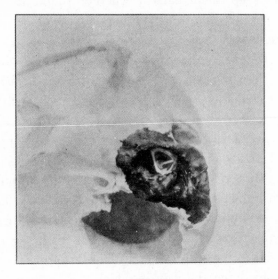

FIG. 85.—Columella in ear of Snowy Owl (magnified 2 diameters).

extending inward from them, beneath the skull, to the broad thin palate or roof of the mouth.

In a chicken the individual movement of the upper jaw is not very great, but in some birds, such as parrots, it is much more noticeable. With a sharp knife we can entirely detach the upper and lower jaws of most birds, without cutting through a bone, the connection consisting only of exceedingly tough tendons. When we found our shark's skull we perhaps wondered what had become

of the jaws with the many rows of teeth, and we may
now guess that they were attached so loosely to the skull
that the action of the water washed them away with
the flesh. This was the case, and in all fishes we find
both jaws as separate bones. Among reptiles we find
the quadrate bone free only in snakes, an admirable
adaptation which enables them to swallow their prey
entire.

The bones forming the palate, or roof of the mouth,
are of the greatest value in classification. No matter
how specialized the habits or the food of a bird may be,
the palate appears to be the last portion of its structure
to respond to any recent outside influences. Thus while
the absence or presence of a keel to the sternum is a
character of little value in separating the ostriches and
their allies from all other birds, yet the radical difference shown by the palate bones in the two groups is
reliable evidence of their early divergence from each
other. These taxonomic characters may be found in
any good book on systematic ornithology and need
not detain us here.

Although we have the skull and both jaws of our
chicken, yet some very important and interesting bones
are lacking, and to find them we must find the tongue
of the bird. For a bird's tongue, as well as that of other
creatures, is not all flesh or horn, but underneath there
is a jointed framework of bone, which is called the hyoid.
We may compare its shape to that of an arrow, with a
central head and four barbs, two very short and blunt
and two long jointed ones.

It may seem to us that the mandibles, the jugal, the
palate, the quadrates, the ear-bones, and the hyoid are
an unmeaning jumble of irregular bones, apparently

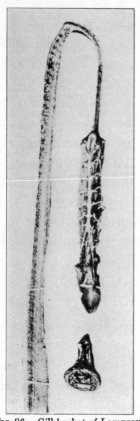

FIG. 86.—Gill-basket of Lamprey.

bearing no relation to one another,
and with absolutely no interest
outside the fact that each is very
well suited to its particular use.
If scientists had studied only the
bones of adult animals, we might
have groped in vain for any answer to the question of how these
bones came to be what they are.
But the science of embryology, or
egg-life, has unfolded wonderful
things, and, as we shall soon see,
nothing more marvellous than the
strange story of these bones.

The eel-like lampreys which
crowd up our shallow brooks in
April to spawn are curious creatures, and not the least remarkable thing about them is the fact
that they have no jaws, although
they have an elaborate cartilaginous net-work protecting and
supporting the gills. We perhaps thought that every
vertebrate animal in the world had jaws of some kind, and
perhaps even lampreys had them long ago, before their
habit of sucking did away with any need for chewing.
But the reason I have spoken of the lamprey is because

it brings vividly to mind the image of an animal which must have once existed—a fish-like creature with no jaws, but with a gristly mass which held up and protected the delicate blood-fringes, or gills, by means of which all true fishes breathe.

Our shark is a very convenient starting-point, and before going further we should mention the technical name

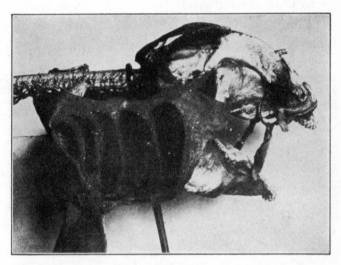

Fig. 87.—Gill-bars of Shark.

of this group — *Elasmobranchs*, or strap-gilled fishes. There are usually five of these gills, and within each strap or fold of skin is a jointed arch of gristle.

All this may be very true, say you, but what bearing has it on the skull of the chicken?

We have seen that in sharks the number of gills has been greatly reduced, and a pair of very loosely attached jaws has been acquired,—and the truth gradually dawns upon us: the jaw of a shark is nothing but a greatly changed gill-arch, which has doubled up, bent forward and hinged to the skull. The skin has grown over the edge, and the bony scales in the skin, standing up on end, have become teeth.

And now to our bird. In the embryo chick four gill-arches are at first distinguishable, but these soon begin to alter their position, to fade away, or to change in some way, and in our bony skull we may trace them as follows (see Fig. 89). The upper half of the first gill-

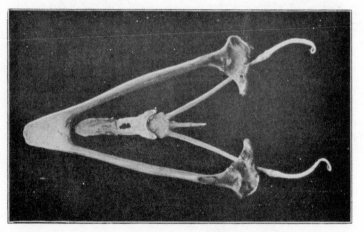

Fig. 88.—Lower mandible, tongue, and hyoid bones of Bald Eagle.

arch forms the bones of the upper jaw, palate, jugal, and quadrate, and the lower jaw completes the entire arch. The central part of the second gill fades into nothing, but the top is present as the columella-bone of the ear, while the base is transformed into the head and two blunt barbs of the arrow-like bone of the tongue. The two long barbs of this bone correspond to the third gill and, from their rod-like jointed character, they look very much like the real gill-arches of a fish. The fourth arch vanishes.

Such is the almost incredible alchemy which Nature has wrought from a plastic rod of gristle,—transforming it into beak, tongue, and ears. Few of us, when watch-

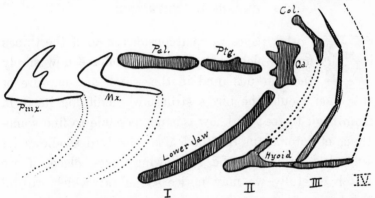

Fig. 89.—Ultimate distribution of the four embryonic gill-arches in the skull of the adult bird. The dotted portions are not developed. (Adapted from Newton.) Compare with Figs. 83 and 88.

ing the gently waving gills of a fish, have realized how much we indirectly owe to them. A noted German anatomist—Karl Gegenbaur—believes that we owe even our hands and arms (by way of the pectoral fins of fishes) to portions of the gill framework, but this theory is not generally accepted.

CHAPTER V

ORGANS OF NUTRITION

N other pages we shall consider some of the things upon which birds feed, and shall see how surely the methods used in the search and capture of this food mould the bird's structure, modifying its form from beak to toe; and now is it not possible to find something of interest in the food after the bird swallows it? Indeed even before the swallowing takes place, if we watch carefully we may notice something which we did not before know.

In the first place the bill of a bird is, of course, a primary factor, not only in procuring food, but often in killing and preparing and also holding it while it is being made ready to swallow. Less confusion will result, however, if we leave the consideration of the beaks and bills to a later chapter.

After the bill (which corresponds to our mouth and lips) come the glands of the mouth and here we again enter the portals of physiology,—for some unknown reason dreaded by many of us, and systematically shunned, as dry and ultra-scientific. On the contrary there are interesting facts awaiting us in all its branches. After a brief consideration of the more important, we shall

surely return to outdoor study of the daily life of these
creatures, with more balanced interest, and a "little
knowledge" which, instead of being a "dangerous thing,"
will, in this instance, add many fold to our appreciation
of the external results of these functions, whose workings are ever concealed from the light of day.

The digestive apparatus of a bird, or indeed of any
creature with a back-bone, is in reality a tube or canal,
which begins at the mouth and extends through the
body. Certain portions are contracted or expanded, and
specialized to store up, moisten, grind, dissolve, digest, or
absorb the food substances which pass through.

The Salivary Glands

The mucous membrane, or lining, of the entire digestive canal is very delicate and requires to be kept constantly moist. The lining of the mouth and throat, being
so exposed to contact with the outer air, requires some
special provision to lubricate it. This is accomplished
by certain glands, some beneath the tongue, others situated in the upper portion of the mouth. These are not
found in fishes, nor in other creatures which live altogether in the water; but in reptiles several groups are
distinguishable. In birds they vary greatly, some having
scarcely a trace, while others have large well-developed
glands. Salivary is the common name given to certain
of these, and we will let that name represent all.

In ourselves, saliva is an important aid in digestion.
Besides moistening the food and softening all hard portions, it exerts active chemical effects, as, for example,

changing starch to sugar and in many other ways making
ready the food, that the important changes which take
place in the stomach may begin at once. In birds, however, the saliva has but little chemical effect on the food,
its principal use being to moisten the substances before
they are swallowed.

It is not often that Nature, when she has produced

Fig. 90 —Nest of Chimney Swift; twigs glued together with saliva.

an organ or special tissue by the elaborate synthesis of
evolution, confines its use to any one function. If birds
were provided with salivary glands intended only for the
purpose mentioned above, they soon found other uses for
them. In a woodpecker we will find very large salivary
glands on each side of the mouth. These secrete a sticky
liquid which covers the long, many-barbed tongue and is
an efficient aid in picking out insects from their holes in
the bark and wood of trees.

Many birds carry in their beaks the grasses and
twigs with which they construct their nests, and if a sticky
fluid helped them to get their food, why would it not
also soften the twigs and make them easy to bend? Not
only this, but certain birds, such as our Chimney Swifts,
are provided with saliva in such quantities, and of such
tenacious consistency, that the entire nest—a mosaic of

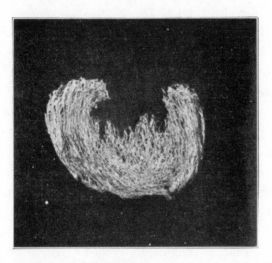

FIG. 91.—Nest of Esculent Swiftlet (edible bird's nest) composed entirely of saliva.

small twigs, each about an inch in length—is set in saliva
cement, and fastened to the vertical side of a chimney
or charred tree-trunk by the same means. Even this is
only a step, or link, in the direction of the extreme usefulness of saliva, for the little East Indian birds known
as Swiftlets (one of which ornithologists call *Collocalia
fuciphaga*) make their nests entirely of saliva or mucus.
The second part of the scientific name, which means an
eater of seaweed, refers to the idea formerly held, that

the nests consisted entirely of half-digested seaweed, but it has been proved that this is not the case. The homes of these birds are the "edible birds'-nests" held in such esteem by Chinese *gourmands*.

The Tongue

If we had a long series of birds' tongues before us, we would be surprised at the great variety of shapes and sizes. Observing the good-sized tongues of sparrows and other small birds, we would turn to a pelican expecting to see an enormous affair to correspond with the huge bill of that bird. On the contrary we will find a tiny inconspicuous flap not larger round than a toothpick. This reminds us of the condition of the tongue in some fishes, where it is a very simple structure indeed. The kingfisher also has a small tongue, and the same is true of many other fish-eating birds, such as pelicans and most of those which feed on large insects. The reason is obvious. The food, which is swallowed whole, is of such large size that a tongue of even moderate proportions would be only in the way.

The tongues of many birds are provided with oblique series of teeth, either soft and fleshy or horny in structure, which point backward toward the gullet and must be of great help to the bird in guiding and swallowing its food. These teeth are especially abundant around the glottis, or opening to the windpipe, guarding it from chafing or from the chance of food choking it up.

In ducks and geese we find tongues large and of complicated appearance. The edges are often toothed or

fringed to correspond with the serrated or otherwise
indented edges of the mandibles.   One which is before me
as I write is very elaborate.   It is that of a wild Mallard
Duck.   At the tip is a thin, distinct flap or lamella, horny
and with smooth edges.   Behind it the tongue enlarges
abruptly into a thick oblong mass, deeply grooved down

Fig. 92.—Bill of Brown Pelican, showing extreme reduction of tongue in a bird
which swallows whole fish.

the center.   The edges of the anterior half are fringed
with a double line of horny hairs, while in the posterior
portion the upper line is replaced with tooth-like structures.   The upper surface is smooth in front, but farther
back two central folds arise and curve over laterally,
forming tube-like grooves.   Still more posteriorly, fleshy
recurved teeth are visible, singly, in groups, or in regular
lines.   The tongue of our common barnyard duck is

similar to this and is well worth examining. The use of such a complicated organ in a bird of so simple feeding habits as the duck is hard to explain.

We will hardly find two tongues that are alike, and even the tips differ, and show as wide a range of varia-

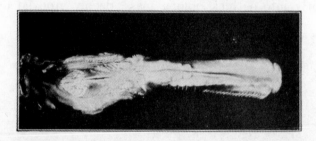

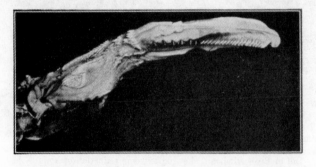

FIGS. 93 and 94.—Top and side views of the tongue of a Mallard Duck, showing complicated structure in the tongue of a bird which sifts its food from the mud.

tion as the remaining portions. In many birds, such as owls, larks, and swifts, the tip is bifid, or double-pointed, bringing to mind the forked tongues of snakes and certain lizards. In woodpeckers the tongue is round and exceedingly long, and can usually be thrown out some distance beyond the tip of the bill.

Our common Flicker, or Golden-winged Woodpecker,

possesses a tongue of remarkable length, even for a woodpecker, and while feeding, the bird will often shoot it

FIG. 95.—Head of Flicker, showing tongue slightly protruding.

out two or three inches beyond the tip of the beak.
Easily and without a hitch it disappears again, appa-

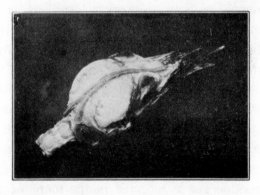

FIG. 96.—Skull of Flicker, showing rear branches of the hyoid bone, curving up
over the skull and down into the right nostril. The front of the tongue is
visible beyond the tip of the beak.

rently down the very throat of the bird. If we carefully
remove the skin from the skull of a dead Flicker, the
magic will become plain. When we spoke of the skull

of a bird, mention was made of the two long bones which branched out from the rear of the tongue and which are all that remain of the third ancestral gill-arch. In the Flicker, the slender, white tongue divides into these two branches just in front of the glottis and from here they extend backward, passing one on each side of the wind-pipe, and on upward, following the curve of the skull, then forward, lying together upon the forehead. Not even here do they end, however, but actually reach some distance into one nostril! So when this bird stretches out its tongue, the tips of the rear branches leave the opening of the nose and shoot around over the surface of the skull until they have gone as far as possible. No wonder the poor ants have but little chance when a Flicker visits their hill and sets the marvellous mechanism of his tongue rapidly to work. And no wonder the enthusiasm of an ornithologist never fails, when he thinks of the scores of similarly interesting structures still await-ing investigation.

The tip of the tongue in the sap-sucking woodpeckers is beset with numerous hairs forming a brush-like instru-ment, but spines take the place of hairs in the species which feed exclusively on insects. It is known that the exact proportion of insects in the diet of any particular kind of woodpecker is reflected in the more or less per-fect adaptation of the minute structure of its tongue to that end.

In the sapsuckers, too, the tongue is comparatively short, doubtless because the sap flows readily from the holes which these birds bore. Hence they require no such extension of tongue as the deep burrows of the ants necessitate in the case of the Flicker.

Thus the tongue of a bird seems a very unstable character, acted upon quickly and radically by any change in the diet of the species. The entire tip of the tongue is frequently frayed out into a kind of brush,

remarkably developed in the parrot-like lories. Yet this curious structure is probably only an elongation of the papillæ, homologous with those which make the tongue of a cat or lion so rough. Cockatoos, although first cousins to the lories, have very different tongues, thick and fleshy with club-shaped tips.

In our common goldfinch, the sides of the tongue curl inward, forming an admirable seed-scoop, while the same or-

FIG. 97.—Thick fleshy tongue of Cockatoo.

gan in the chickadee, being distinctly cleft into several prongs at the tip, has been likened to a "four-tined pitchfork" on which its little owner impales the myriad grubs and insects for which it so industriously searches twigs and leaves. The great particoloured bill of a toucan conceals a very curious tongue—a long thin affair, narrow throughout its whole length and so thickly bordered with a deep, delicate fringe that it bears a decided resemblance to a feather.

FIG. 98.—Feather-like tongue of Toco Toucan.

The tongue of a flamingo is thick and fleshy, filling the entire cavity of the lower mandible and in shape reflecting its crookedness. The upper edges of the man-

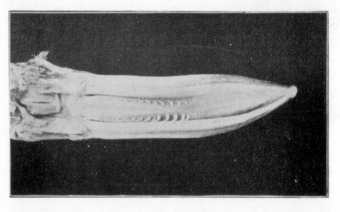

FIG. 99.—Tongue of Flamingo within lower mandible (natural position).

dible approach each other so closely that they permanently inclose the tongue, motion being only possible in

a forward or backward direction.   Along the sides of the
tongue are two series of fleshy teeth, in shape exactly
like the poison-fangs of a rattlesnake.

Mention must be made of the unique and greatly
specialized tongues of Hummingbirds and Honey Creepers.
The outer edges of this organ are curled into two tubes,

FIG. 100.—Side view of Flamingo's tongue, forcibly lifted above mandible, showing fleshy recurved teeth.

which are more or less split and frayed near the tip,
forming delicate brushes—efficient instruments either to
suck up nectar or to flick out insects from the heart of
corollas.

The Crop

From the back of the throat to the stomach extends
a tube, the gullet or œsophagus, through which the food

FIG. 101.—Young Flamingoes, showing position of the bill in feeding.

128

descends after it leaves the mouth. In some birds this is a simple tube of the same diameter throughout, always moist from the secretion of (mucous) glands which are found abundant in its walls, but serving merely as a passage for the food on its way to the stomach.

In another class of birds an enlarged chamber is present, called the crop. This serves a somewhat similar purpose as the external pouch of the pelican; that is, it acts as a receptacle for food. No especial digestive glands are found here, and the only agents acting on

FIG. 102.—Brush, or tube-like tongue of Honey Creeper. Twice natural size.

the food are water, the secretions of the salivary glands, and the heat of the bird's body. The crop exists only superficially in some birds, the dilation being hardly noticeable.

From these we find a succession of more distinctly marked permanent crops, until in grain-eating birds this organ is very prominent. If we examine an English Sparrow after it has made a hearty meal in the chicken-yard, we will find the crop filled with grains of wheat, some cracked in pieces by the bill, others entire.

When we sought the extreme in the provision of saliva in birds, we had to refer to a swift, living in caves in islands of the Malay Archipelago, but to find the highest degree of development of crops is a much easier matter. In the ordinary pigeon the crop is of very great size and divided into two lobes. The capacity of the crop in some birds of this class is astonishing. As many as sixty-three acorns have been found in the crop of the English Wood-pigeon. If we look at the crop of a pigeon before its young leave the nest, we will discover a function of this organ which would otherwise never be suspected. We know that herons and some other birds feed their young on fish half-digested by themselves. This process is known as regurgitation. If we have ever seen a pigeon with the beak of its young half down its throat, pumping something into the offspring's mouth, we have probably thought that a similar habit was being shown,—half-digested grain taking the place of the heron's fish. But such is not the case. At the time of the breeding season, the folds of membrane in the crops of both parent pigeons thicken and secrete or peel off in curdy cheesy masses—"pigeon's milk" some call it—and this forms the food of the young birds So in pigeons the crop not only receives food, but at times provides it.

Now for a glance at some of the oddities in the structure of crops. The Hoatzin—a strange bird of Brazilian swamps—which harks back to its reptilian ancestors in many ways, has a very curious crop. There are strong muscles in its walls, the use of which, it is said, is to squeeze out the juice of the thick leaves of the *Arum arborescens* which forms its food. Thus it has a gizzard-like function, and has become so important in the life-economy of the bird that it has developed out of all proportion, and occupies so much space that the keel on the breast-bone has had to give way in part to make room for it, and even the arms of the "wish-bone" have been bent outward. In this remarkable bird the proventriculus and gizzard are reduced, their functions being usurped by the crop.

The facility with which most birds are able to eject the contents of their crops serves several useful purposes, besides the feeding of the young of herons, cormorants, and others. When vultures have gorged themselves to repletion on the flesh of any animal, they usually retire to some near-by retreat and sleep until digestion has taken place. But if they are suddenly approached or alarmed, they will instantly eject all they have swallowed and, thus lightened, take safety in flight. Pelicans and Wood Ibises also have the habit of 'unswallowing' their fishy meals when frightened. Petrels and many fish-eating sea-birds appear to have a supply of oil always in readiness, which they shoot from the mouth to a considerable distance, surving as an efficient means of self-defence when taken in the hand after being wounded.

In birds of prey generally, but especially in owls, another use for this habit is found. Owls always swallow their smaller prey entire, sometimes crushing the skulls of mice and plucking out the longer wing and tail-feathers of birds. Although their crops are not nearly so muscular as that of the Hoatzin, yet there must be powerful movements of the walls, for the mice and birds are denuded of hair and feathers and even the bones are in some way removed from the body, and all are ejected in a neat oval ball.

If we find some hollow tree where an owl has its

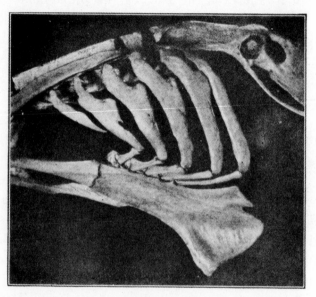

FIG. 103.—Keel of Hoatzin, repressed by crop.

regular sleeping-place, many of these pellets may be found on the ground below, showing the results of each night's hunting. The skulls in them are often in such perfect condition that the species of rodents may be identified. Besides allowing the bird conveniently to get rid of the indigestible portions of its food, this habit seems to be necessary to the health of the bird. In captivity, owls and hawks are never so healthy and active when fed on fleshy meat alone, as when a dead mouse or sparrow, rat or pigeon is given occasionally. In dissecting specimens which have had nothing but a flesh diet for a year or more, I have found the throat and gullet in a very bad condition, as if the lack of some scouring process,

FIG. 104.—Food-pellets ejected by Great Horned Owl, containing remains of rodents.

such as is afforded by the pasage up and down of the indigestible hair and feathers, had actually resulted in the death of the bird. I have seen owls try to eat the straw on the floors of the cages, when not provided with food in the condition in which they find it when at liberty.

In cormorants and birds of similar voracious fish-eating habits, the entire gullet serves as a receptacle for food, while the fish first swallowed are undergoing the process of digestion lower down. Here, as in many other instances, we have a condition very similar to that in some reptiles—crocodiles in particular. These ravenous scaly creatures have such powerful organs of digestion that even bones are dissolved, but the stomach is comparatively small, and when a crocodile makes a large meal, it is at first stored away in the wide gullet.

The Stomach and Gizzard

In the present chapter we might easily be led into

details which would strand us in the midst of dry technicalities, but we will try to avoid all this and choose only the interesting facts.

The chief organ of digestion, in birds as in other animals, is of course the stomach. In many fish-eating birds this organ is merely a simple, more or less enlarged chamber, rather crop-like except that it contains numerous digestive glands.

FIG. 105.—Caracara, showing crop distended with food.

The typical bird-stomach, however, is compound, or formed of two more or less distinct parts. The first portion—known as the proventriculus—is the smaller, and contains very active digestive glands, sometimes arranged in patches, but more usually forming a band. If the lower part of the œsophagus of an English Sparrow is removed, slit open and washed, these glands can be easily seen, being more of a rose tint than the paler tissue of the portion nearer the mouth. The walls are thicker in this glandular area. This can be seen to better advantage in a young chicken, where the glands take the form of conical protuberances which dot the entire surface. Nature has produced curious modifications of this typical fore-stomach, as in snake-birds, which have the glands of this portion enclosed in a sac, in shape not unlike a small crop. Here the food is softened and acted upon chemically by the secretions from the walls.

FIG. 106.—Glands of the stomach of a young chicken.

The second division of the stomach is the gizzard, an organ made to perform most powerful compressing motions, thus crushing and macerating the food, so that when passed on into the intestine, every particle of nourishment may be extracted from it. When we think of beauty of colouring in birds, it is their plumage which at once presents itself to the mind, and yet a gizzard has a real beauty both of shape and hue. This organ, in a chicken, is in shape like a double convex lens. The cavity in the centre is lined with a tough yellow membrane, sometimes almost as hard as bone. Two great tendons spread over the outer surface on each side, and although in life forever buried in the absolute darkness of the bird's body, yet when brought into sunlight they shine with an iridescence like the beam from a spectrum.

It is hardly possible for the gizzard to grind up food in the sense of having much lateral motion, like the movement of the jaws in chewing, but it shuts together again and again with great force. Gravel and sharp stones are swallowed by many birds, and are of great importance in helping to grind the food. The number and size of these stones are sometimes almost beyond belief. I have known a cassowary to swallow over a quart of rubble in one day, and have given a quartz pebble twice as large as a hen's egg to one of these birds and watched it slip down the bird's throat as easily as a cube of carrot. This particular bird preferred smooth white quartz pebbles, and would search through a whole heap, picking out stones of this character. The same preference was exhibited by the gigantic extinct birds of New Zealand called moas.

Mr. Frederick Chapman, writing of a portion of New Zealand where the skeletons of moas were found in great abundance, says: "When we came upon the ground disturbed by the wind (the soil being shifting sand) we soon found a number of distinct groups of gigantic gizzard-stones. It was impossible to mistake them. In several cases they lay with a few fragments of the heavier bones. In all cases they were in distinct groups; even where they had become scattered, each group covered only a few square yards of ground, and in that space lay thickly strewn. . . . The peculiar feature of the stones was that they were almost all opaque, white quartz pebbles. In one place I found a small group of small pebbles of different colour, more like the few brown water-worn pebbles which may be picked up hereabouts. These lay with a set of bones much smaller than the very large bones I found with most of the clusters of pebbles.

"I did not gather these brown pebbles, as I thought it uncertain whether they were gizzard-stones or not, though it is possible that the species to which the smaller stones belonged was not so careful in selecting white stones.

"A glance at the pebbles lying around in the sur-rounding country showed that the quartz-pebbles were not collected here. . . . Mr. Murdock and I collected three sets of pebbles, and these I can pronounce com-plete, or nearly so. It is beyond question, too, that each set belongs to a distinct bird. No. 1 weighs 3 lb. 9 oz.; No. 2 weighs 4 lb.; while No. 3 weighs no less than 5 lb. 7 oz.! This giant set contains individual stones weighing over 2 oz.; indeed, I have picked out eight stones weigh-ing almost exactly 1 pound."

The gizzard of a bird is reflective of its diet, and is very quickly affected by any change in the food. For example, a captive gull when fed exclusively on fish has but little muscular power in the gizzard, but a diet of grain will produce a change in that organ, giving it grinding power sufficient to crush the kernels of corn.

That this is something more than an abnormal condition brought about by artificial means is proved by the fact that in the Orkney Islands the wild gulls feed in winter, spring, and summer on fish, and at this time are gizzardless; but in the fall they change to a diet of corn and develop a very respectable gizzard. So we see that this organ, apparently so independent in function and individual in appearance in many birds, is in reality only a physiological change from the stomach proper.

The history of the development of this organ may be traced in various living species, from the soft membranous sac of a fish-eating bird to the knot of tendons which forms the gizzard of certain Fruit-pigeons. These birds feed on nutmegs and other very hard, almost stony nuts, and to enable the bird to crush these, the lining of the gizzard is covered with several score of conical projections, horny in consistence. These are probably the nearest approach to "hen's teeth" we are likely to find.

What a boon to a business man who indulges in a daily "fireman's lunch," if his masticatory function could be an internal and unconscious one, as in a bird!

A crocodile, which has so much in common with a bird, is provided with a gizzard, which, like that of a chicken, is round, muscular, and has two great side tendons, and no less than five pounds of grinding-stones have been found in one of these reptiles.

Many interesting adaptations are found in the stomachs of birds, made necessary by special requirements in the diet. As an instance of this, the snake-bird has a dense mat of hair at one end of the stomach, the free ends of which point outward, brush-like, and prevent the accidental entrance of any small fish-bones which otherwise might get into the small intestine. The gizzard of a cuckoo, when opened, often gives the impression of a similar coating of hair lining the entire organ, but these are in reality only the hairs of caterpillars upon

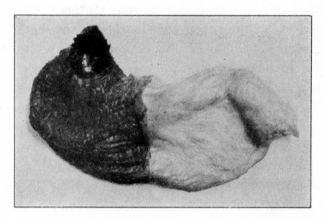

FIG. 107.—Cluster of matted hairs in the stomach of a Snake-bird.

which these birds feed, which have become detached and have lodged in the folds of the gizzard lining.

When considering the crops of birds we noticed the curious way in which a pigeon feeds its young, by regurgitating a cheesy substance which forms in its crop, and we will now speak of something still more remarkable. The strange nesting habits of the hornbills are foreign to this volume, but we cannot leave the subject of gizzards without touching on the manner in which the male birds of this group probably feed their imprisoned mate and young. I say probably, because no one has seen them do this, but as in captivity the operation occurs repeatedly during the breeding season, there can be but little doubt concerning its evident significance. After walling up his mate and her egg in some hollow tree, the male hornbill takes upon himself the labour of supplying her with food throughout the period of incubation and the subsequent rearing of the young bird. Instead of bringing food piecemeal,—nut by nut, grape by grape,—the lining of the entire gizzard peels off at certain frequent intervals, appearing, when ejected at the mouth, like a small bag or purse, the puckered opening (heightening the simile) serving to retain securely the contents of the gizzard,—a dozen or score of grapes or other fruit. This, the male bird, in his native land, doubtless takes in his beak to the tiny opening of the walled-up nest and delivers into the bill of his mate. How admirable a spouse this, who not only seeks and provides sufficient food for his temporarily helpless family, but bears it to them wrapped in a packet torn from his very body—if not a "pound of flesh," at least enough to make a lunch-basket!

The Intestines

Beyond the gizzard is the intestinal canal, which varies greatly in length in different birds. The ostrich has forty-six feet of this digestive tube, while the nectar and tiny insects snatched by a hummingbird in its flight are digested in a delicate hair-like duct but two inches in length. Although comparatively of such great length, the way in which this part of the digestive tract is coiled and twisted in the body cavity of the bird allows it to take up the least possible amount of room.

The function of this long tube is to absorb the nutriment from the food after this has been moistened by the salivary glands, crushed by the gizzard, and acted on by the stomach acids, and secretions from the liver and pancreas. The digestible parts are then taken up by the blood through the walls of the intestine. In many of the lower types of birds, such as the cassowary, ostrich, and screamer, the arrangement of this long digestive tract is very simple, much like the condition to be found in alligators.

CHAPTER VI

THE FOOD OF BIRDS

THE organs and physiological functions of a bird, as of animals generally, are so interrelated and intimately dependent on each other that it is a rather difficult matter to consider any single one by itself without being led into another's province. For example: we have for the subject of this chapter the food of birds, and unless we are very careful, we shall overstep the bounds of our theme. To limit our subject clearly we will consider only adult birds.

We have all seen the pestiferous sparrows picking up grain in the chicken-yard; we have admired the skill which the red-breasted robin exhibits in spying and extracting earthworms on our lawns; our memory recalls the osprey dropping upon his fish, and the woodpecker chiselling to the wood-borer; but did we ever stop a while and attempt a "bird's-eye view" of all the classes of substances which birds find good as food?

The ways in which this food is sought and caught, killed and prepared are wonderfully varied, and some idea of the remarkable variety of substances laid under contribution as food by birds of different orders may be had from a brief review of the principal divisions

into which these substances are classified, and the part
they take in supplying birds with food.

As with all animals, certain mineral salts are very
necessary to a bird's existence, such as the substances
from which the calcium phosphate for the bones, and
the calcium carbonate for the shells of the eggs, are de-

Fig. 108.—Finch, a bird with heavy, thick bill adapted for crushing seed.

rived. The gravel and pebbles swallowed by birds in
the course of their daily feeding should hardly be mentioned in this connection, as this is only done for the
mechanical assistance, derived from the hard surfaces,
in triturating the food.

Vegetable-feeders form a large group among birds, and
they alone would offer an interesting field for study, as

there is such specialization for feeding on particular varieties or portions of plants. We find fruit- and grain-eaters, besides those which feed almost entirely on buds, leaves, berries and nuts, nectar, sap, and even pollen. Lichens form a considerable item in the bill of fare of ptarmigans, the Arctic grouse. We have even dedicated certain plants to birds which show a decided partiality for them,—duckweed and partridge-berry.

Fig. 109.—Vireo, an insect-hunter. with a delicate, hooked bill.

There is no doubt that a great many plants benefit from the cross-fertilization of their flowers by humming-birds carrying the pollen from blossom to blossom. Of one of the sugar-birds of South Africa it is said: "When sucking up the nectar of one of the larger protea-blossoms, the bird perches on the edge of the flower, plunges its long bill and the greater part of its head downwards among the petals, and retains it in this position until

satisfied. As a result the narrow, shaft-like feathers of
the forehead frequently become saturated and stained
with juice and dusted over with pollen, and it is probable
that this bird plays an important part in the cross-fertilization of several species of protea."

Desmids and diatoms, those one-celled microscopic
organisms which are almost on the border-line between

FOOD OF VARIOUS BIRDS.

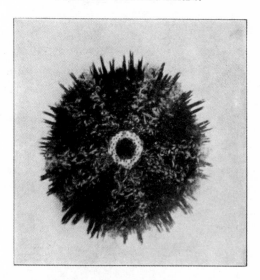

FIG. 110.—Sea-urchin.

plants and animals, I have found in large numbers in
the digestive tracts of ducks and other birds which are
accustomed to find their food by sifting the mud at the
edges of ponds and lakes.

Sponges, at least in a decayng state, are devoured by
crows, as I can testify from observation after dredging
expeditions in the Bay of Fundy.

We should scarcely think that those watery creatures sea-anemones, hydroids, and jelly-fish (some of the latter

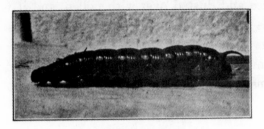

Fig. 111.—Caterpillar.

consisting of over 95 per cent water) could afford much nourishment to any animal, and when crows and gulls are seen tearing large stranded jellies into pieces, it is

Fig. 112.—Cocoon.

probably only for the sake of the semi-parasitic shrimps which make their home in the interior canals of the masses of animate gelatine.   But the fresh-water hydra, belonging to the same division as the hydroids, is eaten in myriads by ducks and geese.   These and many other birds are remarkably fond of duckweed, which they devour with such evident pleasure that they must enjoy it as much as cats do catnip, or canaries hempseed.   As the under surface of these small water plants is the fa-

Fig. 113.—Butterfly with wing torn by bird.

vourite home of the hydra, they necessarily form a portion of the food of these water birds.

Roundworms, flatworms, and leeches are devoured by many aquatic birds, while earthworms form a staple article of diet with such different species as thrushes, woodcocks, and cranes.   A favourite morsel of the curious apteryx of New Zealand is a gigantic species of worm, twelve to twenty inches in length, which is highly phosphorescent.   The apteryx seeks its food by night, and when devouring one of these worms, the whole bird is lighted up, and after its meal the bird's bill is illumined by the mucus which adheres to it.

Starfish and sea-urchins are sought out by crows, ravens and gulls, and perhaps other birds. They break

into them by main force, or else carry them to a height and drop them on the rocks. I have even seen a Bald Eagle, when fish and Fish-hawks were scarce, deliberately break into and devour a green-spined urchin.

If, as is said, immense bow-head whales subsist entirely on minute larval shrimps,

FIG. 114.—Snail.

then it is not surprising that many thousands of shore-birds are well nourished by the myriads of shrimps and prawns, large and small, which every tide leaves exposed.

It is a mere truism to say that insects form the sole food of scores of species of birds, and enter into the diet of many hundreds. It has been said that without birds, within a space of ten years, the earth would not be habitable for man, owing to the unrestricted increase of noxious insects. There is doubtless not a single group of insects which does not suffer from the appetite of one or more species of bird. The eggs and larvæ are dug and pried out of their burrows in the wood by woodpeckers and creepers; those underground are scratched and clawed up to view by quail, partridges, and many spar-

rows; warblers and vireos scan every twig and leaf;
flycatchers, like the cat family, lie in watch and spring
after their prey, only in the air instead of on the ground,
feeding more particularly on low-flying insects; while
swifts, swallows, and martins glean their harvest from the
diurnal hosts of high-flying winged creatures. Many

Fig. 115.—Crab.

times when we think hummingbirds are taking dainty
sips of nectar from the flowers, they are in reality picking minute spiders and flies from the deep cups of the corollas. When night falls, the insects which have chosen
that time as the safer to carry on their business of life
are pounced upon by nocturnal feathered beings—the
cavernous mouths of the whippoorwills engulf them as
they rise from their hiding-places, and the bristles of

night-hawks brush them into rapacious maws, if per-chance they have succeeded in reaching the upper air.

In tropical forests, where insects are everywhere abundant, the birds seemed to have realized the fact that to each is apportioned certain phases of insect life, and that by hunting in large flocks, instead of competition resulting between birds of different species, they play into each other's hands (or rather beaks). It is of such a flock that Hudson writes: "The larger creepers ex-

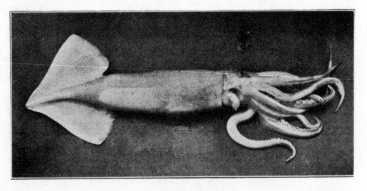

FIG. 116.—Squid.

plore the trunks of big trees, others run over the branches and cling to the lesser twigs, so that every tree in their route, from its roots to the topmost foliage, is thoroughly examined, and every spider and caterpillar taken, while the winged insects, driven from their lurking-places, are seized where they settle, or caught flying by the tyrant-birds."

The Wattled Starlings or Locust-birds of South Africa live in flocks of thousands, and so dependent are they on locusts as food, that their habitat and place of nest-

ing is influenced by the presence or absence of these insects. "When pursuing a flight of mature locusts these
starlings perform various extraordinary and beautiful
aerial evolutions with the object of intercepting and surrounding a portion of the swarm, and in doing this their
movements closely resemble those of another locust-
destroying starling, the beautiful rose-coloured Pastor
of eastern Europe and Asia.   Individually the two species
are very different; collectively and under similar conditions their actions are quite
similar.   Starting in a dense
'ball-like' mass, they suddenly
open out into a fan-shaped
formation, then assume a
semicircular arrangement, and
finally end by forming a
hollow cylinder in which a
portion of the locusts are
enclosed; as the imprisoned
insects are destroyed, the
starlings gradually fill up the

FIG. 117.—Rattlesnake.

hollow of the cylinder until they again assume their 'ball'
formation and proceed to follow the remaining locusts.
The ground below the flock is covered with the droppings
of the birds and the snipped-off legs and wings of locusts.
At other times the starlings station themselves on the
tops of bushes and trees, from which they dart on the
flying insects like flycatchers.

"In Cape Colony the Locust-birds usually breed in
very large colonies, in localities in which the locusts have

deposited their eggs. For hundreds of yards every thorny bush is packed full of cup-shaped nests, even the spaces between the nests being often filled up with sticks or rubbish, through which narrow passages are left for the ingress and egress of the birds. Many starlings that can find no room in the bushes build on the ground, or under

Fig. 118.—Brown Pelicans diving for fish. (Sanborn, photographer. Courtesy N. Y. Zoological Society.)

stones, or in holes, and these unfortunates, together with their eggs or young, ultimately become the victims of the smaller carnivorous mammals or of snakes. It frequently happens also that either the young locusts are hatched in insufficient numbers or that they migrate before the young starlings are fledged. In either case large numbers of birds perish of hunger, the majority of the old birds and the more advanced young following the locusts."

Slugs and snails are eaten by thrushes and many other small birds with avidity, and the name "Snail-hawk" has been given on account of one bird's fondness for these mollusks. The Oyster-catcher feeds on clams and oysters and derives its name from the facility with which it inserts its bill and pries open the shells. The Courlan, a near relative of the rails, feeds on clams and mussels and has a most ingenious method of obtaining its food. In shallow water it feels about with its feet for these mollusks, and when they are found the bird inserts its bill between the valves with a sudden quick stroke, and, thus suspended, the heavy shell and its occupant are carried to the shore, where the shell is forced open and the animal eaten. Crows treat shell-fish in the same way that they do sea-urchins and crabs, carrying them aloft and, after dropping them, descending to feed on the nutritious flesh exposed by the shattered shells.

Squids, the "head-footed" leaders of the division of mollusks, are eaten by penguins at least, and so numerous and at times so conspicuous a feature of marine life are they that probably many other birds also feed upon them. Even deep-water snails and crabs are not safe, as the sturdy sea-ducks will sometimes dive to a depth of one hundred and fifty feet to feed upon them.

Fish count many enemies among birds, which have numerous ways of obtaining their victims from ocean or lake. Some of these are so ingenious that they well deserve notice. In their variety they rival the methods of man himself, and we find many analogies between the two. Penguins earn their food with perhaps the hardest work, as they follow the fast-swimming fish of the open ocean in their own icy element and capture them notwithstanding their speed and quick turns.

We must not forget the slim, evil-looking snake-birds of the tropical swamps, which also dart through the water, but impale their victims on their needle-pointed beaks, suggesting the fish-spears of mankind. Cormorants and sheldrakes also dive after the fish on which they feed.

Next in the list of strenuous seekers after fish we must mention the osprey, which hovers on slowly vibrating wings, treading the air, as it were, over some favourite spot, until a finny back shows itself near the surface, when, giving itself to gravitation, the bird drops like a plummet. It seizes its prey in its talons, while our common kingfisher, after watching patiently from some branch overhanging the water, uses its bill to capture the fish. Terns dive for their fish, gulls usually snatch them from the surface, and skuas and jaegers get theirs at second hand, stealing fish from the more skilful fishers of the sea. When schools of mullet leap in frantic fear from the water to escape the attacks of porpoises, or when the dolphins force the flying-fish above the surface, the merciless Frigate-bird has but to pick and choose. Certain cormorants are the analogues of man's gill-nets, a flock of these birds surrounding a school of fish in a half-circle and driving them ashore or into shallow water.

Fig. 119.—Osprey with fish in its claws. (E. H. Baynes, photographer.)

155

Herons are the 'still-fishers' of the bird world, and stand in the shallows, silent and motionless as the reeds around them, with their lance-like beaks in rest and their necks

Fig. 120.—Great Blue Heron, a still hunter. (Sanborn, photographer. Courtesy N. Y. Zoological Society.)

at a hair-trigger poise. So we see that few kinds of fish, from the lowly lamprey to the jewelled brook trout, escape the sharp eyes of birds, and even when decayed masses of fish are thrown ashore, feathered scavengers are always alert.

Frogs always suggest storks to our minds, the relation being of course solely a gastronomic one, and indeed most of the near relatives of the frog pay their tithe to birds in a similar way.

Fig. 121.—Wild Mouse, the most frequent victim of birds.

Turtles, lizards, and snakes enter largely into the food of certain birds, some of which, such as the Secretary-bird and our native Road-runner, are adepts in the capture and killing of members of the latter division of reptiles. Certain sea-eagles subsist chiefly upon sea-snakes.

The most unpleasant items in the bill of fare of the bird kingdom are birds themselves, although few, if any, hawks or owls feed exclusively on members of their own Class. The most systematic cannibal among birds is the Peregrine Falcon or Duck Hawk, and, where birds are abundant, this fastidious *gourmand* merely eats the flesh of the head and neck and the eyes of each victim, leaving the remainder of the body untouched. Occasionally, as among other animals, a bird of strictly vegetarian habits will attack another bird, even one of its own kind, and kill and eat it in the most matter-of-fact way.

Owls are the terror of many birds, from the tiny Elf-Owl which sometimes finds a sparrow too great a match for him, to the great Strenuous Owl of Australia, which snatches full-grown Lyre-birds from their perches. But these birds of the night are ever ready to vary their diet; as we read of certain owls in India feeding chiefly on fish and crabs which they snatch from the water. In that same country, too, bats form a large part of the Barn Owl's diet.

The eggs of birds are delicacies which many feathered robbers, such as jays and crows, can never resist. There are two birds, however, one a raven and one a hawk, which well deserve the eggs which they steal,—so ingenious is their method of obtaining them. In South Africa, on an ostrich-farm, when a female bird has left her nest for a few minutes, a black form will often appear and hasten toward the great white eggs. Hovering over them the raven will let fall a stone into their midst, instantly swooping down and regaling himself on the yolk pouring out through the crack in the shell. His beak being too weak to break the shell, he has learned to adopt this effective method. A similar remarkable habit is related of the Black-breasted Buzzard of Australia, but in this case it is an emeu which is the victim. After breaking a hole in the thick shell, this bird inserts its foot and carries the egg to its nest.

Perhaps every Order of the higher warm-blooded animals may be included in our list, from the sloth which mutely resigns itself to the terrible grip of a Harpy Eagle to the human child which is powerless before the attack of some bird of prey frenzied with hunger. In certain districts eagles and hawks have been shot smelling strongly of skunk, but whether that fearless animal really figured in their diet remains to be proved! If any entire group of mammals is to be excepted from the birds' bill of fare, it is only that of the whales, although indeed, when one of these leviathans dies from any cause, his blubber and oil furnish food for sea-birds of many kinds.

The small gnawers of wood, the rodents, suffer most heavily, and untold thousands are devoured by hawks and owls, while cranes, shrikes, and ducks make away with their share.

This brief and very imperfect review of the vast variety of substances eaten by birds is at least instructive in revealing vividly the complex interrelations of all organic life on the earth. A counter-list of animate creatures which cause the death of birds would be as

surprising in its numbers and
extent. Every class of living
beings appears, at certain phases
of its existence, to check or come
into intimate contact with other
unrelated groups, radically affecting the most isolated, in ways
too subtle for our observation.
A little green flycatcher snatching a tiny gnat from its hiding-
place beneath a leaf seems
a trivial incident, and yet
the effects of accumulated

Fig. 122.—Red-tailed Hawk
(the watcher) an active
hunter.

events no more important than this are felt around the
world, so delicate is the balance of Nature.

Oddities of Birds' Diet

To give any adequate idea of the vagaries of the diet
of birds would require a volume by itself, but certain changes

Fig. 123.—Red Squirrel (the watched),
food of hawks and owls.
(R. H. Beebe, photographer.)

in feeding habits, due to
some increased pressure in
the struggle for existence,
are too interesting to be
passed by unnoticed. They
show us how plastic and
adaptive birds as a whole
are,—how, often, instead
of giving up and becoming
extinct, a certain race will

instantly accept changed conditions and flourish under
the new *régime*.

As the range of diet of the whole Class of birds is so
vast, doubtless the food of the individual species varies
more than we should ever suppose, but many instances
are recorded of birds regularly feeding on food for whose
capture they seem very ill adapt-
ed. Insects form the staple food
of all flycatchers and tyrant-
birds, but the Sulphur Tyrant and
several others readily devour
snakes. They dash down at one
of these reptiles, catch it up in
their beak, and, flying back to
a branch or stone, hammer the
snake flail-like, until its life is
battered out. Certain small kingfishers living in New Zealand

Fig. 124.—Texas Kingfisher
fishing for insects.

have deserted the habits of their group, and subsist on the
remarkable diet of "flies, young birds, and cherries"!

The change in habits of the Kea Parrot is only too
well known, especially to the sheep-raisers in New Zealand, the home of these birds. Originally exclusive
fruit-eaters, they have lately become so fond of the fat
from the backs of living sheep that they have developed
into ravenous birds of prey, vivisecting their victims and
rejecting all but the choicest morsels. Gulls have long
been known to enjoy an insect diet, and on the pampas
in the vicinity of Buenos Ayres the people look and pray
for flocks of gulls as the only relief from the hordes of

grasshoppers which occasionally devastate that region. In the antipodes we find a gull with crepuscular habits, whose entire food consists of night-flying moths.

Birds in captivity may sometimes be induced to eat food which they would never touch when in a state of freedom, but there are three species of birds the variety of whose natural diet will challenge that of any living creature. The first is a Burrowing Owl. This bird will not disdain vegetable food, and in its underground dining-chambers have been found remains of ducklings, sparrows, mice, and many other small birds and rodents; snakes and frogs, besides spiders, beetles, and apparently all small forms of life which these little birds are able to catch and kill. But leaving even the Burrowing Owl far behind in this respect is the Chimango Carrion-hawk of southern South America. Hudson tells us that nothing comes amiss to these birds. The vulture habit is perhaps strongest, and all offal and decaying meat is pounced upon with eagerness. All wounded and sickly creatures are closely watched until they die, or, if the opportunity offers, are despatched at once. When a large extent of grass is burned, bountiful repasts are ready for these birds in the shape of roasted snakes and small mammals. Eggs and young birds are especial dainties for the Chimango, and young sheep are often attacked, bringing to mind the Kea Parrot. The bird is, at times, a vegetable-feeder, and in fact it would be hard to find any organic object near its home, the edibility of which it has not tested.

The Red-winged Starlings of South Africa during

the greater part of the year feed upon larvæ and insects, but grapes, figs, and other soft fruits are eagerly devoured. They catch locusts and flying ants and occasionally devour the young of small birds. When their travels take them near the seashore they search the seaweed for snails and shrimps, and one of the greatest delicacies is the

FIG. 125.—Moth and Hummingbird. Both half natural size.

fruit of the syringa-tree, "on which they sometimes gorge themselves until they are no longer capable of flight, . . . affected by some narcotic property of the berry itself."

This state of semi-intoxication is by no means rare among fruit-eating birds, when over-ripe or fermented fruit is abundant.

The great extent to which all the external organs and parts of birds are adapted to facilitate the obtaining of food is evident in every species; but in hummingbirds this adaptation is especially apparent, because we can compare these feathered mites with other creatures far beneath them structurally, but with feeding habits and general environment so similar that such a comparison is fraught with interest. These other creatures to which I refer are hummingbird moths. Again and again collectors have shot the moths, mistaking them for hummingbirds, as the manner of flight is the same in both, and the way in which each species poises before a flower, probing it with proboscis or bill, is identical. Of the way this wonderful resemblance is carried out even in details of the body Bates writes: "It is certainly very curious, and strikes me even when both are in the hand. Holding them sideways, the shape of the head and position of the eyes in the moth are seen to be nearly the same as in the bird, the extended proboscis representing the long beak. At the tip of the moth's body there is a brush of long hair-scales resembling feathers, which being expanded look very much like a bird's tail."

It seems very improbable that this resemblance can be attributed to mimicry, as neither has many dangerous enemies, their marvellous powers of flight being an all-sufficient protection. So we are left to conclude that it is solely to similarity in method of seeking their food that the likeness is due.

CHAPTER VII

THE BREAK OF A BIRD

THINK of a mite of a hummingbird shooting southward mile after mile; his singing wings beginning their throbbing in the cool damp air of an Alaskan fall, whirring through the dry heat of deserts and around the wind-eddied spurs of mountain-ranges, until they hum in the warm atmosphere of Mexico or Brazil, where tiny insects are never lacking throughout the winter! How exquisite an adjustment must exist in his organs; how mankind's engines of locomotion are put to shame! The only comparison of which we can think is with an insect,—a sphinx-moth or a beetle, whose wings of gauze lift and carry their owners so easily, so steadily. It will be interesting to keep this similarity in mind, superficial though it is.

Birds require, comparatively, a vastly greater strength and "wind" in traversing such a thin, unsupporting medium as air than animals need for terrestrial locomotion. Even more wonderful than mere flight is the performance of a bird when it springs from the ground, and goes circling upward higher and higher on rapidly beating wings, all the while pouring forth a continuous series of musical notes, the strength of the utterance of which is attested by their distinctness in our ears after the bird has passed beyond the range of vision. A human singer is compelled to put forth all his energy in his vocal efforts, and if, while singing, he should start on a run even on level ground, he would become exhausted at once. The apparatus which gives to a duck the "wind" to outstrip an express train, and to a Mockingbird notes which hold us spellbound as by a *motif* of grand opera, is most interesting, and as easy to understand in its general scheme as it is effective in operation.

The Trachea, or Windpipe

Look into the beak of a sparrow or pigeon and directly back of the tongue, on the floor of the mouth, a narrow slit is visible —the glottis, or opening of the windpipe. In the gaping yellow mouth of a nestling robin this may be seen to excellent advantage, and watched as it widens and narrows with each breath. But give the young bird a mouthful of food, and this air-passage closes instantly and remains so until all danger of an intruding substance is past. No matter how suddenly you may eject a stream of water from a medicine-dropper into the bird's mouth, reflex action will anticipate the danger of choking and close the aperture.

FIG. 126 — Open glottis of a Pelican.

The swollen rim of this opening suffices to close it, and
there is no elaborate trap-door arrangement as in mammals, only a few backwardly directed fleshy points.
Birds have no trace of an "Adam's apple." The vocal
chords and other adjuncts to the voice of mammals
are entirely absent in birds, not a single note or song
being produced in the upper
throat.

Passing down the neck
from this orifice is the windpipe, which follows the
course of the œsophagus, or
food canal, passes to one
side of the crop and be-
tween the two branches of
the wish-bone, and finally
divides into two equal parts
called bronchi, which carry
the air directly to the lungs.

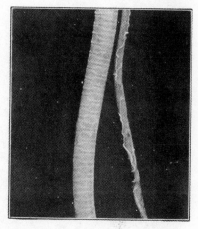

FIG. 127.—Windpipe and œsophagus of
bird compared; the former always distended; the latter soft and collapsed.

Comparison of the two
tubes which traverse the
throat and neck of birds shows them to be very different
in appearance and structure, and consideration of their
respective functions gives us the key to this dissimilarity.
The only occasion for the œsophagus to open is to permit
the passage of food, and thus a limp, fleshy canal answers
all requirements. The windpipe, on the contrary, must
always be wide open, and not only this, but it must be kept
open no matter what the pressure upon it. In addition,
it must be flexible, yielding to every motion of the neck,

and elastic, in order to stretch and contract as the bird reaches out or draws back its head.

We find a most ingenious arrangement fulfilling all these requirements. A series of bony rings is imbedded in the wall of the trachea, beginning with that portion

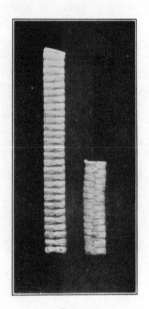 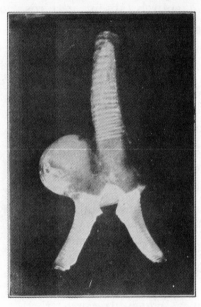

FIG. 128.   FIG. 129.

FIG. 128.—Windpipe of Flamingo, extended and contracted, showing delicate mechanism of supporting rings.
FIG. 129.—Syrinx-drum of Mallard Drake; the windpipe above; the bronchi below leading to the lungs.

immediately back of the glottis, and extending throughout its entire length. The membrane which connects these rings is so elastic that a section of trachea can be drawn out until it is twice as long as when contracted. When in the latter condition (I have in my hand an inch of the windpipe of a flamingo, but the general structure is common to all birds) the trachea appears to be composed of alternating half-rings, but when elongated these are seen to be complete, the illusion being produced by the overlapping of half of each ring by an equal part of the rings on each side. When the trachea is extended, the only hint of this clever device is a small notch on the sides of every ring. The illustration demonstrates the working better than any description.

Nature is ingenious but not perfect, as is seen even in the inch of Flamingo's trachea which I have utilized for illustration and description. Two of the rings do not "jibe" on one of their sides, and overlap the wrong way, but the loss in motion is infinitesimal, the defect being hardly noticeable even when the rings are bent into a semicircle.

In a very young English Sparrow there are about fifty rings around the trachea, appearing to be of a more cartilaginous nature than those of the flamingo. This latter long-necked bird has no less than four hundred and fifty rings.

In some members of the Class of amphibians (frogs, toads, and newts) the trachea is supported by small irregular pieces of cartilage, tending in the higher forms toward ringed areas. Among reptiles an intermediate condition exists, complete rings being present, but of cartilage instead of bone.

The wonderful music of birds is produced in a relatively small area, known as the syrinx. This organ is situated at the point where the trachea divides into the two bronchi. The latter arise as if by a splitting of the windpipe, and the effect is heightened by the rings which extend as far as the lungs, which are half-rings or semi-circles, the inner halves being replaced by membrane. This organ is peculiarly characteristic of birds, there being not a trace of it in any reptile.

But though the syrinx alone is concerned in the production of sound, this may be modified, made resonant, or given a reverberating quality by a special structure or by windings of the trachea before it reaches the syrinx, and which are perfect analogies of human musical instruments. Many species of ducks have an enlarged box of bone, a kind of drum, on the lower portion of the trachea, sometimes of one shape, sometimes of another, serving, doubtless, to give power to the bird's voice. Cranes and swans have veritable French horns in their breast-bones. The windpipe enters between the arms of the clavicles or wish-bone, and describes an S or even a more intricate figure before passing out and dividing into the two bronchial tubes. When a Trumpeter Swan stretches out its neck and utters a musical clang, most maligned by comparing it to a whoop, we should remember the cause of its mellowness. In the majestic Whooping Crane of our Western States, which in a few years will have vanished from the earth, the windings of the trachea reach their maximum. The entire windpipe of this bird is four feet in length, and of this, one-half is coiled within the sternum, or breastbone, giving remarkable volume and resonancy to the voice.

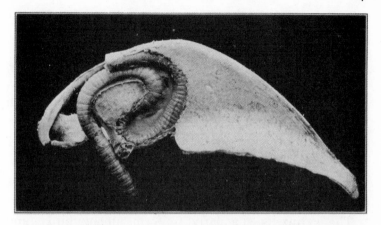

FIG. 130.—Breast-bone of Sandhill Crane.

FIG. 131.—Breast-bone of Whooping Crane, showing convolutions of trachea within the keel.

The Syrinx

This organ is peculiar to birds and, as stated before, is alone concerned in the production of the voice, although the tongue in parrots may be of some aid in distinctness of articulation. But this is not true of any other Order of birds, and the operation of splitting the tongue of a magpie or crow to "make it talk" is as unnecessary as it is inhumanly cruel.

The syrinx is singularly uniform among birds, and this seems the more remarkable when we consider the great variety of vocal sounds which are produced. The position and the structure of this organ vary within narrow limits, but in general it is composed of several modified rings of the lower trachea or upper bronchial tubes. The membranes which cover the inner half of each bronchial tube unite at their juncture with the windpipe and extend some little way into it as a thin median fold of tissue, supported by a bony framework. The tenseness or looseness of this membrane is governed by special muscles, of which there are from one to seven pairs. It is by the action of these muscles that the varying tones of croak, scream, warble, or trill are produced, the air from the lungs rushing out through the bronchial tubes and past the varying aperture controlled by the syringeal membrane.

We may dissect out every muscle and study trachea, syrinx, and bronchi with all the apparatus and instruments afforded by modern science, and yet the mystery of song is not solved. The marvel of the Canyon Wren's melody becomes but the more wonderful; the voice of the Seriema, carrying over a mile, and the never-to-be-forgotten evening song of the Solitaire only impress us with the failure of the scalpel and microscope to explain more than superficially the varied expressions of life.

Lungs and Air-sacs

At the beginning of this chapter a bird was compared to an insect, and the reason will now be apparent. The body of an insect is aerated by means of an intricate system of tubes ramifying throughout the body, which in many instances are connected with air-sacs. The comparison with a bird is not to its lungs, which are small and compact, but to a series of nine air-sacs, distributed through much of the body,—four pairs, and two which have coalesced into one.

When a bird is dissected, the thin membranous walls of these air-cavities are collapsed and rather difficult to make out, being very similar in appearance to other connective tissues of the body. But if we insert a small blowpipe into the trachea of a dead bird, tie it tightly about with a piece of string and blow into it, all the air-sacs will become distended and bladder-like and can easily be made out. It is remarkable how closely these sacs fit around the viscera and muscles, occupying every crevice and filling the whole body of the bird with air, thus reducing its specific gravity, and making it a creature literally "of the air." There is sometimes a layer of air between the muscles and the skin, and when we handle a bird thus aerated the skin crackles under our touch.

The lungs and air-sacs send off tiny membranous tubes which enter the bones of the limbs and skull and sometimes even the small bones of the wings and toes, which are hollow and thus filled with air. It seems incredible, but nevertheless it is true that the connection between the lungs and the upper arm-bone of a bird is so substantial that a bird which has had its wing broken with shot is able to breathe through the splintered end of this hollow bone when its windpipe is completely choked with blood.

We may compare the body of a bird to a submarine boat with many water-tight compartments, and as such a vessel is made buoyant by admitting air to these bulkheads, so a swimming bird may float high out of water by inflating its sacs and filling its bone-cavities with air. Conversely, when we see a grebe slowly and mysteriously submerge its body, we conclude that it has but emptied its lung auxiliaries.

We now come to the most important part of the respiratory system, where the blood and the air come into closest contact and exchange gases, the oxygen of the air vitalizing the entire body. If we follow the two bronchial tubes after they leave the syrinx, we shall find that each enters a lung, and passes through it, giving off a number of side branches which open into the various air-sacs. The lungs are not elastic and, instead of lying freely in the body, are flattened against the back-

bone and ribs, and when carefully removed show furrows made by these latter bones. There is still much
to be learned of the manner of a bird's breathing, but
it is probable that there is a sidewise or dorsal expansion of the ribs, rather than of that portion corresponding
to our chest. In a bird the latter region is chiefly an immense flight-muscle, which could hardly yield to the
action of breathing while carrying on the tremendous
work of keeping the wings in motion, and when a

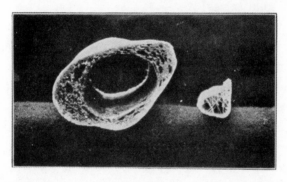

Fig. 132.—Cross-section of wing-bone of Ostrich and Black Swan. In life the
bone of the Ostrich is filled with marrow; that of the Swan with air.

bird squats on a branch with its breast pressed close
to the perch, "chest expansion" must be all but
impossible.

We cannot help being surprised at first when we see
how small are the lungs of a bird in comparison with
the size of its body.

The first thought that occurs to us is that the air-
sacs in birds, and the hollow cavities of the bones, must
function chiefly as aids to flight, and we should expect
to find as best flyers those birds in which the air-cavities

are most numerous, but there are many exceptions. The bones of storks and vultures (birds of great powers of flight) are extremely pneumatic, while the bones of the flightless ostriches are filled with marrow, and in the aquatic penguins even this is reduced to a thread, the bones being almost wholly osseous tissue. A swan, although a heavy bird, flies remarkably well when once on the wing, and is highly aerated, but, on the other hand, terns and swifts—past-masters both in aerial evolutions —have solid bones!

Now an athlete who is trained in running has always a very large lung capacity. Two persons of equal health and strength, one of whom has run many races or who has the power of keeping up a dog-trot for hour after hour, while the other has led a more sedentary life, may show a remarkable difference in the amount of air which they can draw into their lungs—perhaps one hundred or one hundred and fifty cubic inches more in the case of the runner. The average person uses only about one seventh of his lung capacity in ordinary breathing, the rest of the air remaining at the bottom of the lung, being termed "residual." As this is vitiated by its stay in the lung, it does harm rather than good by its presence. When great exertion is required, as in running, the person who can admit the largest amount of fresh air to his lungs in each breath has command of an equally great power of action.

As we have seen, the lungs of a bird are small and non-elastic, but this is more than compensated by the continuous passage of fresh air, passing not only into but entirely *through* the lungs into the air-sacs, giving, therefore, the very best chance for oxygenation to take place in every portion of the lungs. When we compare the estimated number of breaths which birds and men take in a minute—thirteen to sixteen in the latter, twenty to sixty in birds—we realize better how birds can perform such wonderful feats of song and flight.

Birds, having no sweat-glands in the skin, and the action of the capillaries being impeded by the feathers, would have no way of regulating the temperature of the body, much as this is necessary in flight, if it were not that the great quantity of air exhaled with each breath relieves the body of any excess of heat.

However directly or indirectly the air-sacs are concerned with flight, a bird which sings uninterruptedly as it flies upward must be immeasurably aided by the great quantity of air at its command. And again, when a Prairie Hen inflates the orange-hued air-sacs on both sides of its neck, there is only one explanation as to their use, at least at the time of courtship, namely, an added decoration, and as an aid in the "booming"— factors both of which, for aught we know, may help to soften the hearts of the coquettish females.

Looking down the scale of life we find an animal among the reptiles with a lung which at once suggests that of a bird. The lungs of a chameleon are spongy and compact in front, but farther back they are hollow, and give off a dozen or more finger-like tubes or lobes, thus foreshadowing, at least in appearance, the air-sacs of birds.

We have learned that the chick in the egg passes through a stage when it possesses several well-developed gills. This proves that in the dim, distant past the ancestors of birds were once aquatic and fish-like. But how about lungs? Fishes have none, and indeed in their aquatic life such organs would be useless. Nevertheless, as we shall see, the lungs of reptiles, birds, and mammals are legacies from the creatures of the sea.

Many fishes have within their bodies a thin-walled sac, known as the swim-bladder. This is filled with gas, and as the fish ascends to the surface, or dives to where the pressure of the water is very great, the amount of gas varies; so that the specific gravity of the fish changes with that of the water. This swimbladder is generally connected with the throat by a delicate tube; and in these two structures we have the homologues of the birds' lungs and trachea. Proof of this is to be found in the growth of the lungs in all young chicks. A tiny bud appears upon the primitive œsophagus, just behind the little gill-clefts, and increases in size until it is larger than the food-canal itself. It then in turn divides into two equal parts which become diminutive flaps, or canals—the beginnings of the lungs.

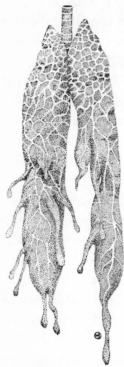

Fig. 133.—Lung of Chameleon, foreshadowing condition in bird.

A simple experiment will show what fishes have a canal, or duct, leading from the throat to the swim-bladder and what have not. If a goldfish and a perch or sunfish be placed in a bowl of water and the air exhausted, the two latter will be forced to the surface, while the goldfish will soon eject a few bubbles of air, or gas, from its mouth and stay at the bottom. Thus we can see the ad-

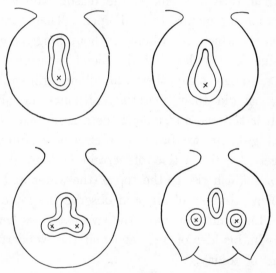

FIG. 134.—Diagram of growth of lungs. X, the lower part of the primitive digestive tract, divides into two parts, XX, the lungs.

vantage of such a canal in enabling the fish to regulate the amount of gas in the bladder.

When the fish-like creatures of old took to living on land, the change from swim-bladder and gas to lung and air was a remarkable example of change of function of an organ, and the more we learn of the lungs of living creatures the more marvellous does this transformation seem to us. In changing, Nature seems to have tried numberless experiments, only a few of which have survived. For example, we know that fish breathe by a sort of swallowing, the water being taken in at the mouth and poured out through the gill-clefts. So in frogs and salamanders we find that, although they possess lungs, yet they still employ a swallowing process to get the air down their throats. This is the reason why a frog will suffocate if its mouth is held open. There are certain salamanders which are wholly without lungs, their moist skin being so vascular that the blood is purified through it. But strange to say, these amphibians still swallow and swallow, as did their ancestors, although no air passes down their throats, and indeed there is no place to which it could go! As we have seen elsewhere, birds exhale air largely by the action of certain abdominal muscles. Watch a goldfish rise to the top of the water and eject or gulp down a bubble of air, and observe the rapid breathing of a bird, and you have the two extremes before you —the swim-bladder of ages ago and the wonderful lungs of a bird of to-day.

The Heart and the Life-blood

Perhaps the most wonderful organ in a bird's body is its heart. In the very lowest of back-boned animals the heart is merely a long tube, in fact a simple artery or vein, which contracts at certain intervals and so propels in a forward direction the fluid which it contains. A fish may almost be said to have its heart in its head, so far forward in its body is it placed; nevertheless, as is the case in all the warm-blooded creatures above it, the heart is nearer the under side of the body—the breast —than near the back. And herein lies an important difference between the two great divisions of the Animal Kingdom, vertebrates and invertebrates,—the former always having the heart near the breast, while in the back-boneless organisms it is near the back.

The heart of a fish is fairly concentrated and muscular, but the blood which passes through it is but an impure and sluggish stream. In reptiles both pure and impure blood is found in the heart, but they mingle, and thus half destroy the purifying action of the lungs. This explains why these animals are cold-blooded, and also accounts for their usual lethargic disposition and low mental plane of life.

In crocodiles we find a significant condition. There are four chambers in the heart, as in mammals and in birds, but this avails nothing; for, leading from the heart are two arteries instead of one, and where these cross each other there is a tiny aperture—a small opening in the partition which allows the impure blood to leak into the stream of pure, red blood, and so a crocodile is only a crocodile, although evolution has lifted his heart almost to a level with birds and the warm-blooded animals. If this tiny hole could become closed, and the two streams of blood be kept separate, the eyes of the crocodile would brighten, his activity increase many fold, and in fact his entire plane of life would be changed.

I have thus briefly reviewed the heart in the lower vertebrates in order to give a more vivid idea of this organ in birds. Here we find an organ remarkably large in proportion to the size of the bird's body—a conical knot of muscle, the power of which is almost beyond belief. The heart of a bird is said to beat a "hundred and twenty times a minute when the bird is at rest. The first flap of the wings doubles the pulsations, and when the bird is frightened or exhausted the number of beats are too many to be counted."

There are four separate chambers, known as right and left ventricles and auricles, and the partition which divides the heart in the middle is blood-tight so that not a particle of "bad" blood can get through and vitiate the life-giving stream which has just come from the lungs.

A Bluebird is perched on a twig near its nest murmuring its sweet warble; a Wood Pewee, half hidden in the shadows of some dense, moist forest, speaks to us in its sad dreamy phrase; how calmly, how quietly they sit! It seems impossible to believe that every drop of blood in their bodies is rushing back and forth with inconceivable rapidity—from heart to head, from body to wings and legs, and back again!

Let us take the blood as it is just leaving the heart in the breast in one of these little feathered beings, and trace its course through the body and back again to the starting-point. The left ventricle opens into the aorta, the greatest artery, or blood-tube leading from the heart, in the body. The clean oxygen-food-bearing stream rushes through this channel, which we may compare to the trunk of a tree, and is carried into branch arteries, dividing finer and finer, just as the trunk of

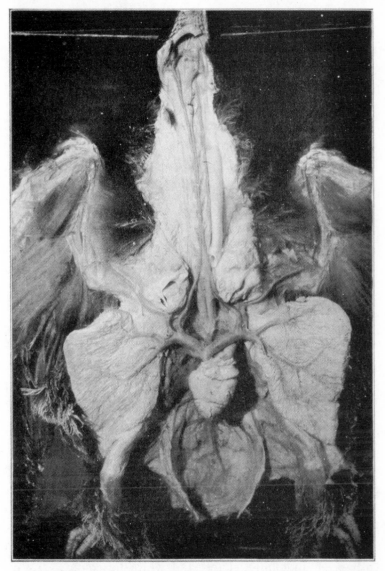

FIG. 135.—Circulatory system of Pigeon (injected), showing blood-vessels rami-fying from the heart to every part of the body.

183

the tree merges into limbs, and these into branches, twigs, stems, and at last into the delicate foliage. This last we may liken to the capillaries or hair-tubes in which the blood does its real work of supplying nourishment directly to the tissues, and where it receives the waste matters, carrying them away in its current.

When we have followed the divisions of a tree out to the foliage, we may find that they touch and interlace with the foliage of another tree, and this is very much like what occurs in the course of the blood. The capillaries run together and form larger vessels, these in turn coalesce, and soon the blood—dark now and filled with the waste matters of the body-cells—is flowing through only two large veins (*veins* always lead *toward* the heart). These enter the right auricle, which opens into the right ventricle. From here the blood rushes to the lungs to be purified and back again to the left auricle and ventricle, and its cycle is complete.

If we look at a drop of bird's blood (or that of any kind of warm-blooded creature) under the microscope, we shall see thousands upon thousands of oval discs, or corpuscles, like tiny platters floating in a fluid. These flow about under the cover-glass through little channels, mechanically and very slowly of course, and giving but a faint idea of the way they must tumble and rush after each other through the veins and arteries of the bird. Scattered among these oval bodies will occasionally be seen others of indefinite shape and white in colour. As we watch one of these tiny cells, the thought suddenly comes over us,—what are birds indeed but collections of untold

millions of one-celled animals! For here before us we
have what is almost exactly like the little flowing drops
of jelly called Amœbæ which we may find in quiet ponds
and watch as they move about in search of food; flowing
around a bit of nutriment, digesting it and flowing away
from the waste matter which is left.   This is just what the

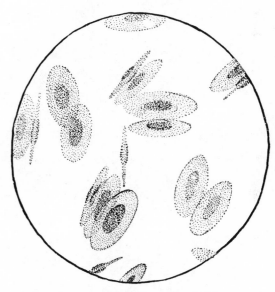

Fig. 136.—Blood-corpuscles of bird.

white corpuscles do; they flow around the food which is
absorbed by the walls of the digestive canal, and in fact
act like tiny independent animals, parts though they are
of the great whole. The oval corpuscles carry and distribute the oxygen, and here we have in a sentence the
inner 'living' of a bird: the food-canal bringing in food
and preparing it; the windpipe and lungs admitting

oxygen; and the blood taking up and transporting both to every part of the body.

The normal temperature of our body is about $98\frac{1}{2}°$; if it rose to 106°, we should soon succumb to the burning fever, while the little bird before us is healthy and comfortable with a temperature of 110° to 112°!

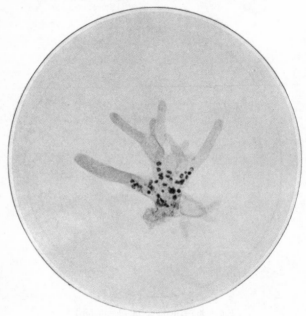

Fig 137.—Amœba, greatly magnified. (Courtesy of Dr. G. L. Calkins.)

The next time you see a wee chickadee, calling contentedly and happily while the air makes you shiver from head to foot, think of the hard-shelled frozen insects passing down his throat, the icy air entering lungs and air-sacs, and ponder a moment on the wondrous little laboratory concealed in his mite of a body; which his wings bear up with so little effort, which his tiny legs support, now hopping along a branch, now suspended from some wormy twig.

Can we do aught but silently marvel at this alchemy? A little bundle of muscle and blood, which in this freezing weather can transmute frozen beetles and zero air into a happy, cheery little Black-capped Chickadee, as he names himself, whose bravery shames us, whose trustfulness warms our hearts!

And the next time you raise your gun to needlessly take a feathered life, think of the marvellous little engine which your lead will stifle forever; lower your weapon and look into the clear bright eyes of the bird whose body equals yours in physical perfection, and whose tiny brain can generate a sympathy, a love for its mate, which in sincerity and unselfishness suffers little when compared with human affection.

Fig. 138.—Chickadee in the snow.

CHAPTER VIII

MUSCLES AND NERVES

Muscles

BIRDS exhibit probably a greater degree of activity than any other class of animals. Some seem never to be still, and, whether soaring, fluttering, running, hopping, climbing, dancing, or swimming, every motion is the result of the action of one or more muscles.

The entire flesh of a bird is divided up into layers or bundles of distinct muscles, each having its function,— raising, lowering, or in some way moving feathers, eyelids, legs, wings, tail, and other portions of the body. The number and intricacy of these muscles can be imagined when it is stated that in a goose there are more than twelve thousand muscles or parts of muscles immediately beneath the skin, which serve to raise or otherwise move the feathers.

In a penguin the muscles immediately beneath the skin are unusually well developed, and for an excellent reason. By means of them the water "may be readily expelled from the interstices of the plumage so soon as the bird quits the water. Were it otherwise, in the low temperature of the Antarctic region, which the majority of these birds inhabit, their plumage would soon be frozen

into an icy mass, the high temperature of the bird being
of itself insufficient to obviate this, although assisted
by the great development of the subcutaneous fatty
layer, which far exceeds in thickness that of the corresponding structure in the member of any other group
of birds, and recalls to mind the fatty deposit of 'blubber' of the seals and cetaceans."

When we looked at the blood of a bird, we saw the
tiny white corpuscles, which in life flow and move in
every direction, constantly changing their outline; and
now if we take a piece of a bird's muscle or flesh and
examine it carefully, after "teasing" it out into shreds
with a needle, we shall see another kind of cell-animal.
These are long and generally pointed, each a single cell
with a tiny spot or nucleus in it, differing from the white-
blood animals in being able to stretch out and contract
in only one direction.   When we will our arm to close
together, bringing our hand close to our shoulder, a thick
colony or bunch of these muscle-animals shortens, becomes stouter, and bulges up under the skin on our upper
arm.

In our own body the bones of the spinal column are
movable, and we can bend in almost every direction,
and so we are provided with many important back-muscles.
But if we have ever carved a chicken, we shall remember that the ribs and shoulder-bones are close to the surface, and but poor pickings are to be had from them.
The breast and chest, on the contrary, are hidden in a
thick mass of muscles, most of which are concerned with
moving the wings in flight.   The immense pectoral or

breast muscle, which makes possible the all-important downward sweep of the wings, weighs one-fifth as much as the entire bird, bones and all. This arrangement of a great weight of muscle hung below the point of attach-

Fig. 139.—Wing and breast of Pigeon, showing immense pectoral muscles, and tendons of wing used in flight.

ment of the wings is, for mechanical reasons, the only one possible in a bird of flight; since any excess of weight above the wings would instantly overbalance the bird.

If we remove the skin from the upper arm of a bird,

we shall see a tangle of bundles of red flesh—the muscles
which unite to make the arm of a bird such an exquisite
flying-machine.   Where a muscle narrows and is fastened
to a bone, its fibres merge into a thin, tough white cord—

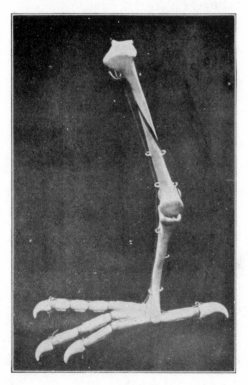

Fig. 140.—Model of bird's foot, showing perching tendons; toes extended.

a tendon.   This is not elastic like the main portion of
the muscle, but is much more tough.

   In the slender legs and feet of birds there is little more
than bone, tendon, and skin.   The tendons which clasp
and unclasp the toes are very interesting, and if we will

bend the tarsus back and forth in the leg of a dead chicken, the workings of these strands of tissue may be traced beneath the scales. Reference to the photograph, where catgut replaces these tendons, will make their workings still more plain.

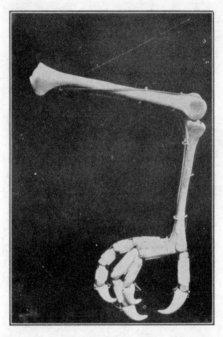

Fig. 141.—Same as Fig. 140; toes contracted.

Many birds cannot flex the leg without drawing the toes up, and we may be sure that these birds are safe when they perch; the closer they sit to the branch the tighter becomes their grip. But this safety mechanism is not found in all perching birds by any means (Fig. 143).

A strange thing about muscles is that there are fine

wavy cross-lines, or striations, on those which are moved voluntarily, such as the muscles of the neck or wing; but those which are moved involuntarily, as the gizzard, are smooth and without the cross-lines.

Fig. 142.—Amazon Parrot in sleeping position, hanging by its toes; illustrating the wonderful strength of the tendons.

Among birds new muscles have appeared, or old ones have split up or so changed in position that it is all but impossible to compare them, muscle for muscle, with other animals. There are so many resemblances between birds and reptiles that we naturally turn to the latter for comparison, but even here we find a great unlikeness. We learned, when we reflected on the number of ribs of a bird, that the repetition of so many similar structures was merely the last remaining vestige of ancestral body segments, which reach their extreme development (in number and similarity) among the worms; but in regard to muscles birds show little or nothing of this. In lizards we may count dozens upon dozens of bands of muscles succeeding one another, all more or less alike, from head to tail, but it is only in the neck of a bird that we shall find anything like this.

In order to give to muscles a firm anchorage, they must of course be attached to the bones. At these points of attachment deep furrows or cavities are often found in the surface of the bones, and in still other ways we are reminded, even in fossil bones, of the flesh and muscle which once moved them. These muscle impressions are often a valuable source of identification in naming the bones of creatures which, many thousands of years ago, disappeared from the earth. And indeed so great variety exists in the muscles of living birds that many of them, those of the upper arm for example, are of considerable value in classification.

Nerves

The last great system of internal organs which we shall consider, and perhaps the most mysterious of all, is that of the nerves. We have learned that the back-

FIG. 143.—Young Black-throated Green Warbler, roosting close to its perch.

bone supports the entire body and gives a point of attachment for the limbs, but long before limbs were found among animals on the earth, in fact long before bone existed, a sheath of cartilage surrounded and supported the primitive spinal cord of creatures which lived long ago in earlier epochs of the earth's history. So we may say this protection to the nerve-trunk is the most important, as it was the original, function of our vertebræ. When "brainy" creatures appeared, that is, when the front end of the nerve-cord became enlarged, it needed some special protection, so a box—the skull,—first of cartilage, then of bone, was evolved.

One more fact which may hark back to old, old times, and then we shall leave the past as perhaps trespassing too much on the province of the chick while he is yet within the egg. Birds (and all the higher classes of animals) have what we may call two separate systems of nerves, although in some ways they are insolubly connected with each other. The brain and spinal cord send numerous branches which subdivide into countless nervelets, permeating every portion of the body, as we can easily prove by the feeling, on pricking our skin anywhere with a needle. This is the principal nervous system of back-boned animals, and it is by this that birds, and all creatures with well-developed nerves, see, hear, taste, smell, and by which they send messages to the muscles when they desire to move them. Below the vertebral column is another lesser system which sends nerves to the digestive tract and other organs, the movements and functions of which are not under control of the will, and

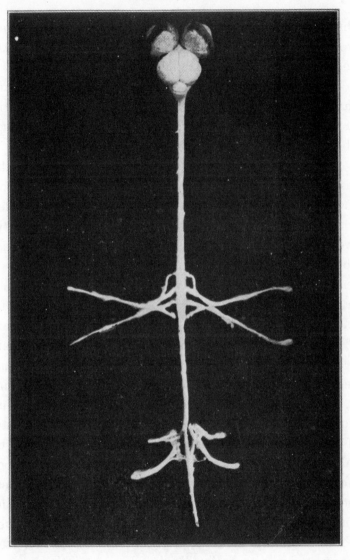

FIG. 144.—Nervous system of Pigeon, showing large **eyes and brain**, and nerves leading to wings and legs.

this is the sympathetic or reflex system. It is a very wonderful thing, this not having to think about the heart beating or the lungs expanding.

We can understand how a muscle (such as the heart) can pump the blood through the body, but we know little or nothing of the action of nerves. An eagle soars high above the clouds; a rabbit is discovered crouching in a field far below; the eye of the eagle telegraphs this discovery to the brain; a message is sent along the spinal cord, switches off to the wings, repeats to the muscles, which half close and set the great pinions firmly; the eye is the pilot, never leaving the mark; a triple message now goes out, to the wings to hold back, to the legs to reach forward, to the talons to open and clutch! All is done without a break or hesitation, so quickly that one's eye can hardly register the act, and all by means of impulses sent through the finest of white, hair channels, consisting of a substance so unstable that it tears and falls apart, like wet tissue-paper, when we examine it. And if the sending and receiving of impulses seems wonderful to us, what can we say of the brain, the master of all, where instinct, mind, soul,—no matter what we call it,—directs the whole life? It is here that fact upon fact, experience upon experience, is stored from the moment the bird breaks its shell throughout its whole lifetime, and it is from the brain that the benefit derived from this perception of experience, failures and successes, causes and effects, is intelligently brought into play and made to redound to the bettering of the subsequent life.

When we carefully remove the upper part of a bird's skull, we find that the brain occupies the whole interior,

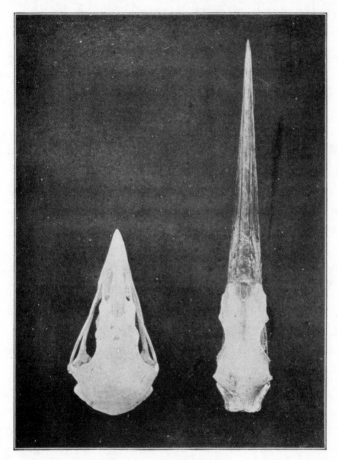

FIG. 145.—Comparison of skulls of Heron and Hawk, showing unlikeness caused by difference in manner of procuring food.

the shell or box of bone which protects it being very thin, although strong.   It would be very interesting if we could compare the short and thick bullet-shaped skull and brain of a rapacious hawk with the thin-templed head of a timid heron and say, "phrenologically," in the first we have the bump of combativeness well developed, analogous to a prize-fighter; in the second case, timidity is prominent! But unfortunately, characteristics such as these are compound, and made up of many simple factors, the synthesis of which is not confined to any particular "bump."

At the first sight of the bird's brain we are struck with the very great size of the two larger masses of brain-matter—cerebral hemispheres these are called. It is in these that the higher faculties reside, and when these are destroyed, all knowledge, all power of voluntary movement passes from the bird. These great brain-halves are much larger than in the brain of a reptile, in fact the cerebral hemispheres, set deep in the great buttressed skull of a full-grown crocodile, are no larger than those of the duck which he snaps up. Not only this, but in the days of the *Archæopteryx* (which had a typical bird-brain), the monster Dinosaur, *Triceratops*, 25 feet long, had, in its 6 feet of skull, a brain proportionately only one tenth as large as that of a modern crocodile! When compared with a mammal there is seen to be a conspicuous difference, since the outer surface is perfectly smooth in birds, but is wound about in convolutions in the higher four-footed animals. This latter condition is said to indicate a greater degree of intelligence, but when we look at the brain of a young musk-ox or walrus and find convolutions as deep as those of a five-year-old child, and when we compare the wonderfully varied life of birds, and realize what resource and intelligence they frequently display in adapting themselves to new untried conditions, a smooth brain does not seem such an inferior organ as is often inferred by writers on the subject. I would willingly match a crow against a walrus any day, in a test of intelligent behaviour!

Between the hemispheres is a small projection which

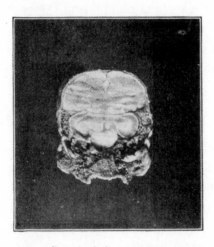

FIG. 146.—Vertical section through skull of bird, showing great size of brain.

is called the pineal body. It is very tiny, and we know little of its function at present, but its history is one of the most interesting chapters in the evolution of the bird, which we shall leave to the chapter on the senses.

The other most conspicuous part of the brain is the cerebellum, or "little brain," a section of which shows a most remarkable tree-like appearance. This has been called the *arbor vitæ*—the tree of life.

It is in this portion of the brain that a few tiny drops

of blood are found when a bird dies of fright, which occurs more often than in any other class of animals. Sportsmen have fired at a bird, missed it completely, and yet
have seen it drop dead as suddenly as if it had received
the full charge.   In captivity, herons succumb more
frequently to fright apoplexy than other birds. When
we assume the care of any creature, bird or beast, we
should treat it as a timid child, and the person who moves
quietly but unhesitatingly will win the confidence of
wild creatures much sooner than when he alarms them′
by sudden motions, or arouses their suspicions by jerky
half-hearted approaches.

There are twenty-four nerves given off in pairs from
the brain, which pass out through minute holes in the
skull, and energize eye, ear, tongue, and other organs.
Each of these has an individual name, and as they are
homologous with similar nerves in ourselves, the same
name is retained, such as the olfactory, or that leading
to the nostril; and the pathetic, the function of which
is to control the obliquely raising eye-muscle, producing
a pathetic expression, although it must be confessed that
the effect of this in the immobile face of a bird is not
especially affecting.

Back of the cerebellum is a thickening of the spinal
cord, and after again narrowing it enters the bones of the
neck and back, as the true spinal cord. At the base of
the neck and near the thigh-joints this cord increases
in size, large nerves being given off at these places to the
wings and legs.   It terminates in a fine white thread.

CHAPTER IX

THE SENSES

E have seen that the brain is the storehouse of facts and experiences, but whence come these and how do they gain admittance to that soft gray matter which is one of the wonders of the world? There are five channels (and sometimes there seems the shadow of a metaphysical sixth) which are cognizant of and receptive to environmental influences. These are the nostrils, eyes, ears and tongue, and the tactile nerves of the surface of the body; or in other words the bird is in direct connection with his surroundings on land or water or in the air, by means of the senses of smelling, seeing, hearing, tasting, and feeling.

The Sense of Smell

The sense of smell is dependent upon the diffusion in the air of minute particles of objects, and naturally is effective at very short distances compared to the senses of sight and hearing, which require only vibrations in the atmosphere. When we remember that the nostrils of birds are usually encased in horn and that there is no exposed moist surface, as in the nose of a dog, we shall see how it is that this sense is but little developed among feathered creatures.

FIG. 147.—Nostrils of bird encased in horn.

FIG. 148.—Nostrils of deer encased in moist flesh.

In all animals the mucous membrane which lines the nasal cavity is very delicate and filled with nervelets. These nervelets unite and form a single nerve on each side which passes to the brain and transmits the impressions derived from the odours in the air. The thin bones within the nostril, which, in dogs and deer, curl and recurl in delicate lines and scrolls and thus expose such a large surface to the odour-bearing air, are but poorly represented in birds. The simple curve of the bone in the nostrils of birds is very similar in structure to that found in reptiles.

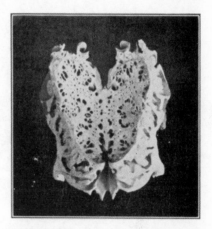

The question whether vultures perceive their prey by sight or smell has

Fig. 149.—Turbinal scrolls of dog. In a bird these bones are far more simple.

been decided in favour of the former sense. Lacking the ability readily to distinguish delicate odours, we find among birds none of the glands which are so common among hairy-coated creatures: the oil-gland is the only one on the body, and this is practically odourless. But slight as is the scent which diffuses from birds, it is sufficient to enable a dog, with his wonderful keenness of smell, to detect a crouching bird some distance away.

The woodcock of our inland swamps and marshes, and the apteryx of New Zealand, probably have the

sense of smell most acutely developed, although in both
cases it is the delicate nerves of touch in the bill which
are most helpful in detecting the presence of the earthworms which constitute the food of these birds.

To whatever degree the nostrils of land birds aid
their owners in procuring food, it is certain that those

FIG. 150.—Head of Apteryx, showing tactile hair-like feathers, nostrils at tip
of beak, and small eyes.

species which feed entirely on fish, which they swallow
whole, have little use for nostrils, except for breathing.
Thus Nature, ever on the watch to economize, has reduced these organs, in such birds as pelicans and cormorants, and, at least in the adults, the nostrils are completely filled up with bone and horn.

The Sense of Sight

Birds, so wonderful and interesting in all their structure and life, have that most treasured of all the senses— sight—so highly developed that there is nothing with which we can compare it among living creatures. With our great telescopes we can see to a greater distance than any bird; with the high-power lenses of our microscopes we can distinguish infinitely smaller objects than any feathered creature is capable of perceiving, but where else on the earth is there an organ of vision which in a fraction of time can change itself from telescope to microscope; where is the eye that, seeing with wonderful clearness in the atmosphere, suddenly adapts itself to the refraction of water, or (less slowly, although no less surely) to the darkness of night?

Next to our powers of reasoning, we value sight above all things, and fortunate indeed should we be could we but exchange our imperfect vision for sight like that of an eagle! Little need of spectacles or binoculars has he, for the perfection of his eye enables him to become near-sighted or far-sighted at will.

"The eye," says Professor Coues, "is an exquisitely perfect optical instrument, like an automatic camera which adjusts its own focus, photographs a picture upon its sensitized retinal plate, and telegraphs the molecular movements of the nervous sheet to the optic 'twins' of the brain, where the result is translated from the physical terms of motion in matter to the mental terms of consciousness. But no part of the nervous tract, from the surface of the retina to the optic centre, sees or knows anything about it, being simply the apparatus through which the bird looks, sees, and knows. In this Class of vertebrates the optic organs, both cerebral and ocular, are of great size, power, and effect; their vision far transcends that of man, unaided by artificial instruments, in scope and delicacy. The faculty of *accommodation*, that is of adjusting the focus of vision, is developed to a marvellous degree; rapid, almost instantaneous changes of the visual angle being required for distinct perception of objects that must rush into the focal field with the velocity at least of the bird's flight. Observe an eagle soaring aloft until he seems to us but a speck in the blue sky expanse. He is far-sighted, and, scouring the earth below, descries an object much smaller than himself, which would be invisible to us at that distance. He prepares to pounce upon his quarry; in the moment required for the deadly plunge he becomes at once nearsighted, seizes his victim with unerring aim, and sees well how to complete the bloody work begun. A hummingbird darts so quickly that our eyes cannot follow him, yet he instantaneously settles as lightly as a feather upon a tiny twig. How far off it was when first perceived we do not know; but in the intervening fraction of a second the twig has rushed into the focus of distinct vision, from many yards away. A woodcock tears through the thickest cover as if it were clear space, avoiding every obstacle. The only things to the accurate perception of which birds' eyes appear not to have accommodated themselves are telegraph-wires and light-houses;

thousands of birds are annually hurled against these objects to their destruction."

A bird's eye is very large in proportion to the size of its head, and is correspondingly perfect and delicate in its workings. It rests in a deep cavity hollowed out of the skull, and is protected by soft cushions of fat and controlled by bands and pulleys of muscle which control its motions.

Looking closely at the eye of a live bird, we at once remark its brightness—that alertness of expression which so truly reflects the virile life of these creatures. The eye, more than any other part of a living organism, is an index to the relative power of its intelligence—more surely than all the other facial features taken together. The eyes of a sloth are expressionless black spots, and even those of an orang-utan are bleary and watery. But a crow or magpie, or any other bird you may choose, though with horny, shapeless lips, nose, and mouth, looks at us through eyes so expressive, so human, that no wonder man's love has gone out to feathered creatures throughout all his life on the earth. A dog is a four-legged, hairy animal with the eyes of a bird.

The eye of a bird appears perfectly round, and is composed of a central area of black, encircled by a ring, sometimes hardly distinguishable from the inner division, or again it may be highly coloured. The circular centre or pupil is always of a uniform black, and no wonder, for "it is not a thing—it is the hole *in* a thing." As when we look through the lens of a camera, only the blackened inside of the bellows is reflected to us, so in the eye of a bird, the delicate living lens, itself invisible, reflects the black pigmented tissue at the back of the eye-ball. The image passes through this lens and is thrown upon the curtain of jet, and here the brain nerves find it and know it—how, we cannot even guess.

If the eye-camera of the bird has no long bellows to focus out and back, it has something infinitely better—the coloured ring or iris which surrounds the pupil. We

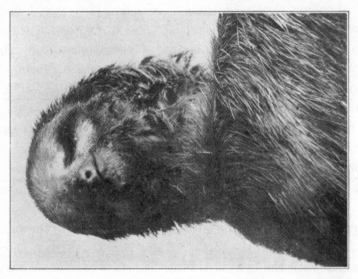

FIG. 151.—Head of living Sloth.

are all familiar with the way the oval iris of a cat narrows to a slit in bright sunlight and broadens at night to let in all the light possible. Look closely at the eye of an owl or parrot, even in broad daylight, and the circle of the iris will be seen to contract and enlarge at the will of the bird. We have always been inclined to pity the poor "blind" owl during the daytime, but the truth is that, because of this power of adjustment, almost all owls *can* see very well, even in sunshine, although of course their eyes are especially adapted for use in the dim light of the evening and of the stars. In Nova Scotia I have noticed Barred Owls flying about and feeding at noonday.

FIG. 152.—Duck Hawk. (Courtesy of N. Y. Zoological Society.)
Compare the alert expression with the sloth in Fig. 151.

Birds have well-developed lachrymal glands, although it is seldom that they actually shed tears. Still I have seen a flamingo in a flying-cage weeping copiously from terror, anticipating all sorts of torture from a harmless condor which was playfully galloping around the frightened bird.

Millions of years ago, in the geological period of time known as the Jurassic, there existed gigantic sea-lizards, which we call *Ichthyosauri*. All we know of them we have learned by study of their fossil bones which, through the ages, have been preserved in rocks. One notable

Fig. 153.—Brown Thrasher with eyes wide open.

thing about them was the great size of their eyes—measuring as much as twelve and fourteen inches across. These orbits were surrounded by a series of bony plates, and in certain birds of to-day we find a similar circle of small overlapping bones.

To make the simile between a camera and an eye hold good, we must show that the latter is provided with a

FIG. 154.—Brown Thrasher with nictitating membrane drawn.

FIG. 155.—Same with eyelids closed.

shutter, and in fact our bird has not one, but *three*—eyelids we call them. So "between winks" all day our bird is taking snapshots, inconceivably more perfect and continuous than any cinematograph ever produced. We have but two eyelids, and every time we wink these shoot toward each other, moisten the surface of the eyeball, clear it of dust, and are back in their places so quickly that we are not aware of any interruption of our vision. The upper lid has most to do with covering the eye. In almost all birds this condition is unusual and the lower lid comes far upward over the eyeball. Perhaps the most notable exception to this is among the Great Horned Owls, where the action of the two lids is like that of our own.

When birds are sleepy these lids close, but usually in winking, the third eyelid, or nictitating membrane, alone is drawn across the eye. This lid is a delicate, semi-transparent sheet of tissue, which, when not in use, lies snugly packed away in folds at the inner corner of the eye, held back out of sight by its own elasticity. It is drawn across the front of the eye by a slender thread of tendon which is suspended, pulley-like, from a muscle which keeps it from pushing against the optic nerve.

When you see an owl in the daytime with eyes dull and glazed, this third eyelid is drawn partly across them, diluting the strong glare of light and yet enabling the bird to distinguish much that is going on. When an eagle turns his head upward and looks full at the sun, it is not "unwinkingly," but with the help of this eyelid shield.

It is interesting to know that this membranous lid is found in many other creatures, from sharks to monkeys, although usually much less perfectly developed than it is in birds. Alligators, however, have it fully functional. In the inner corner of our own eyes we may detect a trace of it, useless to us, but showing that far back in dimly imaginable geological epochs our forebears had need of a third eyelid.

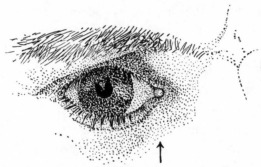

FIG. 156.—Vestige of nictitating membrane in a human eye.

The Sense of Hearing

"The Gauls," says Livy, "having discovered that the rock Carmentalis was accessible, one night when it was pretty clear, sent a man to examine the way, without his arms which were afterward handed to him. Others followed, lifting and assisting each other, according to the difficulties which they encountered in the ascent, till they reached the summit. They proceeded with so much silence that neither the sentinels nor even the dogs, animals usually so vigilant as to be aroused by the slightest noise, took any alarm. They did not, however, escape the notice of the geese, which, being sacred to Juno, had been fed by the Romans notwithstanding the famine caused by the siege. This saved the capitol; for, by their cackling and beating their wings, they roused Marcus Manlius, a brave soldier and formerly consul, who, snatching up his arms and giving the alarm, flew to the ramparts, set upon the Gauls, and by precipitating one of them over the rocks terrified the rest so much that they threw down their arms." So also Pliny, Ælian, and Columella vaunt the hearing of Geese. But leaving legendary lore, it is certain that birds would not have the power of producing the most varied as well as the sweetest sounds in all Nature, had they not been provided with powers of hearing, correspondingly acute and discriminating.

The organ of hearing is complicated and there are many points about it which are still mysteries to scientists. The flap of skin to which we give the name of ear is entirely absent in birds, and indeed in ourselves is a very unimportant part of the auditory apparatus, serving only as a collector of sound-waves. The opening of the inner ear on each side of the head, in birds, is usually protected by a cover of feathers which are bristle-like, partly denuded of barbicels, doubtless to avoid any muffling of sound-waves. In owls this opening is of very large size and protected by a movable flap of skin which may serve to aid in focussing the sounds from below— a very useful function to an owl at night, silently winging its way over field and meadow in search of mice and other terrestrial prey. A rather singular fact is that in many owls the two ear-openings are unlike, one being larger and of a different shape from the other, and this asymmetry extends even to the form of the skull itself.

Two membranes are stretched across the ear-tube, and between these a tiny bone, the columella, is suspended, taking the place of the chain of three bones in the ear of a mammal. When sound-waves strike against the outermost membrane, or drum of the ear, vibrations are transmitted by the little bony suspension bridge to the inner membrane, and this in turn troubles the fluid

Fig. 157.—External ear of Barred Owl.

which fills the inner ear. The hair-like endings of the nerve of hearing are affected by the vibrations of the fluid and thus is hearing accomplished. Rather say, thus the disposition of the physical components of the ear may be explained; but *how* anything more than the monotone of a sea-shell's cavity is translated to the brain, no one can say.

The fluid contained in three semicircular canals, situated in the inner ear—which occupy the three planes of space,—exercises a most important function, that of equilibration. They have been compared to the glass tube filled with water and a shifting bubble of air, by centring which a surveyor knows his instrument is perfectly level.

If these canals be injured or cut, the bird loses all control of his actions; if a certain one of the three canals suffers, the bird moves its head rapidly sideways and spins around in a circle; if another of the trio is by an accident severed, the motion of the head is back and forth, and the bird is compelled to execute forward somersaults; when the third of these canals is cut the bird continually falls backward. In reptiles and mammals the same thing occurs, so the wisdom of Nature in protecting these delicate organs by a sheath of hard bone is very apparent.

The Sense of Taste and Touch

"The hands of birds being hidden in the feathers which envelop the whole body,—their feet and their lips and usually much, if not all, of their tongue, being sheathed in horn,—these two faculties would appear to be enjoyed in but small degree."

The sense of taste is probably the least developed of all. The nerves which find their way through the pores of the bill and tongue are more properly those of touch than of taste, and this seems the more credible when we consider the food of many birds, which is swallowed entire, besides being so hard that nerves of taste would be useless. Parrots and ducks, with their fleshy tongues and ample membranes of the mouth, doubtless possess this sense to a considerable degree, while in birds which are exclusively fish-eaters we may expect to find taste least developed, the character of their food precluding all need for this faculty.

But from no bird is taste entirely absent, as we may easily see by presenting some nauseous insect, which will be instantly rejected with very evident signs of disgust, the bird wiping its bill on a branch and shaking its head violently.

The sense of feeling, although much deadened by the feathery and horny character of a bird's integument, is most active at the tip of the tongue and the beak. At the base of the feathers, especially those of the wings and tail, tactile nerves are found, so that even a touch on the tips of the feathers awakens a response in the nervous system.

The delicacy of the tactile touch is remarkable in those long-billed birds which seek their food in the muddy bottom of shallow water, detecting by means of their sensitive bills the presence of worms and snails,—aided little or not at all by eyesight. In the woodcock and apteryx this dependence on the senses of touch and smell has even wrought a change in the position and character of the eyes. The upper mandible of the woodcock is probably unique in being so sensitive and mobile that the distal third can be curved some distance upward, the base of the two mandibles remaining close together. This is an admirable provision by which, when the bird has driven its beak deep down into the moist soil, it may feel about

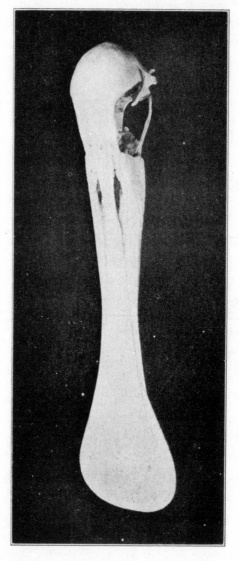

Fig. 158.—Skull of Spoonbill, showing openings for tactile nerves at the end of the bill.

220

and seize the earthworm for which it is seeking. The
eyes have become unusually large in consequence of its
nocturnal habits and in addition are placed far back
upon its head, permitting a clear lookout for danger,
above and even behind, while probing with its head held
close to the ground.

Fig. 159.   Fig. 160.

Fig. 159.—Photograph of living Woodcock with bill closed.
Fig. 160.—Same with bill open, showing mobility of upper mandible. The bird
   is thus enabled to feel about and seize the earthworms deep down in the mud.

Thus ends our brief survey of the five senses; that of
smell taking note of minute particles of matter diffused
in the air; sight and hearing depending on vibrations of
the atmosphere; the sense of taste detecting matter which
is dissolved in water, and that of feeling making the bird
cognizant of the qualities of bodies by actual contact.

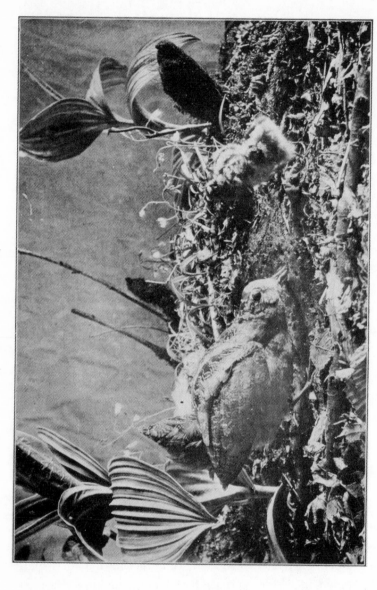

Fig. 161.—Woodcock probing for worms. (From a photograph provided by the American Museum of Natural History.)

222

CHAPTER X

BEAKS AND BILLS

TIE a man's hands and arms tightly behind his back, stand him on his feet, and tell him that he must hereafter find and prepare his food, build his house, defend himself from his enemies and perform all the business of life in such a position, and what a pitiable object he would present! Yet this is not unlike what birds have to do. As we have seen, almost every form of vegetable and animal life is used as food by one or another of the species. Birds have most intricately built homes, and their methods of defence are to be numbered by the score; the care of their delicate plumage alone would seem to necessitate many and varied instruments: yet all this is made possible, and chiefly executed, by one small portion of the bird—its bill or beak.

If one will spend an afternoon at a zoological park, or with any good collection of live birds, watching the ways in which the bills of the various species are used, one will not boast of his own accomplishments, when it is realized how much more, comparatively, the bird is able to achieve with the aid of two projecting pieces of horn.

More than a single volume could be filled with interesting facts about the bills of birds and the uses to which they are put,—hardly any two species using their beaks in a similar manner. The general way in which the vast subject of the adaptation of the bird to its needs and to its surroundings is treated in this volume will, it is hoped, be a stimulus to the reader to observe for himself,—to discover the thousand and one facts to

FIG. 162.—Beak of Snapping-turtle. (Courtesy of N. Y. Zoological Society.)

which Nature has not yet given us the key. Our language is too often lacking in phrases expressing delicate shades of meaning, and thus we are compelled to identify structures among the creatures which rank below us with portions of our own anatomy corresponding only in relative position or a general vague likeness of function. We are accustomed to speak of the *mouth* of a starfish, the *arms* of a sea-anemone, the *foot* of a snail: in these respective cases, structures specialized for receiving food, reaching about, or for progression being understood. But no one would think of alluding to a bird's lips or nose; both are included in the terms beak, or bill, and nostrils.

The finding and securing of food being the most important problem which birds have to solve for themselves, it is for these purposes, and especially the last mentioned, that we find bills most adapted. This is so universally

Fig. 163.—Bill of American Raven.

the case that we may often judge accurately of the kind of food of a certain bird from a glance at its beak.

As is the case with so many other avian structures, the horny, toothless beak or bill is duplicated elsewhere in Nature only in a group of reptiles, the turtles and tortoises, whose mandibles furnish a splendid example of parallel evolution.

In certain of those long-extinct *Dinosaurs,* such as

Triceratops, an interesting transitional condition is found. The front of the mouth was beak-like and horny, while farther back were the masticatory teeth.

Starting with the generalized beak of the *Archæopteryx,* which, we remember, was furnished with teeth, we are almost at a loss in which direction to turn, so many and so varied are the beaks of modern birds. No trace of teeth, however, is to be found in the adults of any of them. The bill of a crow or raven and, to a lesser extent, that of his near relatives, the jay and the blackbird, is perhaps in shape most like that of the 'bird of old,' and is suited to the many purposes which the varied life of these intelligent birds requires.

The crow or the raven is an excellent example of a modern bird with a remarkably generalized diet, in striking contrast to those birds whose bills show them to be fitted for feeding only on some strictly defined food. With his strong, ample beak the crow can dig up recently planted corn, or crack the hard shells of acorns; he enjoys stealing the eggs and the young birds of thrushes, orioles, sparrows, warblers, and quail, and I have seen a crow chase, capture, and carry off a half-dozen wild Mallard ducklings in one morning! These birds are, in addition, able to capture insects of all kinds, besides picking berries, and ducking their heads under water in quest of the shrimps which live in tide-pools. In short, their bill serves them well in procuring many kinds of food, from earth, water, or tree; as well as in carrying great quantities of sticks, which they use in the construction of their nests. These birds are so skilful with their

Fig. 164.—Beak of Gannet.

Fig. 165.—Beak of Cormorant.
Birds closely related, but procuring food in different ways.

beaks that a new trick is learned in a very short time. In captivity a crow, when it thinks no one is watching, will often take a morsel of food, thrust it beneath a piece of sod, and cover it up with grass, almost with one motion of the beak.

Functional or adaptive radiation is beautifully illustrated by the beak of a gannet, cormorant, snakebird, and pelican—birds which are closely related to one another structurally, also having in common a fish diet, swallowing their prey whole. The gannet's beak is thick and very strong, and along the inner edge is a series of fine serrations pointing backward. The bird dives, from a great height, into the water and seizes the fish in a grip of steel. The upper mandible of the cormorant is furnished with a large, sharp hook, with which the bird gaffs its prey, pursuing it under water. The snake-bird, or darter, has a bill like a needle, with which it spears the fish, impaling it through and through; while the pelican, because of its great pouch least vicious of all in its methods, simply engulfs the fish, the water in which it is swimming and all, then straining out the liquid, tosses the unfortunate into the air and swallows it head first. The under mandibles of this bird are long and pliable and so arranged that they can bend far apart, thus making of the great bag of skin beneath the bill and throat an admirable fish-trap.

This is one of the many instances where several closely related species, with needs so similar that there is danger of fatal competition, are able to exist in great numbers and to avoid all undue struggle for existence by having

Fig. 166.—Beak of Snake-bird.

Fig. 167.—Beak of Pelican.

Birds related to each other and to Figs. 164 and 165, but with different feeding habits.

each an individual method—a niche into which it fits
perfectly in the great scheme of Earth's hungry creatures.   The snake-bird's prey is in the water of dense

Fig. 168.—Brown Pelican catching fish, showing bag-like distension of lower
    mandible.   (Sanborn, photographer.   Courtesy of N. Y. Zoological Society.)

swamps and bayous; cormorants and pelicans amicably
share inland lakes and tidal waters; while the haunt of
the gannet is the high seas.
    Even more closely related to each other are terns

and Black Skimmers. Except in their bills these birds
are almost identical in structure, but the bill makes a

FIG. 169.—Bill of Tern.

FIG 170.—Bill of Skimmer
Closely related birds which differ in their feeding habits.

vast difference in the appearance of a bird, as is very
apparent when these two species are seen flying about

together on their breeding-grounds,—low, sandy islands along our coast. The small, delicately pointed beak of the tern finishes off its neat appearance, and the entire bird is the personification of grace, as it dashes through the air, or plunges headlong into the sea,—to rise almost immediately with a small fish in its beak.

The beak of the skimmer lends a heavy aspect to the whole bird. It is long and high, and the lower man-

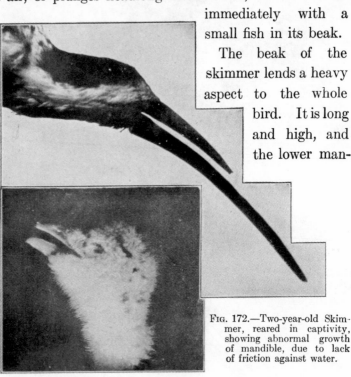

Fig. 172.—Two-year-old Skimmer, reared in captivity, showing abnormal growth of mandible, due to lack of friction against water.

Fig. 171.—Bill of young Skimmer, showing under mandible already slightly the longer.

dible extends a full inch beyond the upper. Both are as thin and as pliable as paper-knives. A unique method of obtaining food is the secret of this apparent deformity: the strong wings of the bird enable it to fly very close to

the surface of the water, so close in fact that the lower
mandible dips below the surface, thus ploughing a zig-
zag furrow and catching up any organisms, shrimps or
fish, which chance to be floating on the water.

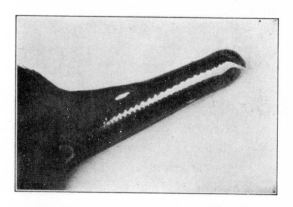

Fig. 173.—Bill of Merganser, a fish-eating duck.

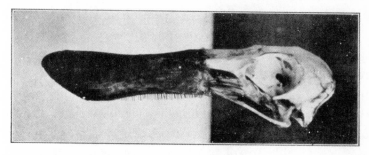

Fig. 174.—Bill of Shoveller Duck, a bird which strains its food from the mud.

Among ducks, we find those which feed on fish, and
those which sift their food from the mud at the bottom
of ponds, and these differ radically in respect to their
beaks. The fish-eating merganser has perhaps, of all
living birds, the nearest resemblance to a toothed beak.

The deep serrations, however, are but indentations in the substance of the strong, narrow bill of the bird. When once in this saw-like grasp, the most slippery fish is helpless. The beak of the Shoveller Duck shows how well Nature has provided for its wants. The beak is arched and spatulate, while the sensitive epidermis is prolonged at the edges into a series of comb-like teeth,— analogous to the whalebone in the mouth of a whale. Through this sieve the water is drained out, leaving entangled the edible worms and insects.

If we should elevate our Shoveller Duck, placing him on long, slender legs and providing him with a correspondingly long neck, he would indeed be in a predicament, since only the tip of his beak could be brought to bear in feeding. Now a flamingo is really a long-legged duck, which feeds in much the same way as the Shoveller, and the difficulty mentioned is overcome in a most ingenious way. The mandibles are bent downward, almost at right angles, so that, when the head reaches the ground, not the tip but the whole inverted bill is in a position to sift out food. To meet the reversed condition, the lower mandible is deeply arched, instead of the upper as in the Shoveller Duck.

We are able to follow the probable evolution of such remarkable beaks as those of the flamingo and skimmer by observing the growth of this organ in any individual from the time when the bird hatches from the egg until it is full-grown. In the very young flamingo chick there is no sign of the subsequent deflection, the mandible being short, perfectly straight, and rather slender. As the

FOUR STAGES IN THE DEVELOPMENT OF THE BILL OF THE FLAMINGO.

Fig. 175.—Young bird in down.

Fig. 176.—Young in gray plumage.

Fig. 177.—Young in gray plumage, later stage.

Fig. 178.—Adult living bird.

bird at first feeds upon regurgitated food, taking it drop
by drop from the bill of the old bird, it of course has
no need of the curved beak of its parents. Later, when
its bill has increased in length and has begun to be marked
by the ultimately sharp angle, the birds begin to sift
from the coral mud the small mollusks of which their
food consists.

Until its wings are full-feathered the young skimmer
is compelled to limit its wanderings to the sand-dunes
along the shore near its nest. Thus, although at birth
the lower mandible is a trifle longer than the upper, yet
even when the birds are half-grown the disparity in length
between the two mandibles is but slight. Later, when
the young bird is able to join its parents in their skimming
of the seas, the lower mandible quickly attains its full
development. The friction of the water upon the bill
must be considerable, as in a skimmer which I have had
for years in captivity, the lower mandible grew remarkably fast, measuring $6\frac{3}{4}$ inches from base to tip when
the bird was eighteen months old.

Herons and ibises, through all the years, sought their
food in much the same places as have ducks; the straight-
billed herons seizing their living prey with a single light-
ning dart, as it swims past them; the spoonbills spatter-
ing in the shallows; and the curved-beaked ibises probing every crevice along shore. The spoonbills swing
their necks and heads from side to side, as they walk
slowly through the water, gleaning their food with the
motion of a mower wielding his scythe. Two of the
herons are interesting enough to hold our attention for

a moment. The common Black-crowned Night Heron
is abundant throughout most of North America, and he
fishes in legitimate heron fashion; but his near relative,
the Boat-billed Heron, is a more tropical species. In
voice, appearance, and structure there is little to choose
between the two birds,—except that the latter has a broad,
scoop-like beak,—a pelican's fish-trap in miniature, which
seems to answer every requirement of this strange-looking bird.   From the
muddiness of the water
in the tropical swamps
from which I have
flushed these birds, it
seems probable that much
of their food may be
lesser fry than fish.

Pebbles and shells,
which shelter so many
toothsome morsels along
the shallows of our sea-
shore, offer sumptuous

FIG. 179.—Bill of Great Blue Heron.

feasts to birds furnished with beaks adapted to prying
and probing, and we find all sorts of sizes and shapes.
A collection of bills of various wading-birds would look
like a complete set of surgical tools! There is the stilt,
whose bill is almost straight; the ibis, with mandibles
curved downward to probe the crevices between the
pebbles on which he stands; the avocet has a pair of
recurved pliers, which search out the worm or snail in
the deepest fissures ahead of him. At the slightest touch

of such a beak, the oysters and other large bivalves close with a snap, defying these birds to penetrate their living armour. Indeed, more than once a gull or wader has rashly pecked at the sweet flesh, when the two tight-fitting doors have suddenly closed, pinning the bird help-

Fig. 180.—Boat-billed Heron.
Figs. 179 and 180 represent birds with slightly different feeding habits.

less and holding it captive despite its struggles, until the rising tide has ended its life.

But along comes a bird, well named Oyster-catcher, and woe to the mollusks now. It allows them to close tightly upon its bill, the mandibles of which are thin like blades, many years antedating man's oyster-knives. The mollusk is wrenched free by the sturdy bird, carried from the water still gripping the bird's bill, and is

FIG. 181.—Spoonbill, with spatulate mandibles.

FIG. 182.—White Ibis, showing curved bill.

FIG. 183.—Bill of Avocet, recurved for probing.

then pried open and eaten. The bill of this bird shows
the wear and tear of forcing apart the shells, and it is
sometimes slightly bent to one side. The short-billed
gulls are denied the power of opening these oysters and
mussels, but they sometimes get an unlawful feast by following up and robbing the Oyster-catchers of the shells
which the latter have opened.

The bill of the Shell Ibis of India may be likened to
an ordinary lemon-squeezer, having a cavity in which

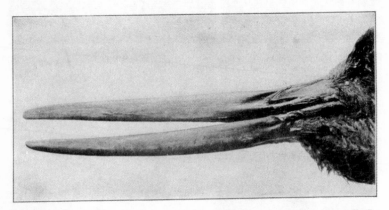

Fig. 184.—Bill of Oyster-catcher; used for prying open the shells of mollusks.

the half-lemon rests before it is compressed. When
the mandibles of this bird are closely opposed the central
portion of the beak gapes slightly. In this cavity the
bird firmly holds the shells of the land-snails upon which
it feeds, until it can bring the pressure of both mandibles
to bear and so crush the shell of the mollusk.

The asymmetry of the bill—as seen in the Oyster-
catcher—is not accidental, but constant, in the Crook-
billed Plover of New Zealand. In this bird the bill is

permanently bent to the right, a beautiful adaptation
to help the bird in its search for insects, which, in the
dry country that it inhabits, are found almost entirely
under stones.

As a rule, beaks are rather immovable throughout
their length, but in the woodcock, and to a less extent

Fig. 185.—Bill of Crook-billed Plover, for probing under stones.

in the Dowitcher Snipe, the extremity of the upper mandible can be raised some distance (Figs. 159, 160). This
extreme sensitiveness is especially necessary, as the eyes
of the woodcock are placed very far back on the top
of its head, and are of little or no use in seeking food.

What an interesting study the various beaks of land
birds would offer, were we able to devote to them the

space which they deserve! They defy classification and refuse to be arranged in any linear sequence. The majority of those birds which have their beaks armed with a strong hook feed upon living prey,—from the great mandible of the Golden Eagle to the tiny vireo, which snaps up the dancing gnats.

The owls and the parrots, which, by the way, are much more closely related than most of our classifications would indicate, have bills very much alike, and afford

Fig. 186.—Bill of Golden Eagle, hooked for tearing prey.

a striking example of two large related groups of birds whose diet has become radically unlike, although even in this case "blood will tell" and the Kea Parrot slips back into carnivorous habits with ease.

Owls tear their prey apart with their beaks, or swallow it entire, but parrots gnaw and gnaw upon their nuts and seeds, reducing their food to powder. This grinding and rasping is aided by several file-like ridges which many parrots have within their beaks. The hinging of the upper mandible with the skull is more evident in a parrot than in any other bird.   This arrangement allows much freedom of motion.

It is not clearly known what use the immense beaks of toucans may serve, although there seems little excuse for this ignorance in those who know the birds in their native haunts.   The delicate, spongy texture renders the

Fig. 187.—Toucan, showing enormous bill used perhaps for reaching fruit on the tips of branches.

clumsy-looking appendages exceedingly light, and they are usually banded or marked with brilliant hues,—blue, yellow, red, brown, green, or black.   But light as the beaks are in these birds, in the unrelated but similarly monstrous-beaked hornbills the weight must be considerable, for the first two vertebræ of the neck in these latter birds are fused together, to yield a firmer support for the muscles of the neck.

Chimney Swifts and hummingbirds both feed upon insects and are rather closely related to each other, but here again the most decided difference is to be found in their bills.   The broad, flattened mandibles of the swifts

Fig. 188.—Bill of Toucan; cut open to show its light, spongy structure.

open wide, as the birds dash through the air, engulfing gnats and flies with wonderful skill; while the humming-birds, as we all know, probe the deepest calyxes.   Could two bills more unlike be imagined?   In very young hummingbirds the bill is short and broad, very like the swift type, and later its long and slender shape is acquired very rapidly, as we can see in Figs. 190 and 191. There are many resemblances between hummingbirds and insects, due entirely to the similarity in their feeding habits. Certain flowers are especially adapted in structure to attract certain bees or moths, which in return unconsciously cross-fertilize the blossoms; and certain of the various bills of hummingbirds reflect the exact contour of the corollas in which the birds seek their food. Among hummingbirds the various shapes of bills of other groups are reproduced again. Humming through the air about us in the tropics speed miniature avocets, ibises, stilts, mergansers, and we realize, as never before, the never-ending devices of Nature, providing for the needs of all, from the greatest to the least; endless patterns paralleling each other, but never identical. Indeed, in the great family of South American birds known as Wood-hewers the diversity in shape, size, and direction of bills is so great that it seems as if not a niche, or crack, or hollow in the bark of any tree in the forest where these birds abound would afford a safe retreat to an insect!

It remains to mention the woodpecker's bill, which is used chisel-like, for excavating his home as well as in boring for grubs. With his beak the nuthatch hammers his acorns, and the tailor-bird sews his nest. The thick conical beaks of all sparrows and finches are for cracking seeds; while the weaker, more slender beaks of warblers, thrushes, and wrens reflect a diet of insects.

Among the finches is a group of several species which, by a thrust of the bill, have at their command a new source of food, one which there are none to dispute with

Fig. 189.—Bills of adult Hummingbird and Chimney Swift. showing great dissimilarity in form, due to different methods of procuring food.

Fig. 190.—Bills of young Rufous Hummingbirds, showing swift-like character.
(Photograph by Finley & Bohlman.)

Fig. 191.—Slightly older Hummingbirds, with bills half as long as the adults.
(Photograph by Finley & Bohlman.)

them. Both mandibles of the crossbill are curved into
sharp hooks which cross one another, either to the right
or left, thus forming a unique pair of pliers, with which
the bird pries out the seeds shut tight behind the overlapping scales of pine-cones.

Fig. 192.—Two extreme types of Hummingbirds' bills, adapted for insertion
in flowers with shallow and with deep calyxes.

The beak of a bird is always growing, and in captivity,
from lack of proper use, the mandibles sometimes grow
to a great length, and, if not trimmed, will often interfere with the bird's feeding.

Perhaps the most remarkably adapted beaks in the
world are those of the male and female Huia birds—

natives of New Zealand — in which not only is the bill
of the species designed for a special method of procuring
food, but the bills of the two sexes are very different in
form and use, and complement each other's methods.
Concerning the peculiar use of the bill in the Huia birds,

FIG. 193.—Bill of Purple Finch and Crossbill compared; the latter specialized
for extracting seeds from pine-cones.

Professor Newton writes: "Its favourite food is the grub
of a timber-boring beetle, and the male bird with his short
stout bill attacks the more decayed portions of the wood,
and chisels out his prey, while the female with her long
slender bill probes the holes in the sounder part, the hard-
ness of which resists his weapon; or when he, having
removed the decayed portion, is unable to reach the grub,

the female comes to his aid and accomplishes what he
has failed to do."

The bill of a bird, besides serving in so many other
ways, is invaluable in preening the plumage, arranging
disordered feathers, drying them, and, most important
of all, in pressing out the oil from the gland on the lower
back, and with it carefully dressing all the feathers, giv-

FIG. 194.—Bill of male and female Huia Birds, showing difference of the bill
in the two sexes.

ing to them that brightness and gloss and also the water-
proof quality—so surely a sign of perfect health in a
bird. When, after the bath of a caged bird, you see the
drops roll from its feathers, literally like "water off a
duck's back," then the good health of the bird is certain.

The all-important use of the bill as a needle, shuttle,
pick and shovel, auger, or trowel in nest-building does not
concern us here, nor does its function in expressing emotion, or in taking the place of the voice or of the foot.

All this is expressive rather of the mental than the physical life of the bird.

Within a period of five minutes I have observed the following uses of the beak of a parrot perching in my study. With its mandibles it picked up a sunflower seed and comminuted it; it then hooked the upper mandible into a wire and swung itself along; gnawed at a nesting-hole it had begun to excavate; nibbled gently at my finger, showing affection; bit fiercely in anger and fear at a dead snake which I presented; preened several feathers of one wing, smoothing out all the dislodged barbs; rattled its beak along the wires to make a sound to attract my attention; and finally seized its water-pan and turned it over in pure playfulness!

CHAPTER XI

HEADS AND NECKS

THE head of a bird is indeed a wonderful object, when we consider its comparatively small size and yet realize that it contains the brain, as well as being the seat of the five senses. It also supports that most important organ the beak, which, as we have seen, takes the place of hands and tools in the life of its owner.

Of expression, with the exception of that caused by raising its feathers, the bird has but little; although fear, that emotion which must needs be expressed all too often in the life of these timid and comparatively defenceless creatures, is made apparent by the dilating eyes and the open, panting beak. The only exception which comes to mind is the Crowned Crane, Fig. 206, the suffusing of whose bare, white cheeks indicates the changing emotions. Perhaps the best index is to be found in the crest, which we will find to be developed to a very remarkable degree.

The eyes of most birds are placed at the sides of the head, in such a position that the bird cannot bring both to bear simultaneously upon the same object, but is compelled to turn its head and look sideways. As birds spend so much of their time in the air, or in trees, where danger may threaten from all sides, above or below, this arrangement is most useful to them, giving them command of almost their whole surroundings, whereas, without turning the head, we can see only ahead of us. In much the same relative position, the two ears are placed,

FIG. 195.    FIG. 196.

FIG. 195.—Head of Dove, with eyes at side
FIG. 196.—Head of Owl, with eyes in front   Showing difference in position of eyes in a pursued and a pursuer in Life's race.

and the absence of a directive outer ear renders the bird susceptible to sounds coming from every direction.

Owls, for very obvious reasons, are interesting exceptions to the above statements. Living most of their active life at night, playing always the rôle of *pursuers*, these raptorial birds have few enemies to fear; and their subsistence depends upon the keenness of their senses when focussed in one direction—downward. When its strong, soft-feathered pinions carry a mousing owl over field and stubble, the head, like the nose of a hound, is held low, and, that not a rustle nor a motion of the little field-mice may be lost, the ear-openings are turned downward and the eyes look full upon the ground. Look a Barn Owl in the face and you will see the entire circumference of both eyes, but a dove—one of the *pursued* in life's race—shows in the front view only the profile of the eyeballs. The same story is told in the eyes of the fox and the rabbit—examples of Nature's parallels, which are never repetitions.

It is interesting to compare the eyes of owls with those of mammals in general. With the exception of man, and of some of the monkeys, we find that when the eyes show but slight divergence the animal is invariably a lover of the dusk, or is wholly nocturnal. We know that when we are asleep, or are under the effects of ether, our eyes tend to roll upward and outward, and now we realize that the cause of this is the old ancestral pulling outward, toward monocular vision, as in the fish or rabbit or dove. Our distant ancestors, far from having books or work which focussed their attention directly in front, had most vital need of looking out for dangers in all directions.

Another adaption found in the eyes of almost all nocturnal birds is the great size of the orbit, fully one half of the skull being hollowed out to receive the eyeballs. No degeneration of the eyes, as a result of nocturnal habits, is recorded among birds, such as exists in moles and bats, except in the case of the apteryx, the diminutive New Zealand representative of the ostrich-like birds. The

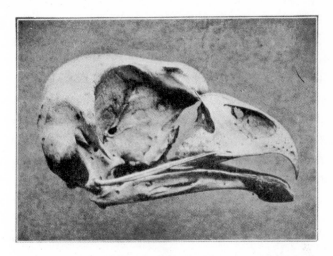

Fig. 197.—Skull of Owl.

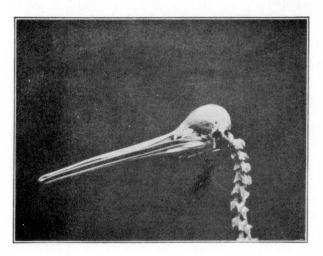

Fig. 198.—Skull of Apteryx.

Showing opposite effects of nocturnal habits on the size of the eyes.

small eyes of this bird become dazzled by strong light, its food being detected by the senses of touch and smell.

The eyes of the woodcock show an interesting adaptation to its habits. The bird feeds at night in marshes, probing the mud for worms and, being in frequent danger of attack from owls or other foes, it has need of constant vigilance. So we find that its eyes, which are large and lustrous, are placed far back on its head and also up near the top of the skull. Useless in guiding the bird in its search for food, they have become altered in size and position and so best fulfil their function of aiding their owner to all but look through the back of its head.

Even the iris of a bird's eye may share in the wonderful colour scheme of its feathers, although the most common hue is a hazel-brown. And in birds of two related species or races, there is sometimes a marked difference in the colour of the iris; such, for example, as between the Red-eyed and White-eyed Vireos, or the similarly named Towhees. Puffins have blue irides, pigeons pink ones, while young Bald Eagles have brown eyes which, in the adult, turn yellow. The eyes of Barred Owls seem to be a deep, lustrous black, but they are really dark brown; while the great yellow eyes of Snowy and Horned Owls are the most brilliant bits of colour about these birds. In cormorants the irides are a glittering emerald-green.

It might be thought that "making eyes" was confined to the more frivolous of our own race, but certain it is that, whether or not it plays a part in charming the females, the irides of the males of a number of species of birds change, at the season of courtship, from a dull hue to some bright tint, either red, green, or yellow.

Although eyelashes, as we understand them, are merely stiffened hairs which have been inherited from hairy-coated ancestors, yet among birds we sometimes find lashes similar in appearance and function, but structurally derived from feathers. The ostrich has well-

Fig. 199.—Head of Seriema, showing eyelashes.

developed eyelashes, which must be of value in helping to exclude the dust of the desert; but why such birds as hornbills and the Seriema should possess them we cannot say.

A savage thrusts feathers into his hair, warriors of old bedecked their helmets with flowing plumes, the opera hat of milady is by way of wonderful and strange creations; but withal feathers are *really* beautiful only

where they by rights belong—upon a bird. Among
birds we find a more remarkable development of crests
than in any other class of animals. Indeed nearly all
birds have the power of slightly raising the feathers on
the head.

Fig. 200.—Crest of Java Peacock.

Most, if not all, plumes and crests are probably ornamental, and, since many are more highly developed in
the male sex and at breeding-time, we must conclude
that they are of value in attracting and holding the attention of the females during the period of courtship.

What a list of these crests we may compile in a walk
through a zoological park! The photographs show the
grace and delicacy of these feathers, to which words can

add nothing. Note the slender shafts which rise from the head of the Indian Peacock, each one tipped with a dainty feather tuft; and the variation in the crest of its splendid cousin from Java. In one of the Birds of Paradise, six long, fan-tipped shafts extend backward from the head, much longer than, but similar to, the crest of the Indian Peacock. The California Partridge has a tiny,

FIG. 201.—California Partridges, showing difference in crest of male and female birds.

club-shaped crest which points in a forward direction, and, when the bird is excited, the feathers which compose it spread out, breaking into a fan. The ornament of the Plumed Partridge is a long, sweeping plume. The crest of the curassow is most peculiar, being composed of curly, recurved feathers, resembling in texture and appearance jet-black or parti-coloured shavings.

The nuptial plumes of the Night Heron hang far down upon its shoulders, and the soft barbs are curved inward, forming a slender tube. The glory of the Great Crowned Pigeon is a maze of lavender lacework,—one of the most beautiful of all crests; while the most graceful, perhaps, is the mist of filmy whiteness which, at the slightest breath of air, floats about the neck of the Snowy Egret, like the mantilla of a *señorita*. Cockatoos are decorated with a profusion of beautiful crests, each characteristic. These are under the complete control of the birds, and take an important part in expressing changing moods and emotions. The crests may lie so flat as to be ordinarily invisible, when, in a flash, the whole head is surmounted by an auriole of colour or whiteness. An excited Leadbeater Cockatoo is a wonderful sight. Before the crest is raised, all that is visible is a single, rather elongated white feather, but a wealth of colour is hidden, which flares out, showing a band of scarlet close to the head, next a streak of bright yellow, then a second band of red, and finally the white tips of the crest feathers. The nod or jerk of the head in spreading wide the crest reminds one of the sudden flick with which a fan is thrown open.

Concealed crests bring to mind the Kingbird and the Ruby-crowned Kinglet, both of which derive their names from their crowns of ruby. It is said that the former bird is aided in its search for food by the bright spot of colour which, flower-like when exposed, attracts insects. This, however, should be confirmed before being accepted as a fact; although in a tropical flycatcher, which has a beautiful red and purple transverse crest, the evidence of this novel use seems fairly well corroborated.

FIG. 202.—Crest of Banded Curassow (female).

FIG. 203.—Crest of Victoria Crowned Pigeon.

Fig. 204.—Harpy Eagle. (Courtesy of Dr. Frank Baker.)

The Laughing Thrush of the Himalaya Mountains has every feather upon its head lengthened and permanently erect, forming a soft, spreading halo.

FIG. 205.—Hooded Merganser. (From a photograph provided by the American Museum of Natural History.)

In almost every Family of birds we find certain species with long, well-developed crests. Among the ducks, the Hooded Merganser has a compressed, semicircular halo of delicate feathers, while the Mandarin Duck has a broad, many-coloured, erectile crown, which is con-

spicuous even in contrast with the gorgeous ornamentation of the body of this feathered harlequin. Of birds
of prey, the Harpy Eagle has perhaps the most imposing
crown of feathers.

Sometimes the crest is sharply set off from the rest
of the bird's plumage, as in the scarlet-plumed woodpeckers, whose crests give them the appearance of having
long hair, which is gracefully brushed straight backward
and upward.

We must not discuss the subject of crests without mention of two birds of extraordinary appearance, the Crowned
Crane and the Umbrella-bird. The former illustrates
admirably what strange and unfeather-like forms, feathers
may assume in the course of evolution. The illustration
shows better than words can describe the dense, velvety
cap of plush-like feathers, and the glorious crown of a
myriad radiating points—a decoration unrivalled, even
among birds, in exquisite colour and delicacy. In addition to this, the cheeks are entirely bare of feathers, and
the lower half suffused with blood, which shows through
the skin,—an ever-changing blush of deep pink.

The decorations of the Umbrella-bird are as beautiful
as they are bizarre; while if shorn of its crest and streamers,
this bird would resemble a small crow in appearance.
The crest really bears a resemblance to the article which
has given the bird its name—a high, arching mass of
feathers, overshadowing the entire head and beak, continually spreading and partly closing again, as the bird's
emotions change. From the neck of the bird dangles a
streamer of black feathers, as long as the bird's entire

Fig. 206.—Crowned Crane.

Fig 207.—Demoiselle Crane.

body and which, when it flies, blows back between its feet. The filament of feathers looks for all the world as if a strip of the bird's plumage had caught on a thorn and torn loose. The core of the streamer is a very slender

Fig. 208.—Umbrella-bird.

ribbon of skin which hangs from the neck. Would that we could state the causes and the manner of the development of these curious structures which our fancy likens to an umbrella and a feathery handle!

One or two small tufts of feathers may spring from

some part of the head of a bird, such as the feather "horns" of owls, motmots, and larks. In Screech Owls these prominent "ears" certainly play a useful part in breaking up the outline of the bird, rendering it very difficult of detection when it is perched upon some jagged limb or stub. Or again, tufts or pencils of feathers may arise from near the ear, or over the eye; as shown by the Demoiselle Crane (Fig. 207), some of the Puffins, and the Manchurian Pheasants (Fig. 209). The Great Bustard has long tufts of chin-feathers which, like wide-spreading whiskers, spread to each side, and the Bearded Vulture has a similar goatee of stiff, black bristles.

Of the wonderful crests, frills, ruffs, breastplates, and cloaks of hummingbirds there is no room to speak, and indeed no words or pictures can aught but parody them. The eye alone can record their marvels, in the collection of a museum, or, better still, in the living birds, as the little creatures hover over their favourite flowers, or vibrate before us, fanning the air in our very faces with their invisible wings.

Brief mention should be made of two Birds of Paradise, those beautiful creatures inhabiting a region where the eye of man seldom sees them.

The Six-shafted Bird of Paradise is found only in New Guinea. "The plumage appears at first sight black, but it glows in certain lights with bronze and deep purple. The throat and breast are scaled with broad, flat feathers of an intense golden hue, changing to green and blue tints and certain lights. On the back of the head is a broad recurved band of feathers, whose brilliancy

Fig. 209.—Head of Eared Pheasant.

Fig. 210.—Head of Great Horned Owl.

is indescribable, resembling the sheen of emeralds and topaz, rather than any organic substance. Over the fore‑head is a patch of pure white feathers, which shine like satin; and from the sides of the head spring the six wonderful feathers."

Fig. 211.—Six-shafted Bird of Paradise (a mounted bird). (From a photograph provided by the American Museum of Natural History.)

Head decorations reach the acme of strangeness in the King of Saxony's Bird of Paradise. The bird itself is sombre-hued and small, about the size of our robin, with nothing unusual about its appearance, except for the two streamers springing from opposite sides of the head. They are twice (or more) the length of the body, and, far from being feather-like, they are best described as a series of thirty or forty tiny flags of blue enamel, each separate, each hanging pendent from the main shaft (Fig. 212). It would seem as if Nature herself could go no farther in unusual decoration than this.

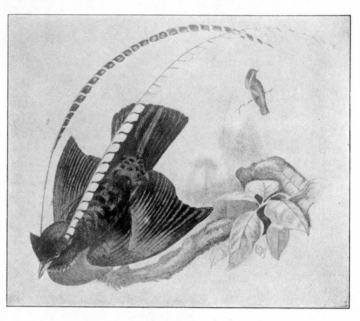

Fig. 212.—King of Saxony Bird of Paradise. (From a photograph provided by the American Museum of Natural History.)

In the Double-crested Pigeon of Australia the core or fleshy covering of the beak is completely feathered; while some of the birds known as plantain-eaters are feathered to the very tip of the short beak with plumes of delicate green, tipped with white. The extreme of feathering is shown by the Cock-of-the-Rock, in which the whole beak, in fact every part of the head except the eyes, is buried in a maze of soft, orange plumes.

As the antithesis to this condition, we find many birds which have the head partly or entirely bare of feathers, such as the vultures and some of the waders.

In the former group this lack of feathers is doubtless

Fig. 213.—Head of male Condor

of value in enabling the birds to avoid soiling their plumage, when engaged in their scavenger work. The great Condor of South America has, just below this naked area, a necklace of the whitest of fluffy down, and in addition the male has a large wattle of skin upon the front of the head. The Caracara of Mexico is partly vulturine in its habits, and the feathers have disappeared from part of its face. Wherever the skin of the head and neck is even

FIG. 214.—Caracara. partly vulturine in habits.

FIG. 215.—Young King Vulture.

partly bare, ornamentation often takes the form of many-shaped and often highly coloured wattles, such as we see highly developed in a King Vulture.

The most common example of this is seen in a domestic rooster or a turkey, but in many other birds these wattles of skin are very brilliant in hue. Indeed the cassowaries are resplendent in their gorgeous hues of blue, yellow, red, and many other intermediate shades. Turkeys too, at the breeding season, develop bright colours. The Yucatan Wild Turkey, which has thus far resisted all attempts at domestication, has the bright blue naked skin of the head, dotted with tubercles of the most brilliant orange, while a long tube-like wattle, also tipped with orange, dangles down over the beak. The wattles, or caruncles, of the Bell Bird are interesting as being connected with the windpipe in such a way that they become inflated with air when the bird utters its wonderful note.

In the White Ibis the face only is bare, in the spoonbill the head and face, and the whole head and neck in the Marabou Stork; the effect of this condition in the latter bird being heightened by the enormous pouch which hangs suspended from the neck. The same is true of the Adjutant.

A close inspection of the neck of one of these storks will show that, while ordinary feathers are absent, there is a scanty covering, here and there, of what looks like soft, curling ringlets of chestnut hair. The resemblance is absolutely perfect, and no naturalist in the world, if shown one of these locks, would say that it came from a bird and not from one of the hair-covered mammals!

Fig. 216.—Head of domestic cock. Extreme development of comb.

Fig. 217.—Head of domestic cock. Extreme development of crest.

274

We must pass by all the strange ornaments of horn upon the heads of birds, such as the scarlet plate of the gallinules, the immense recurved casques of the hornbills, the use of which is as yet unknown, unless it be purely ornamental. But the impressive helmets of the cassowaries,

Fig. 218.—Head of Wild Turkey.

Fig. 228, demand especial notice in this volume, as being very useful adaptations to life in a dense forest. These great running birds are the only members of their Sub-class which inhabit thickly forested regions, and in speeding with great leaps and bounds through the undergrowth, the tall, smooth helmet of horn protects the head of the bird

FIG. 219.—Head of Adjutant.

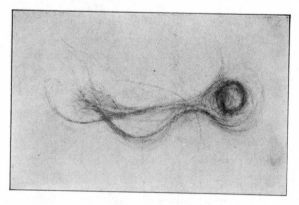

FIG. 220.—Ringlet of hair from the neck of an Adjutant.

and shunts off the hanging lianas and vines which would otherwise impede its progress.

In our hasty paragraphs we have seen to what a remarkable extent the ornamentation of the heads of birds is carried, and as many extraordinary examples could be given of decoration of the neck. The Loon has a speckled black and white throat with a long colour bandage of black feathers wound about its neck; the cervical ruffs of our Ruffed Grouse are like wings in miniature; in the Golden and Amherst Pheasants this form of ornament is extended into a circular ruff of black and gold and black and white respectively; while in the Superb Bird of Paradise a shoulder-cape flares back, large enough to cover almost the entire body of the bird, giving it the appearance of being clothed in two distinct sets of plumage! The nuptial attire of the Ruff, a species of sandpiper, is as greatly developed, except that it forms a double cloak over the breast.

This cloak or shield of feathers in the Ruff plays a vital part in the life of the bird. We must first notice the remarkable variation in the pattern of this cloak of battle,—for such it really is. If we could see fifty Ruffs standing side by side, some would be seen to have ruffs of pure white, others of gray, black, orange, buff, or chestnut, while the waving ear-plumes are also independent in colour, varying from white to purple, green, or blue. Then there is a type of Ruff with barred cloaks, another with spotted patterns, and so on in almost endless variation. This condition of affairs is wholly unlike the uniform pattern of colouring of other wild birds.

Fig. 221.—Lady Amherst Pheasant.

Fig. 222.—Casque of Hornbill.

We can only compare these little Joseph-coated birds
with the unnatural sports among domestic poultry and
pigeons.

But whatever their colour, these Fighting Snipe find
their ruffs of service in their encounters at the breeding
season.   Four male birds which I observed in captivity

Fig. 223.—Ruff with battle-cloak partly moulted.

were adorned respectively,—plain gray, dotted gray,
chestnut barred with black, and a rich golden rufous.
Though no females were present, yet their fighting instinct
often cropped out and a pair of them would dart and side-
step about each other, bills held low and far advanced,
ruff spread out from the breast and trailing low, hiding
almost the whole body.   Now and then one of the fencers
would make a vicious dash, sending his bill through the

feather shield of his opponent. But the force of the blow would spend itself on the inch of space between the shield and the feathers of the bird's breast. When, in his native haunts, the Ruff has conquered his rival, his triumphant dances before the female are most elaborate. While these facts are not exactly pertinent to the physical

Fig. 224.—Breast ornament of a Wild Turkeycock.

life of the bird, yet I mention them to show to what practical, as well as æsthetic, uses the development of some portion of the bird's plumage may be devoted.

What a contrast to the cloak of the Ruff is the pectoral decoration of the Wild Turkeycock: a great tuft of coarse, black hair-like feathers, like the tail of a horse in miniature, growing almost a foot in length from the centre of the breast!

The length of the neck of birds is often correlated with that of the legs,—a long-legged bird of necessity requiring a long neck to permit its bill to reach the ground. Geese and swans are an exception, and in their case we

Fig. 225.—Flamingoes   Correlation of long neck with long legs.

find that the long, mobile neck is of great use in making up for the awkwardness of their waddle when on land, and in allowing them to reach beneath them while floating in shallow water, thus feeding along the bottom.

Herons are uniformly so light of body that they would have difficulty in steadying themselves in the air, were it not that, when in flight, their necks become compressed to an incredible thinness, thus acting as does the cut-

water of a ship's prow. The perpetual crook in the necks
of these birds is significant of their method of fishing—a
patient watch until the prey comes within striking distance.
In the snake-bird this crook, or Z-shape, has, by the

Fig. 226.—Swan.   Correlation of long neck and short legs due to feeding habits.
(Sanborn, photographer.)

adaptation of three of the neck-bones, become a veritable
trigger, by the springing of which the bird literally spears
the fish.

If the mention in this chapter of a few examples of
crests and other decorations has seemed in the least to

verge upon the monotony of a mere catalogue, my plea is that they have been cited with the intention of emphasizing the fact of the remarkable degree which decoration, pure and simple, plays in courtship. Viewed from such a standpoint, these facts and comparisons become important data in the observation of the courtship of birds,

Fig. 227.—Snake-bird, showing crook in neck.

which in its turn is one of the most important and interesting corollaries of the psychology of these beings. Whether female birds have highly developed æsthetic feelings, or whether the songs and dances and colour masses act more along the line of the passes of a hypnotist, is yet to be ascertained.

It is also hoped that a realization of the more immediately practical uses of such structures as the cassowary's horny helmet, the feather shield of the Ruff, perhaps the crest of the kingbird, and many others as yet unknown, will impel amateur observers to further efforts in the investigation of the life-habits of birds.

CHAPTER XII

THE BODY OF A BIRD

IN experimenting with balloons and flying-machines, weight is a question of prime importance, and among birds there seem to be certain limits to the bulk of the body, beyond which flight is impossible. The tiny hummingbirds, with bodies weighing less than some insects, have remarkable powers of flight, and throughout all the groups of larger birds we find certain species with exceptional flight ability, until in the birds of widest extent of wing, such as the condor and the albatross, flight seems to reach the acme of perfection. But the flying birds of actual heaviest bulk are perhaps the Wild Turkey, the Great Bustard, and the Trumpeter Swan, the two latter reaching weights of thirty-two and twenty-five pounds respectively. Even the gigantic *Pterodactyls*, those flying reptiles of olden time, some of which had heads a yard long, and an expanse of eighteen feet or more of bat-like wings, are estimated to have weighed but twenty pounds or thereabouts.

But when the necessity for flight ceases, a bird may begin to assume larger proportions and greater weight without detriment; just as a mammal which adopts a life in the dense medium of water may attain a much more gigantic size than one which has to support its body in the thinner atmosphere: a whale is to a horse as an ostrich is to a dove.

The ostrich is the largest of all living birds, a full-grown male being able to reach to a height of nine feet and weighing as much as three hundred pounds; but even these figures were exceeded by its extinct relative of Madagascar, the moa, whose height is variously estimated at from ten to eleven feet, and whose massive leg-bones show that its weight must have been much greater than that of the ostrich.

There is a great difference in the relative condition of the body in various birds. Herons, even when fish are abundant, with opportunities of feeding from morning to night, are thin to emaciation. Truly they belong to the "lean kine." A fat heron would be an anomaly. On the other hand, the flesh of many sea-birds seems as constantly encased in thick, oily layers of fat. Petrels are used by the inhabitants of some islands as candles, simply by threading the body of the dead bird with a wick, the excess of fat burning steadily until the whole is consumed. Penguins are well protected against the icy waters of their Antarctic home by a layer of fat under the skin, so thick in proportion to their size as to remind one of the blubber of whales.

If we were writing of the bodies of the fur-bearers instead of birds, we would have much to say concerning the various kinds of scent-glands and secreted odours; but in birds the only gland is that above the tail, which furnishes the oil with which the bird preens its plumage, thus both cleansing it and rendering it water-proof. That birds, and especially those which, like quail, are found in flocks, possess odours is borne witness to by the ability of dogs to point successfully the hidden game; but that this is of much use in enabling the birds to find one another is doubtful, both from the fact of the slight development of the sense of smell, and because of the loud call-notes which are so characteristic of these birds. One exception, however, may be noted, that of the apteryx, which is said to have a strong and persistent odour, with correspondingly well-developed nostrils.

Again, among fur-covered animals we find usually a poor development of the sense of sight and but few of them exhibit bright colours, while, as we have seen, birds excel in the power of seeing, and, correlated with this, possess an unparalleled array of colours upon the body.

There are many ways in which the body or its feathers are adapted to aid the bird in some special way. For example, the Puff-back Shrike of Africa has a habit of suddenly puffing out and erecting a patch of long, loose, white feathers on its back, giving the appearance of a large powder-puff, an act so startling and unexpected being well calculated to make any attacking hawk or other bird hesitate.

The general texture of the body feathers is usually an accurate index to the bird's power of flight. Although the feathers of the breast and back are never as compact or as stiff as those of the wings and tail, yet in birds of good flight their barbs are quite firmly connected. In a small African bird, called from its habits the Rock-jumper, the wings are so small that the power of flight is almost *nil*, and we find an interesting corollary in the plumage,

FIG. 228.—Cassowary, showing the loose plumage of a flightless bird.   (Sanborn, photographer.   Courtesy of N. Y. Zoological Society.)

which is so loose and fluffy that it blows about in the least wind.   In the ostrich and rhea this down-like character is still more noticeable and extends even to the feathers of the wings and tail.   The extreme is to be found in the apteryx and emeu (Fig. 23). Compare a feather of the latter with one of a condor and the difference is remarkable. So unfeatherlike is the emeu's plume and so loose are its barbs that it brings to mind the much-divided leaflets of an Acacia.

The plumage of the snake-bird is inexplicable. This bird is so emphatically aquatic that we would expect a dense, compact covering of the body; but in reality it more nearly resembles hair or fur, soaking through so quickly and thoroughly that, after immersion for some time, the bird becomes waterlogged and has to hang itself out to dry by seeking some sunlit perch, opening wide its wings and waving them to and fro.

The feathers of the penguin are small, flat, and rigid, approaching in these respects the scales of fishes—an interesting reacquiring of characters consequent upon an all but wholly aquatic life. It is interesting to compare the colouring of such a bird as the Scaled Partridge with a fish like the Carp, the dark margins of the feathers and scales bringing about a remarkable resemblance.

Taking up the subject of colour in general, we realize, after even a superficial glance at a collection of birds, that in gorgeousness of hue and diversity of shade and pattern, they are to be compared only with insects. In a former chapter we have briefly considered the chemical and optical causes of colour in feathers; but the causes due to environment (using that word in its widest sense) cover a vastly greater field and one as yet comparatively unexplored.

Advancement of actual knowledge of any subject in

science depends upon two things: first, the accumulation of facts; and secondly, a philosophical spirit capable of generalizing and bringing order out of the chaos of

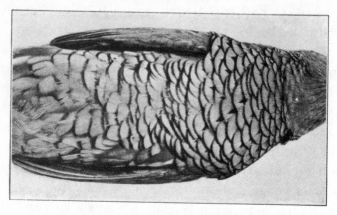

FIG. 229.—Breast of Scaled Partridge.

FIG. 230.—Carp, a fish with distinctly marked scales. (Keller, photographer.)

these myriad observations. A knowledge of museum facts is of but slight use in such a subject as the one under consideration, which requires more adequate knowledge

than we now possess of the life-habits and the psychology
of birds. This is especially true of the great number of
cases which we can explain only by calling them ornamental and decorative. Hence we find one ornithologist

Fig. 231.—White-throated Sparrows. The light-coloured bird is in normal plumage; the dark bird was subjected to moisture-laden air through two moults.

explaining a certain colour as due to one cause, while
another scientist gives an entirely different interpretation
of the same fact.

From personal observation among the birds of the

New York Zoological Park, I have had opportunity to record many cases of the effect of food upon colour. An experiment very commonly known is that of feeding canaries on red pepper, thus causing their plumage, after

Fig. 232.—Variation due to climate, etc., in races of North American Song Sparrows
(From a photograph provided by the American Museum of Natural History.)

successive moults, to become of an intense orange colour. This is the more remarkable since the actual red pigment, or, capsicin, of red pepper is not the direct cause of the canaries' changed hue, but a fatty substance known as triolein, which is a constituent of the pepper.

It is generally thought that the fact that, in captivity, Purple Finches and orioles frequently moult into yellowish hues, instead of their rightful tints, is due to some change in food. Indeed in many species the bright colours are wholly lacking after a year or two in captivity. But I have transferred a male Purple Finch, which had for several years moulted yellow, from a dark cage to one which was exposed to bright sunlight, and in one moult the bird assumed his original and normal colour.

A more probable example of the effect of food upon colour is seen in our American Flamingoes. In captivity these birds fade out moult by moult, until they become almost white, like the European species. By mixing with their food a quantity of some strong but harmless dye,

Fig. 233.—Effect of environment on Bobwhite, shown by specimens from Minnesota, Florida, and Cuba. (From a photograph provided by the American Museum of Natural History.)

I have had them either retain their original colour for years, or at least the fading process has been appreciably lessened.

The effect of climate upon colour is even more readily proved, and may be noticed in wild birds as well as in those in captivity. In regions which have a very dry climate, the birds, and in fact all of the animals, are of a much lighter hue than those living in an atmosphere of great humidity, where moisture does not readily evapo-

FIG. 234.—Male Scarlet Tanagers, showing moult from the scarlet summer dress, (*a*), through the parti–coloured garb (*b*), into the green winter plumage (*c*).

rate.   In such a place birds tend to be very dark-coloured. In the case of captive birds, I have seen White-throated Sparrows and Wood Thrushes become almost like blackbirds in colour when confined in a bird-house where the air was constantly moist.   Correlated with the effect upon colour is often a difference in size, and in many instances among birds the more northerly individuals are larger, those inhabiting warmer regions being less in stature.

Among wild birds, the Quail, or Bob-white, shows an almost unbroken series from the northern, light-coloured variety, ten inches in length, to the Cuban bird, very

FIG. 235.—Siberian Black Lark, male bird in the spring.

much darker in shade and measuring only eight inches from beak to tip of tail.   The race of Bob-whites seems very susceptible to climatic influence; as in Mexico there are nearly a dozen different geographical races, each inhabiting a distinct portion of the country.   Many other wide-spread groups of birds, such as the Song Sparrows, vary in a similar manner.   It is strange what a marked effect this greater or less amount of moisture has upon birds, even in very limited districts.   A South American pipit, the individuals of which spend their lives on very circumscribed plots of earth, exhibits two colour forms entirely different, and thought to be due solely to the amount of moisture in the ground on which it lives. Very dark-coloured and very pale individuals live within a few hundred yards of each other, in dry and swampy situations respectively, each, it is said, keeping entirely to its own little beat.

We are all familiar with the changes of colour due to

Fig. 236.—Nighthawk perching lengthwise on a fallen branch.

age, as, for instance, in the young Rose-breasted Grosbeaks, which are very different from the male parent, and the young Bald Eagles, which lack the white colour of the feathers of head and tail. Certain wild pigeons show marked differences in colour patterns between the young birds and the adults, and very good evidence of the gradual evolution which must have preceded these changes is to be found by plucking out a few of the feathers of the young bird. Those which replace the ones pulled out will show intermediate stages, which have long since been dropped from the sequence of patterns, as observed in the regular moults of the birds.

Another important phenomenon is the seasonal moult, which was spoken of in the chapter treating of feathers· In the fall of the year the brilliant Scarlet Tanager assumes the olive-green dress of the female, and the Indigo Bunting and the Bobolink likewise don the dull garb of their mates.

There is another very interesting cause of change in colour, namely, the wearing off of the brittle tips of the feather-vane. An excellent example of this is seen in the Snowflakes, which come south in the depth of severe winters, flying in small flocks about our fields, like an animated flurry of the actual crystals. When we see the birds at this time they are brownish and brownish white. In the spring in their northern home, they change to a clear-cut black and white, not by shedding the entire plumage, but merely by the breaking off of the brown feather-tips. By a similar process the Bobolink changes from the buffy female dress to his rich black-and-white spring suit, and, as we saw in Chapter II, Fig. 35, the English Sparrow gains his cravat of jet.

Another excellent example is found in the Black Larks of Siberia, the males of which, in winter, are of an almost uniform sandy colour, like a Skylark, but by the wearing off of the buff tips of the feathers, the birds become jet-black in the summer—a most remarkable and radical change.

FIG. 237.—Wild Ptarmigan. Their fearlessness of the photographer is due to their unusual immunity from danger. (Whealton, photographer.)

The relation of a bird's colours to its haunts and its habits of life is a subject of intense interest. This is, of course, not in the same category as the subjects of the foregoing paragraphs, but indeed includes them all. The most common class of colours is known as protective. These are such that the bird resembles its environment or surroundings and is thus given a better chance of escaping the observation of its enemies. It is evident that, in a study of this nature, observation of the bird in its natural haunts is of far greater value than any other method.

We find that the majority of sparrows, sandpipers, and quail are gray or brown, like the grasses, sedges, and leaves among which they live; while the birds which spend their lives higher up among the branches of trees are greenish, or at least more brightly coloured.

Many birds which are protectively coloured are dark above and white or whitish beneath. The significance of this pattern of coloration has been beautifully demonstrated by an American artist, Mr. Abbott Thayer. His experiment, which is as follows, may be repeated by any one: Take two wooden decoy ducks, and place them against a sand-bank. Colour one the exact tint of the sand, or even coat it with that substance. Repeat this with the upper parts of the second decoy, making its back darker than the surrounding sand, but grade the under part of this one to pure white below. At a little distance away, decoy number one will still be distinctly seen; while number two will absolutely disappear, merging perfectly into its background. The reason for this is

that the conspicuous white of the under surface of the
second bird is, when normally lighted up by the sun,
neutralized by the shadow of the bird, and the darker
upper parts are softened and toned down by the strong
direct light; while if the entire bird be unshaded, although

Fig. 238.—Sooty Tern on her nest.

coloured like the environment, the dark shadow beneath
will reveal it clearly.

Whether or not birds really appreciate the value of
the protective colour of their plumage, it is certain that
a quail or ptarmigan will remain crouching on a brown
bit of turf, until all hope of evading danger is gone; while
birds which are very evidently not protectively coloured
are invariably more wary and difficult of approach. When

FIG. 239.—Seven young Flickers clinging to a tree. (R. H. Beebe, photographer.)

a ptarmigan, while yet in the brown garb of summer, is exposed against a hillside of snow, it becomes very wary.

It is interesting, in this connection, to observe how a Nighthawk carries out its colour resemblance to a knot or a rough piece of bark, by perchiyg, not crosswise, but lengthwise, along a branch or fallen tree-trunk.

A volume might easily be written of the various ways in which protective coloration works out among birds, but there is so great a difference of opinion, and indeed so many exceptions to every theory which may be advanced, that it is better, for the most part, to go to Nature without *a priori* theories, and putting ourselves as nearly as possible in the position of the creatures themselves, to hope for better ability to see with their eyes. And it is right along this line that we most need fresh data and experiments, namely, the actual ability of birds and insects to distinguish shades, colours, forms, and motion,—whether efficient in certain ways or not. We know that many men cannot distinguish a scarlet ball lying upon green grass; that is, they are partly colour-blind. If this were the case with certain hawks, a male Scarlet Tanager would be forever safe from them among the green foliage.

An important fact, which for years had been apparent to me, but unexpressed until Mr. Abbott Thayer put it into words, is that colours which we would ordinarily term conspicuous are often exactly the opposite when found in the plumage of a bird. Writing of the Motmot in my volume "Two Bird-lovers in Mexico," I say: " I have often wondered, when I saw mounted specimens in museums, with what special immunity from danger these birds were blessed, their beautiful colouring would seem to be such a startling advertisement of the bird's whereabouts. But in reality the very diversity in hue is their protec-tion, and they merge per-fectly into their environ-ment of green foliage and bright sunlight."

Indeed absolute uniform-ity of coloration instantly reveals the outline of the bird entire, and renders it very conspicuous. Birds which have but few ene-mies are often thus mono-crome in hue. But look at the photographs and see how a broken colora-tion baffles the eye. If

Fig. 240.—Brown Creeper circling up the trunk of a spruce.

the Sooty Tern, Fig. 238, were totally black, it would be conspicuous even against a patch of dark-coloured mottled shingle. But the transverse lines of white across the back totally destroy the symmetry of form, while the white wing-edges fairly force the eye to call them, not part of a bird sheltering her eggs, but only two among a myriad irregular edges of coral rock!

Observe closely the seven young Flickers clinging to their natal stump. As the warriors of Jason sprang forth from the ground fully armed, so the very bark, mottled

with spots of lichen and sunlight, seems to have gendered
these baby birds. Yet they were hatched in a dark hole
from the whitest of white eggs. Is this and a thousand
of other resemblances to be termed *accidental?* Then
is all Nature one great accident! When the Flicker flies
with swift wing-beat from tree to tree, then the white

Fig. 241.—Laughing Gull on nest.

rump blazes forth. At such moment no protection is
needed; but in these young Flickers upon the tree-trunk,
how exquisitely do their spots deceive the eye! They
are, we say, perhaps sunlight splashes,—nothing more.
Yet others which, like the Brown Creeper, haunt the
tree-trunks of the forest, seem veritably to be but stray
bits of roughened bark creeping here and there.

Fig. 242.—Black-necked Swans. (Courtesy of A. E. Brown.)

Let us glance at one more bird upon her nest,—a Laughing Gull. At a distance we see a shapeless blotch of white sand among the reeds, that is all. We walk over a hundred other similar patches; but when near enough, we at last are able to distinguish the dark head and wing-tips, all but invisible among the shadows, and even through the centre of the head we can see two spots of light beyond,—or no, it is the little subtle ring of white about the eye!

Two majestic Black-necked Swans may swim closely along in full view near the opposite bank of a pond, and yet be totally unrecognizable; showing to the eye as bodiless necks or neckless bodies, according to the changing conditions of light and shade around them.

We see a troop of ostriches rushing past. Surely nothing could hide birds such as these! Again we see one of these birds prone upon the ground, and a mighty creature towering eight feet or more above the earth, becomes naught but a dark ant-hill, which the photograph picks out clearly, but which in the desert, dotted with ant-hills, would seldom be noticed even by the hungriest of lions.

Of course, like most other theories, this of protective coloration can easily be carried too far, but there are hundreds of instances where it seems to answer every requirement of the case. Few fields offer such opportunities for original work of the most delightful character. As one example out of untold numbers, what explanation can we give of the Blood-breasted Pigeon or Bleeding-heart Pigeon, which, as its name denotes, has a splash

FIG. 243.—Group of Ostriches on the run. (Cawston, photographer.)

FIG. 244.—Ostrich as it hides from an enemy.

of blood-like scarlet in the centre of its breast? The remarkable and inexplicable resemblance is heightened by the stiffened vanes of the centre feathers, causing them to appear bedraggled and clotted, as if by an actual wound! The photograph does but little justice to the bird's real appearance.

Another class of colours, while still protective, is so for a purpose very different from those cases which we

FIG. 245.—Bleeding-heart Pigeon.

have been considering. The colours which we are now to mention have been aptly called aggressive colours, as, by their means, a bird of prey is enabled to approach its victim more easily. So, throughout the entire animal world we find two phases of phenomena constantly present: on the one hand the *pursued* ones, striving to escape by all means in their power; and on the other hand the *pursuers*, ever trying to outwit those upon which they prey. If a duck acquires great speed of flight, the Duck

Hawk must learn to fly still faster. If the duck learns to crouch close to the reeds when his flight-feathers are moulted and he is helpless, the hawk must develop ever sharper eyesight. We may puzzle and puzzle over a characteristic habit or a colour of some bird, finding no solution, until we discover some special enemy or other factor in its life which makes all clear.

So, among aggressive colours we may mention the garb of the penguin, which is steel-gray on the back and silvery white below; not to protect it from danger, but to enable it the better to approach fish without alarming them. It is curious how fish-like the coloration of these birds really is, and they are said frequently to lay feet and tail together and, drawing their flipper-like wings to their sides, spring clear of the water again and again, by a single motion of the back muscles, exactly as the mammalian dolphins leap ahead of a vessel's bow.

Again, while we find the ptarmigan mimicking the snow in colour, we find the Arctic Fox, the Snowy Owl, and the Gyrfalcon, all of which are enemies of this bird, also garbed in white. The ptarmigan may crouch upon a drift, but it must ever be on the alert, lest from amid the snowflakes a white death come suddenly upon it. Nature is terribly just in her plan of life's battles.

In the same region with these lives the Ivory Gull, immaculate as the ice-floe over which it flies, and in its whiteness we can perhaps read two purposes: a better chance to elude the fierce Gyrfalcon, and a better chance to float cloud-like unperceived over the unsuspecting fish which it seeks for food.

FIG. 246.—Black footed Penguin.

FIG. 247.—Pickerel. (Keller, photographer. From life, swimming.)
PREDACIOUS, AQUATIC ANIMALS, SHOWING AGGRESSIVE
COLORATION.

An instance of what has been called unconscious mimicry seems to exist in the cuckoo of the Old World, which, like our cowbird, is parasitical in habits, making no nest of its own, but depositing its eggs in the nests of other species of birds. The cuckoo bears a striking

FIG. 248.—Ivory Gull. Aggressive and protective coloration in an Arctic Gull.

resemblance to a small hawk, both in general pattern and in its darting flight. The name Hawk-cuckoo has been applied to a genus of these birds in India; the name being given because of the resemblance to a hawk. This similarity may be of great use in temporarily frightening away the owners of the nest in which the bird wishes to deposit an egg. A few other instances are known, as where a fierce, bird-killing hawk resembles a harmless, insectivorous species, perhaps by this deception deluding small birds.

FIG. 249.—Gyrfalcon. Aggressive coloration in an Arctic Hawk.

Many of the plovers have one, or even two, bands of black encircling the neck or breast, and in the Crook-billed Plover of New Zealand there is a most interesting modification of this apparent ornament. This bird feeds by running rapidly around boulders and inserting its crooked bill beneath them to obtain the insects which compose its diet. The pectoral ring of black, instead of being complete, is said to be often less developed on the left-hand side. Buller accounts for this fact by arguing that that side of the bird is much more exposed to danger, as it continually scurries about the boulders, keeping always to the right, and thus the side next to the stone needs no protective colouring; and so we find this one-sided development of the band. How much, in this and in many other so-called protectively coloured birds, other factors, such as the direct effect of light on

FIG. 250.—Snowy Owl. Aggressive coloration in an Arctic Owl.

the plumage, enter into the causation, can only be solved by future thorough investigation.

Albinos are occasionally found among widely different

Families of birds; but white blackbirds and such freaks
of Nature have but slight chance for life when keen-eyed
hawks are ever on the lookout, and owls are alert for
every tell-tale plume. Again and again hawks have been
known to single out white or whitish birds from a number,
making them the object of attack. When any species
of bird, through change of habit, absence of enemies, or
any other cause, is able to increase greatly in numbers,
albinism is likely to occur more frequently. A good example of this is to be found in the naturalized English
Sparrows of our cities and towns, among which a remarkable number with white feathers, or even with the entire
wings and tail white, are to be seen. This is one of
Nature's remedies to reduce the excess number, all need
for protective colours having disappeared in the new
environment of these birds. We may be certain that if,
by any fortunate means, hawks or shrikes can be induced to live within the limits of the cities, the albinistic
individuals will be the first to fall victims.

Black phases of plumage occur among some birds,
and a double colour-scheme is found in the common
Screech Owl,—red and gray individuals being often found
in the same brood, the two phases existing independently
of age, sex, or season.

A vast field for future study and investigation lies in
the meanings of the differences in colour between the
sexes, and in the young birds from both. A hint of the
value of ultimate results in this field (which is without
the scope of this book) is to be found in our young American Robin, whose lower parts, from throat to flanks, are

FIG. 251.—Snowy Egrets in full breeding plumage.

315

FIG. 252.—Young Robin.

FIG. 253.—Fallow Deer fawn one day old.

BOTH SHOWING SPOTS WHICH ARE ABSENT IN THE ADULTS.

316

thickly spotted. This gives a clue to the coloration of its ancestors,—birds probably resembling our Wood Thrush, and lacking the rufous, immaculate breast of the parents. We find a similar condition existing among many deer, whose young are spotted, entirely unlike the brown coats of their parents.

FIG. 254.—Nestling Turkey Vulture. (T. H. Jackson, photographer.)

In many cases the colouring of the downy young is the opposite of the adult, as in the Turkey Vulture, the nestling being clad in down of purest white, and ultimately moulting into the blackish plumage of the parent birds.

It would be out of place in this volume to speak further of the wonderful colours which the Class of birds, as a whole, exhibits, or of the beautiful plumes which, as in the case of the Snowy Egret, are assumed only during the season of courtship. The great majority are now explained either as decorations to charm the female, or as mere by-products of the vitality of the bird, according as to whether one believes in a greater or less degree of æsthetic appreciation among birds. When we consider the nervous, high-strung natures of birds and realize with what ease they are thrown into what seems a kind of trance, it seems unnecessary to credit them with too great an appreciation of pure beauty. The repetition of many similar bright spots, as, for example, the eyes of a peacock's train, may well serve to attract and hold the attention of the female; while the antics and sounds which many birds bring into play in courtship may appeal in some more directly psychic way than we know. That birds do have a certain appreciation of beauty and harmony there can be little doubt. When we remember the jarring discords and clashing tints in which a human savage takes delight under the name of music and beauty, we should be very willing to admit some degree of appreciation to the demure Impeyan Pheasant hen which chooses among her suitors, clad each in hues such as artist could never imitate; or the fair Hermit Thrush, which selects a singer from the incomparable choir of her serenaders. I believe that future field study and experiments with caged birds will reveal much that we do not suspect in regard to the *causes* of coloration.

CHAPTER XIII

WINGS

EFORE the front limbs of any creature had become adapted to flight through the air, they served to assist the hind legs in locomotion on the ground, and, ages before this, a many-rayed membrane stretched across the primitive fin, aided its owner in cleaving a way through the water. So, like a palimpsest, if we look beneath the outer covering of feathers, we see, in the wing of the modern bird, the three fingers hinting of widely different ancestral habits.

The general structure and appearance of the bills, the feet, and wings of various birds is the result of a function characteristic of each. The bills are used to procure food, the feet to walk or perch, and the wings to propel the bird through the air. But, as we have seen in the case of the bill, these organs are put to many other uses besides the one for which they were primarily adapted. This is only what we should expect when we consider the relative high position which avian intelligence holds, and the remarkable extremes of environment with which these structures—bill, feet, and wings—are brought into close touch.

The photograph of the young heron's wing shows

the two principal divisions into which the flight-feathers
are divided: the primary feathers, or those growing on
the fingers and wrist-bones, and the secondaries which
sprout from the bone of the forearm.   The several feathers

FIG. 255.—Young Green Heron, showing various divisions of wing-feathers.

supported by the thumb are also very distinctly shown.
When a wing is greatly elongated it is the secondary
feathers which are increased in number, the two extremes
being represented by the hummingbird and the albatross,

each of which has ten primaries, but the one has six and
the other forty secondaries (Figs. 259, 260).*

Let us observe the wings of living birds in the woods
and fields or in a zoological park and see what of interest
we can discover. We have all noticed how well adapted

Fig. 256.—Great White Heron stretching its wing. (E. R. Sanborn,
photographer.)

to its owner's many uses is the foot of a parrot—how
hand-like it is,—and now if we again watch one of these
birds we will see that, as we should expect from its being

* Extremes in regard to the number of primaries are the three flightless
groups, penguins with approximately 36, ostriches with 16, and cassowaries
with perhaps but 2 feathers which can be called primaries.

so much like a human hand, it is not a good walking foot.
When a parrot is in great haste to reach some object
on the ground without flying, it waddles awkwardly, "toe-
ing in" and frequently tripping up.   When this happens,
out fly the wings, and, as if reverting to some clouded
memory of the habits of its pre-Jurassic forefathers, it
walks on *all fours*.   A young Canada Goose, when climbing about its nest, or a Fish Hawk in the downy nestling

Fig. 257.—Nestling Catbird, supporting itself, lizard-like, on all four limbs.

plumage, does the same thing, and young birds of many
species, when too young to stand, push themselves along
the ground with feet and wings; a young grebe doubtless
being the most accomplished in this motion.   In certain
adult birds, such as the swan, Osprey, Turkey Vulture,
and the various ostrich-like birds, there are perfect claws
at the tips of one or more of the skin-bound wing-fingers.
These are true relics of a lizard-handed ancestry.

Before going on to find the more curious uses to which

wings are put, we will look at certain birds whose flight can teach us something interesting. If a pheasant in captivity becomes suddenly alarmed, or its spacious aviary tempts it to rise from the ground, we hear a great whirr,— broad, round-curved wings buzz in a half-circle of haze around the bird and it is off like a shot to the farther

FIG. 258.—Young Green Heron, reaching out with its wing toward a branch which it hooked with the sprouting feathers, and steadied itself for a new foothold.

end of the runway. It may go right through the sash and pane of glass—such is the impetus gained in this mad rush. Fortunate it is for these birds, and for their cousins, the grouse and quail, that they can thus spring up and escape from foxes and other enemies to whom their scent so often betrays them. If the pheasant were at liberty, we should see that this burst of speed would end in a long, slowly descending sail, and with wings held motionless the bird would sink into the nearest cover. It is most interesting and exciting to walk through a field of tall grass where many pheasants are feeding, and see them shoot up to the right and to the left; a hen with her brood waiting until one's foot is almost upon her before booming away.

In a zoological park we may observe another extreme of bird flight by watching a condor take wing. He waits until a breeze is blowing and then, facing the direction from which it comes, he runs with all his might, flapping awkwardly until sufficient headway is gained, when strong downward strokes carry him to the perch he has selected. We may, at first thought, pity him, but if we could see him soaring for hours high among the cloud-peaks of his native Andes, we should instead pity the low-flying pheasant.

These two examples—the pheasant and the condor—show what differences may be found in flying birds, and as we examine the wings of other species, we find that each is perfectly adapted to the wants of its owner. A wing is a most delicately adjusted organ; its feathers being just strong enough to lift the body of its owner into the air, and, like evenly balanced scales, the least excess or lack of use is quickly met by a reaction. Compare the Black Skimmer of the seas, which is only eighteen inches in length, but whose long wings expand four feet, with a stubby-winged quail or grouse.

There are some species of flycatchers with wonderful

FIG. 259.—Wing of Hummingbird with 16 flight-feathers. 1/2 natural size.

FIG. 260.—Wing of Albatross with 50 flight-feathers. 1/28 natural size.

powers of flight. When perched on a branch, they can
evade the shot from a shot-gun. It is said that one will
sometimes "chase another for three or four minutes,
doubling, turning, twisting, and shooting, now brushing
the grass, now rising to a height of at least two or three

FIG. 261.—Condor about to take flight.

hundred feet, and all the movements so rapid that the
eye can scarcely follow them; and at the end of it would
go back to his own chosen weed-stalk, apparently without
a feather ruffled."

Any attempt to explain the mechanics of the way of a
bird in the air would at most be imperfect in the present

state of our knowledge. Suffice it to say that if we will think of a bird flying through the air when we ourselves are swimming in the water, we can realize the achievement more vividly than from any amount of descriptions and diagrams.

The under surface of a bird's wing is concave; and

FIG. 262.—Wing of living Golden Pheasant; rounded and curved for short, sudden flight.

while the front edge is rather straight and firm, the hinder rim of the feathers is soft and yielding; thus a downward stroke both raises the bird or holds it sustained at the height already reached and urges it in a forward direction. Similarly we push our hollowed palms backward and propel ourselves through the denser medium of water.

The manner of flight varies greatly in different birds

and is often so characteristic that when too far off to distinguish the colour of its plumage, or for its notes to reach our ears, the bird may be recognized by the undulations or the directness of its flight.   No one who has ever visited the tropics can have failed to admire the

Fig. 263.—Wing of living Herring-gull; long and narrow for slow, continuous flight.

soaring vultures,—spots of black swinging across the heavens or swooping low in grand arcs over the palms. Gulls and their kindred fly steadily with continuous wing-beats, which, however, are much less rapid than in the flight of a duck or a parrot.   Many sparrows have an abrupt jerking motion, hitching themselves over trees and bushes; while goldfinches and woodpeckers swing past in long undulations, a loop and a catch, a loop and a catch,—with wings wide extended, then quickly closed. Hummingbirds have a remarkably insect-like flight; the rapid reflex whirr of the wings holding them perfectly still, poised in mid-air.

When ornithologists think that they have formed a correct theory of flight and that, given such and such conditions, certain results must follow, such a bird as the Crested Screamer soars into their mental atmosphere and upsets every calculation. Such a bulky and short-winged bird, by all good "rules" of flight, should confine itself to short laboured efforts, barely skimming the low bushes of its South American haunts! But it refuses to be thus limited. Of this species it is said: "The Screamer is a very heavy bird, and rises from the ground laboriously, the wings, as in the case of the swan, making a loud noise. Nevertheless it loves soaring, and will rise in an immense spiral until it wholly disappears from sight in the zenith, even in the brightest weather; and considering its great bulk and dark colour, the height it ultimately attains must be very great. On sunny windless days, especially in winter and spring, they often spend hours at a time in these sublime aerial exercises, slowly floating round and round in vast circles, and singing at intervals. How so heavy and comparatively short-winged a bird can sustain itself for such long periods in the thin upper air to which it rises has not yet been explained."

I find in my journal the following account of a flight of vultures which we saw in a desolate alkali desert in western Mexico: "One of the most wonderful exhibitions of bird-flight came to us to-day as we left the alkali plain and rode among the mesquite scrub. A confused mass of black appeared in the air which, as we advanced, resolved itself into hundreds of individual black specks.

FIG. 264.—Crested Screamers.

The atmosphere was so deceptive that what at first seemed to be a vast cloud of gnats close at hand, was soon seen to be a multitude of birds, and when a quarter of a mile away we knew them to be vultures. Three *burros* lay dead upon the plain. This we knew yesterday, and here were the scavengers. Never had we seen Vultures more numerous or in more orderly array. A careful scrutiny through our glasses showed many scores of Black and Turkey Vultures walking about and feeding upon the carcasses of the animals, and from this point there extended upward into the air a vast inverted cone of birds, all circling in the same direction. From where we sat upon our horses there seemed not one out of place, the

Fig. 265.—Turkey Vulture soaring.

outline of the cone was as smooth and distinct as though the birds were limited in their flight to that particular area. It was a rare sight, the sun lighting up every bird on the farther side and shadowing black as night those nearest us. Through one's partly closed eyes the whole mass appeared composed of a myriad slowly revolving wheels, intersecting, crossing each others' orbits, but never breaking their circular outline. The thousands of soaring forms held us spellbound for minutes before we rode closer. Now a change took place, as gradual but as sure as the shifting clouds of a sunset. Until this moment there was a tendency to concentrate at the base of the cone, that portion becoming more and more black until it seemed a solid mass of rapidly revolving forms. But, at our nearer approach, this concentration ceased, and there was perfect equilibrium for a time; then, as we rode up a gentle slope into clearer view, a wonderful ascent began. Slowly the oblique spirals swing upward; the gigantic cone, still perfect in shape, lifts clear of the ground and drifts away, the summit rises in a curve which, little by little, frays out into ragged lines, all drifting in the same direction, and before our very eyes the thousands of birds merge into a shapeless undulating cloud which rises and rises, spreading out more and more until the eye can no longer distinguish the birds which from vultures dwindle to motes, floating and lost among the clouds."

Concerning the greatest extent of wing which any bird possesses, there are records of a Wandering Albatross which measured fourteen feet from tip to tip, but the condor of South America exceeds this, certain individuals having an expanse of fifteen feet.

Having considered the finest flyers among the birds, we may now begin to go down the scale and see what has happened when certain species have deliberately discarded the wonderful power of flight with which Nature has provided them and for which human inventors are so earnestly striving. But always we must remember that this restriction and disuse have been to subserve some good and useful purpose,—food perhaps being more easily obtained, or enemies avoided by terrestrial or aquatic locomotion. Functional radiation, working always for the good of the race, once gave to all birds the power of traversing the globe, passing high over sea and land; but later this was withdrawn, until in some cases their wings have become a mockery. The wings of the Owl Parrot of New Zealand are of full size, but the muscles are so encased in fat that they are useless for flight. These parrots feed on ground-mosses, and being nocturnal and therefore having few enemies, their only use for wings is occasionally to sail gently to earth, like a Flying Squirrel, from the trees in the hollows of which they sometimes roost. For this purpose their flabby muscles are perfectly suited.

The Spotted Tinamou of South America is one of a number of birds which have not quite lost the power of flight, but in which, as in the first attempts of a young bird, almost no control is possessed over the direction or height of their flight. In fact, the condition is much the same as that of a man in an ordinary balloon, who is at the mercy of the wind and the sustaining power of the gas. Hudson gives the following interesting account of this bird: "It is an exceedingly rare thing to see this bird rise except when compelled. I believe the power of flight is used chiefly, if not exclusively, as a means of escape from danger. The bird rises up when almost trodden upon, rushing into the air with a noise and violence that fill one with astonishment. It continues to rise at a decreasing angle for fifty or sixty yards, then gradually nears the earth, till, when it has got to a distance of two or three hundred yards, the violent action of the wing ceases, and the bird glides along close to the earth for some distance, and either drops down or renews its flight. I suppose many birds fly in much the same way; only

FIG. 266.—South American Tinamou.

this tinamou starts forward with such amazing energy that, until this is expended and the moment of gliding comes, the flight is just as ungovernable to the bird as the motion of a brakeless engine, rushing along at full speed, would be to the driver. The bird knows the danger to which this peculiar character of its flight exposes it

so well that it is careful to fly only to that side where
it sees a clear course. It is sometimes, however, compelled
to take wing suddenly, without considering the obstacles
in its path; it also often miscalculates the height of an
obstacle, so that for tinamous to meet with accidents
when flying is very common. In the course of a short
ride of two miles, during which several birds sprang up
before me, I have seen three of these tinamous dash
themselves to death against a fence close to the path,
the height of which they had evidently misjudged. I
have also seen a bird fly blindly against the wall of a
house, killing itself instantly. A brother of mine told
me of a very curious thing he once witnessed. He was
galloping over the pampas, with a very violent wind blowing in his face, when a tinamou started up before his
horse. The bird flew up in the air vertically, and, beating its wings violently, and with a swiftness far exceeding
that of its ordinary flight, continued to ascend until it
reached a vast height, then came down again, whirling
round and round, striking the earth a very few yards
from the spot where it rose, and crushing itself to a pulp
with the tremendous force of the fall. It is very easy to
guess the cause of such an accident: while the tinamou
struggled blindly to go forward, the violent wind, catching the under surface of the wings, forced it upward, until
the bird, becoming hopelessly confused, fell back to earth.
I have often seen a swallow, gull, or hawk, soaring about
in a high wind, suddenly turn the under surface of its
wings to the wind and instantly shoot straight up, apparently without an effort, to a vast height, then recover

itself and start off in a fresh direction. The tinamou, when launched on the atmosphere, is at the mercy of

FIG. 267.—Feathers of Ostrich and Condor.

chance; nevertheless, had this incident been related to me by a stranger, I should not have recorded it."

So in this bird we have a most rare and suggestive

instance of a condition where an important organ is actually in process of losing its primary function, and in so doing becomes a source of danger to the bird.

In the waters of the sea near the Falkland Islands is a duck known as the Steamer or Side-wheel Duck. The young birds of this species are good flyers and whistle through the air on strong pinions. But maturity, instead of bringing, as in most birds, a fully perfected power of flight, takes from them what they have, and after the first moult they are helpless to rise above the great waves of their haunts. However, this duck finds another use for its wings, and the stiffness which forbids their being used in the air makes of them bladed paddles which are all the better for their lack of flying power, and with wings and feet these birds make remarkable speed through the water—"twelve or fifteen miles an hour"—and they are thus able to live out their lives in safety. Thus the study of the flight of these birds carries us a step farther than the tinamou, with the all-important difference that, in this case, loss of the primary function is compensated by a direct adaptation of the wing to the new conditions of life.

In the ostriches and their near allies the extreme reduction of wings is to be found, and yet in the true ostriches and rheas the great expanse of soft feathers is a considerable help to the birds when running at full speed, acting as a sail or aeroplane to assist in the onward motion. But the contrast between a loose, open-work feather from the wing of one of these birds and a compact, firmly vaned plume from a condor's wing is very striking. The cassowary has from four to six flight-feathers, but, far from being of any use in supporting his great frame, they are so vestigial that they look exactly like black slate-pencils projecting in a row from the little fleshy flap which contains the evidence of his full-winged ancestors

A full-grown ostrich was once imported to this country from Abyssinia. When the native keepers learned that the bird was to be sent away, they surreptitiously plucked the

FIG. 268.—Wing of Cassowary, showing degenerate flight-feathers.

poor creature, until but few feathers were left on its body. The bird was tame, and, by keeping its attention busy with a basket of carrots, I inserted a piece of white cardboard beneath one of its skinny, denuded wings and secured an excellent photograph (Fig. 269). This clearly shows the black, curved claws on the first two fingers. In this same bird I noticed that occasionally the crooked forearm would be raised, the claw at the end of the wing drawn up, and the ostrich would scratch its body or head with this interesting finger relic! When the plume feathers of the wing are full grown, the foot or leg is thus used,

Fig. 269.—Wing of Ostrich, showing reptile-like claws.

the head or neck being rubbed against its roughened scales.

The Great Auk—a sea-bird which has become extinct within the last sixty years—was without the power of flight, and its living allies, the Razor-billed Auks and Murrelets, have very small wings and are rather weak flyers. The latter, in fact, use their wings, the feathers of which have very stiff and long quills, as much in diving under water as in flying in the air, and, strangely enough, they are said to swim breast upward, propelling themselves by means of both wings and feet. Grebes, too, are very weak of wing, and these birds cannot rise from level ground, no matter how much of a fluttering run is taken, and even in the water much splashing and headway are needed.

Perhaps the most wonderful birds in the world are penguins, and the strangest part of these strange birds is the wing. There is no doubt that they are descended from birds which possessed the power of flight; but the penguins have discarded this gift and have returned to a life in the sea, whence in long ages past their forebears had crawled out upon land. As in the ostriches, the relics of flight-feathers have increased greatly in number, but have become small and scaly, and the wings have virtually become flippers or fins. Instead of a given number of feathers, divided into well-marked series, the paddles of a penguin are covered thickly with small feather-scales, and the rigidity of the wings, together with the rotary movement at the shoulder-joint, make the propeller of a ship an apt simile. The colour of the feather-scales on the upper side of the wing is dark, like the back of the bird, but those on the under side have run rampant, the white and black being mixed irregularly, not corresponding even in the two wings of an individual bird.

The outline of the wing is exactly like that of a shark's fin, the flatness and breadth including even the bones, while (also like a fin) all of the bending quality of a wing

Fig. 270.—Great Auk and Razor-billed Auk, showing relative size of wings.
(From a photograph provided by the American Museum of Natural History.)

is lost,—all the flexibility of wrist and elbow. With these propellers the penguins fly through the water, with almost the identical motion of a bird in the air. Though it is usually asserted that the wings move alternately, this was never the case with a pair of Black-footed Penguins which I carefully observed. As regards the speed of swimming, I found that one of these birds, though in bad health at the time and so weak that it could take but a few steps on land, was able to progress under water

Fig. 271.—Penguin swimming with its wings.

considerably faster than a man could walk an equal distance on land. The greatest speed was about seven miles an hour; but I have no doubt that when in full health this rate can be far surpassed.

Surely no fairy-tale can match the marvellous evolution of a penguin's wing: fin becoming hand, hand evolving into wing, and wing reacting to the environment of long ago and again taking on all the outward characteristics of a fin!

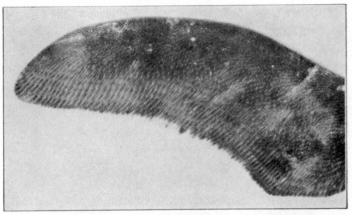

FIG. 272.—Wing of Black-footed Penguin, top view.

FIG. 273.—Wing of Black-footed Penguin, side view.

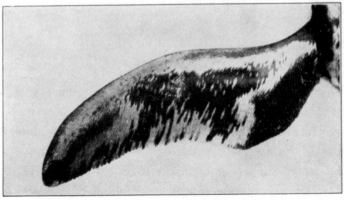

FIG. 274.—Wing of Black-footed Penguin, under surface of wing.
ALL FROM THE LIVING BIRD.

We have seen how wings guard their owners from the risk of sudden surprises from enemies, and now let us observe how, in a sleeping bird, the tender nostrils and eyes are protected against cold and other dangers. Birds do not put their heads *under* their wings, but *behind* them, often using the shoulder-feathers as cover. It is inter-

Fig. 275.—Green Heron with head behind wing.

esting to see how many birds, from all quarters of the earth, have this same habit. The pelican, however, departs from this custom and snuggles his tremendous bill between the feathers in the centre of his back, and flops both wings up so as completely to cover it. Even the cassowary vainly tries to tuck his bill behind his absurd wing. His smaller wing-coverts are mere soft, loose hair-like shafts, while the larger quills, as mentioned before, are reduced to four or six horny sticks.

If we watch an owl flying about its cage at night, or if, in the woods, an owl passes near, his shadow in the moonlight is all that warns us of his presence. The feathers of an owl's wing are soft and downy, and the bird moves as lightly as a falling leaf. Little warning, except by

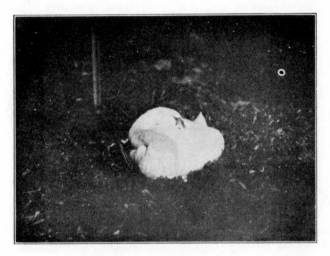

Fig. 276.—Trumpeter Swan asleep.

sight, the mice and birds have of its deadly presence. Few birds have a flight as noiseless as that of owls, and in some species the motion of the wings makes, as we noticed in the pheasant, a very audible sound. When a widgeon rises from the water, the whistling of its quills, so dear to the ears of the sportsman, is quite shrill. A dove claps its wings together above its back while gaining impetus for flight. The characteristic sound from which a hummingbird takes its name is well known.

When wild geese and swans nest in captivity, their wings are put to most excellent use as weapons of defence, and of course this use must come into play frequently when nesting in their native haunts. I have seen a man knocked breathless by a Canada gander who thought his nest in danger. When preparing for attack, the bird approaches hissing, with head stretched low along the ground, and suddenly, without warning, launches

Fig 277.—Trumpeter Swan preparing to attack an intruder with its wings.

itself straight at one's breast and, clinging with bill and claws, beats a tattoo with the hard bend of its wings. One is not likely to forget such a drubbing for a long time. The wings of certain birds are armed with weapons of offence, such as the Spur-winged Goose, Jacana, Plover, and Screamer. The Spur-winged Goose is a really dangerous antagonist and can strike incredibly strong blows, bringing the sharp spur to bear with telling effect. These

spurs are not claws, but correspond in structure to the
ordinary spurs on the legs of a rooster.

The great heavy-headed and heavy-bodied hornbills
fly with great effort, and it is said upon good authority
that when passing low overhead they make a noise like
a steam-engine. Although not strictly within the prov-

FIG. 278.—Spur-winged Goose.

ince of this volume, mention should be made of the inten-
tional use of the wings as instruments of sound,—to attract the females, as in our Ruffed Grouse and other birds.
A little Bush Warbler of Africa has indeed never been heard
to utter a note, seeming to depend upon an occasional
whirr of wings, in lieu even of the usual call-note or chirp.

In the woodcock we find the vane of the three outer primaries of the wing remarkably narrowed and stiffened; probably a direct adaptation for the production of the high, whistling sound which plays so important a part in its aerial courtship performance.

FIG. 279.—Wing ornaments of Twelve-wired Bird of Paradise.

As upon all other parts of the bird's body, we find beautiful decorations upon the wings—inexplicable unless we are willing to credit the females with appreciation of, or at least a reaction to, these beauties. Otherwise we know not the uses of the brilliant wing-mirrors of ducks, or the scarlet wax-like tips of the Cedar-bird's feathers,

or the bizarre decoration of the Twelve-wired Bird of
Paradise.

A strange appendage is found in the wing of the West
African Goatsucker. Conspicuous enough when the bird
is flying, it is wonderfully protected when the bird rests,

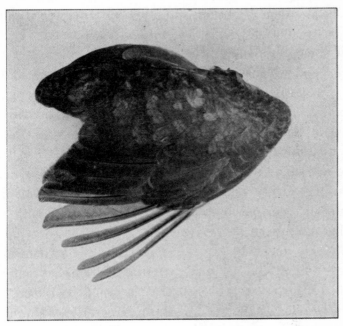

Fig. 280.—Wing of Woodcock.

as is its wont, upon the ground among tall, feathery-
topped grasses. From each wing a single long feather
extends in an upward direction, almost bare of barbs
for most of its length, but tipped with a mottled, loose-
vaned tuft which corresponds very perfectly with the
flower-heads of the grasses among which it lives. As

this decoration, so protective and yet so beautiful, is assumed only during the breeding season, its use is doubtless to aid in attracting the attention of the females.

Herons and other birds make still another use of their wings and the long, tough flight-feathers: as shields for parrying the blows of a rival, or to catch the poison of a snake when it strikes and thus give an opportunity to seize and despatch the reptile. Two Snowy Egrets will sometimes fence with each other in play, and use beak and wing as a soldier would use sword and shield.

I once saw the wing of a bird used in an entirely original manner—a use peculiar, doubtless, to this individual. Several spoonbills suffered severely from the frozen ground upon which they were forced to stand, and no method of relief was found, except by one of their number, who every night stretched one wing beneath him, drew up one foot deep into his plumage, and with the other *stood upon the tips of the primaries.*

Much might be written concerning the swiftness of birds' flight, but so much of exaggeration has entered into estimates of this kind that it would be difficult to select facts and figures of indisputable verity. However, it may be asserted as at least within the actual facts that ducks can attain a speed of ninety miles an hour. An apparently well-authenticated record of a swallow's flight at Antwerp is as follows: A gentleman arranged a flight of homing pigeons from Compiègne to Antwerp,—a distance of one hundred and forty-eight miles,—and with the pigeons he liberated a swallow captured on her nest under the eaves of his house in Antwerp. The swallow, which

FIG. 281.—Osprey showing typical wing of a bird of prey. (Baynes, photographer.)

351

was marked for identification, covered the distance in one hour and eight minutes, or at the extraordinary speed of about two miles and three hundred yards per minute. The first pigeon to arrive took four hours and a quarter to make the journey.

FIG. 282.—Terns in flight.   (Photograph provided by the American Museum of Natural History.)

CHAPTER XIV

FEET AND LEGS

CARRIED far and wide by the power of flight, no two species of birds have exactly similar environments. When the wings cease their labour and are folded close to the sides, the bird must depend upon its feet to carry it to its food and to keep it out of danger, whether its footing be in a tree-top or on a cliff; in shallow water or on the deep; in mud, sand, or snow. Thus we realize the need for many varied adaptations in the way of feet and legs.

Although birds are descended from five-toed ancestors, yet no living wild bird, and none of those which we know only as fossils, has more than four toes on each foot. The disposition of these toes—four, three, or two, as the case may be—is always in accordance with the habits of the bird.

The most common type of avian foot is that in which the arrangement is of three toes in front, with the fourth, corresponding to our great toe, pointing backward. This was the arrangement in our *first* bird, the *Archæopteryx*, and for perching birds, as well as for many others with very different habits, it has stood the test of six millions

353

of years, or thereabouts, since the days of its venerable prototype.

This is the kind of generalized organ which, we should think, would be able to cope with changes in the bird's surroundings more successfully than any other; but that this theory fails when put to the test is proved by the variety of specialized toes and legs which we may observe

FIG. 283.—Foot of Alligator.

among the birds on the earth to-day. Indeed, in the variety of uses which they subserve, the feet and legs of birds are second only to the bills.

A classification of birds, generally accepted for many years, was based on the uses of the feet, or mode of loco-motion. In this scheme birds were divided into runners, scratchers, climbers, swimmers, perchers, etc. Although these, as exact divisions, have long since been abandoned, yet it is worthy of note that even in the most modern classifications many of these groups hold good in the main, although based on other and more fundamental

FIG. 284.—Foot of Brown Pelican.

characters. Examples of these are the ostrich-like birds, or runners; the fowl-like birds, or scratchers; and the Passeres, or perching birds. But there is no doubt that several unrelated groups have independently acquired the

specialized type of foot which is adapted to climbing or
to swimming, so that any classification based on such
similarity of locomotion is obviously false.

From the tiny limbs of a hummingbird to the gigantic
shanks of an ostrich, the legs of birds, with a very few
exceptions, are covered with scales, most emphatic reminders of the reptilian ancestry of both these extreme
forms of feathered life. The real foot of a bird, as the
term is used in speaking of other animals, extends to the
backward-bending joint, or heel. Part of the lower leg

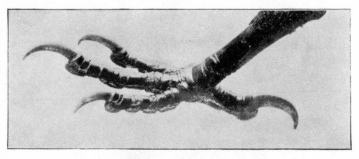

FIG. 285.—Foot of Raven.

is thus concealed by the feathers and skin, while the upper
leg, or thigh, is generally wholly within the body, as we
saw in the chapter treating of the framework.

As before, we must call on the crow, in many respects
standing very near the top of the scale of bird life, yet
which has found it good to hold to the typical bird's foot.
And indeed it serves him well, for with it he can walk on
snow or ice; wade in shallow water; perch in trees; scratch
or claw the ground and hold down a crab's carapace,
while he extracts the edible portion. Not only this, but
he can hop like a sparrow or walk like a lark at will.

We have hardly to leave the group of birds to which the crow belongs to find dozens of interesting and unexpected adaptations of the feet to unusual habits. For example, the Rhinoceros-birds of Africa attach themselves to some of the larger mammals, such as buffalos, rhinoceri, or antelopes, and spend much of their time in freeing these animals from troublesome ticks and other parasites. The power which these birds possess in their feet and legs is remarkable. Millais says of them: "The prehensile power of the claws is, as I found by experience, so great that when a dead bird which had grown stiff was thrown on to the back or sides of an ox, so that the feet touched the animal's hide, the claws held fast at once and could not be withdrawn. It is most interesting to note the way in which a party of these birds will move about on the body of a horse or ox, searching every part of him as they run or hop over it in the most lively fashion. At the risk of being accused of telling a traveller's yarn, I must state the fact that they can hop backward quite as well as forward, and they often make long drops downward from the shoulders to the foreleg, or down the side of the animal whose coat they are engaged upon. It is quite immaterial to them how or in what direction they move."

No hard and fast laws can be laid down, but it is generally the rule that birds which are especially at home in the trees usually hop with both feet simultaneously when on the ground. Ground nesters and feeders, such as the Meadow Lark, Bob-white, and Vesper Sparrow, usually walk or run.

The great Order of perching birds (*Passeres*) shows to what varied uses the typical foot can be put. All birds of this Order have three toes in front and one behind, and there is scarcely a place on the globe to which these birds have not adapted themselves; and recently too, as would seem probable from the similarity of the foot-type running through all.

This very foot holds much of interest too, if we consider it from another point of view. Many apes and monkeys, and we ourselves, still have the five fingers and toes which we suppose was the number originally developed upon the limbs of the vertebrate prototype; while horses and deer—animals much lower in the scale of life—have had the five original digits reduced to one or two. So among birds the ostriches and some other low forms have become extremely specialized in the same respect, possessing but two or three toes, while those birds which in mental and physical attributes excel all others of their Class are still more reptilian, and thus more primitive—more Archæopteryx-like—in possessing a larger number of digits—four. Thus when we speak of an animal as high or low in the scale of life, we must carefully distinguish between mere specialization and actual upward progress, mentally or physically, toward some ideal goal. The branch of a tree, which stretches horizontally farthest from the parent trunk, is not likely to be the one which reaches upward high enough to catch the first rays of the morning sun.

The majority of the Passeres are arboreal and the strength of the tiny tendons which run down the leg and through each toe is sufficient to clasp and unclasp a thousand times a day, and to hold and balance the bird on whatever bending twigs or wind-blown foliage it chances to alight. In this matter of perching the hind toe plays an important part, so much so that when the necessity for grasping ceases, this digit begins to wax flabby and weak and often becomes reduced in size.

FIG. 286.—Nuthatch on tree, clinging upside down.

FIG. 287.—Nuthatch clinging to a gloved hand. (Bowdish, photographer.)

The creepers, Fig. 240, are passerine woodpeckers in habit and forever wind their spiral paths about the tree-trunks. But the nuthatch is the marvel of the whole Class of birds in this climbing ability. With no support whatever from the tail, and without special adaptation of toes, it defies all laws of gravitation and creeps up and down or around the vertical trunks, as if on a level surface. Never a misstep, never a slip, but each foothold as secure as if its feet were vacuum-cupped.

In the swallows the feet are very small, having fallen into disuse with the great increase of the power of flight. Orioles and weaver-birds make occasional use of their feet to hold a strand of grass or string which they are weaving with their beaks into their elaborate nests, and certain flycatchers pounce upon and hold their insect

Fig. 288.—Swallow, showing small size of feet.

prey as an owl grips a bird, or a jay clings to a nut; but with the exception of a few such cases, the feet of perching birds serve principally the function of locomotion.

As variation in habitat or haunt depends so much upon the power of locomotion, it will not be out of place to mention here, in rather more detail than usual, a splendid example of adaptive radiation which we can all verify for ourselves.

There is no more wonderful fact in Nature than the way

in which birds have inherited the earth. When we realize
the immense advantage which the power of flight gives
to them, we do not marvel at this remarkable distribution, but the more we think about it the more wonders
appear. The utmost efforts which man has made to
reach the North Pole have shown flocks of birds winging
their way still farther to the North, heedless of the terrible cold. In the heat of deserts and the sweltering
jungles of the tropics, birds find congenial haunts and
abundant food. Thousands of miles out at sea, on the
highest mountains, and even in dark underground tun-
nels; the whole day—twilight, midnight, and dawn,—
all have been conquered by these tireless, energetic feathered ones.

When we see a large collection of birds, we can appreciate how they are adapted to such varying conditions
of temperature, of moisture, of light, and of altitude.
Their bodies, wings, legs, feet, and tails—in fact every
organ and member is of all sizes and shapes, and shows to
what condition of life the individual is suited. But when
we come to know birds better, and we realize that there
are wheels within wheels, that behind these very evident
divisions into Families and Orders there are lesser groups,
among the members of which the competition is no less
keen, we look for and find gentler gradations and adaptations which, in their way, are more to be wondered at
than the larger, more radical differences; for these birds
have changed their habits and haunts without waiting
for Nature to adjust their wings or their feet. They have
taken the initiative as it were, and, like a man of letters

who is suddenly forced to work at some arduous manual
labour, they have entered on new ways of life—ways to
which their structure seems but ill adapted, and yet,
by the very daring of their efforts, they have won success.

The great-grandfathers, many times removed, of the
modern Families of birds lived lives which were much
broader and more generalized than those of their descendants of to-day, and it is this variety, this seeking of new
opportunities and overcoming of new difficulties by the
feathered *sons*, which makes the study of birds so fascinating a pursuit.

Let us follow the diverging paths of the later generations of some of our own birds. Take the wood-
warblers of our own country. The only way we can
imagine what the earlier ancestors of the warblers were
like is to make a composite of the whole Family. All
its members are tiny, delicate birds which feed on the
smallest insects, their bills are slender and pointed, and
their feet and toes like the finest wire. Yet, far from
waiting for Nature to alter these delicate organs, they
have struck out boldly for themselves and, to avoid a
fatal competition with one another, have varied their
methods of hunting and the limits of their preserves so
successfully that a dozen may live in close proximity
and yet never poach on each other's domains.

Our well-known little Maryland or Northern Yellow-
throat has chosen the low bushes of a marsh as his sphere
in life, and, although he has hidden his face behind a black
mask, yet he is a true warbler, and the blood of his fathers
forces him up now and then into some exposed position,

where he bursts into a joyous bubbling and warbling, calling to his brethren of the tree-tops that, though his haunts are changed, his heart is true to the clan. His cousin, the Worm-eating Warbler, is tending in his direction, living in low bushes and in his habits drifting ever marshward, where there may not be sufficient competition to prevent his eventually sharing it with his more original kinsman. The Yellow Palm Warblers, although more conventional in their ordinary tree-top haunts, have departed from ancient customs in their feeding habits. They dine on the ground, then fly back to the trees; observing, like some humans, the traditions of their family in the spirit, if not in the letter.

The brilliant Redstart clings even more closely to the ancestral ideas of high trees, and cares little what kinds he may find himself in; but he has a failing for water, and if he may not descend, as have his two cousins mentioned above, yet he overlooks them and often swings low through the air toward them. For in his feeding habits he is one of the most radical of warblers. Has he not seen the little green flycatchers in the woods, sitting so lazily upon some favourite perch, and with an occasional swoop snapping up an unfortunate insect? Why, indeed, search all day for the tiny mouthfuls? Why not wait for them to appear? So Redstart attempts flycatching and with perfect success.

But the active blood which surges through his veins will not allow him to assume the patient waiting tactics of the genuine flycatchers. He may imitate their methods of actual capture, bagging his game on the wing, but

he is still ever on the move, from twig to twig, from tree
to tree.   Nevertheless, he has gained an advantage which
ensures to his race a long life; for in a tree whose foliage
and twiglets are being scanned with the microscopic glances
of his relatives, he gets more than the others by watching for the many insects which are alarmed at the dis-
turbance of the tiny hunters, and which flutter out in
the bright sunshine only to flutter straight down his
throat.   Mother Nature has seen his efforts in the new
field with satisfaction, and has given to him a little re-
ward; for from either side of his mouth several stiff bristles
project, and many times, when he has misjudged the distance or the dodging powers of his prey, these little hairs
shunt the gnat or fly into his mouth.

The Myrtle Warbler is an expert catcher of flies, and
has in addition another string to his bow, which bids fair
to place him at the head of the list of new departures
in warblers.   He has learned that bayberries are not only
an occasional welcome variety to the everlasting diet of
insects, but that a warbler can comfortably live upon
them when the cold has benumbed the little winged and
crawling creatures.   So, instead of migrating south at
the first hint of winter, these hardy little Myrtle Warblers
sometimes remain with us throughout the whole season of
cold and snow.

A most daring departure from old-established principles of the warbler clans is that of the Water Thrushes.
Ages ago, perhaps, we may imagine that some member
of this group, while drinking at a stream or pond, watched
the little bobbing sandpipers as they scurried past along

the brim, now wading in a short distance, then leaping to a soft rim of clay, everywhere finding the most delicious morsels abundant. A strange fascination took hold of the tree-haunting warbler, and although perhaps you and I would have said he was a very silly bird and that such a thing as a warbler turning into a sandpiper was utterly absurd, yet the little fellow and his descendants persisted. Sandpipers and sandpipers only they wished to be, and Nature has given them their wish.

Study the Water Thrushes of to-day. Their whole life is spent along some stream or pond, searching for worms and snails in true sandpiper fashion. Not only this, but even the dipping gait of the pipers has been copied, and though we cannot give a reason for this characteristic, yet the warblers have learned it by heart, and many an amateur bird-lover do they confuse! But the heart of the old clan instinct can never be entirely eliminated, and even if a warbler should attempt to hum away his life on the wing like a hummingbird, or to run with the speed of the wind through dry deserts like an ostrich, yet, like the Water Thrushes, he would occasionally drift back to the old tree-tops and there sing of the happiness which is within his heart.

A strange whim of evolution in one member of the warbler tribe results in his mimicking the sandpiper as far as terrestrial locomotion, a walking gait, and the peculiar tilting habit go, but the fondness for water did not accompany these changes, and so we find the Oven-bird content with the deep woods where he builds his home upon the ground. He often returns for a time to the trees, but, like a college boy whose whole ideas of life have been changed by absence from his rural home, the Oven-bird carries aloft with him the mincing gait of the littoral sandpipers, walking sedately along the limbs among his agile, hopping, creeping cousins.

Of the conventional aristocracy of the warblers there would be much to say had we the space. The Black-and-white Creeping Warbler has been transformed into a woodpecker, as far as mode of progression goes; and lucky for him too, for he never fails to find cocoons and small edible things among the cracks and crevices of the bark, no matter how vainly the others may be searching the overworked twigs and leaves. And Nature has helped him, too. She has dipped him in a bath of the essence of these very same crevices and cracks, and out he has come, covered with the semblance of the rough surface and the long, dark shadows which may shield and hide him from many enemies.

Of the typical tree-loving species, the Pine Warbler haunts the growths which have given him his name; the Black-throated Green also loves the evergreens, and the beautiful Magnolia delights in thick forests of spruces.

Thus we have taken a brief survey of the recent branching of the warbler's genealogical tree. Each has found a niche in which to live, and the food and safety which permit him to rear a nestful of young each year. So far so good, but we must not forget to give a thought to the untold thousands and tens of thousands of generations which have failed in their attempts. Nature has removed all traces from view and in the general advancement of the race as a whole they are forgotten, but it is well for us to think of them occasionally: their birth, the chance which came, which seemed so full of promise, which they so eagerly accepted and which betrayed them; the myriad little dead forms which gave up their lives in ages past, and upon whose bodies and whose efforts the birds of to-day have risen to their present high place in the scale of the creatures of the world.

We might have used this same illustration, or many others like it, in connection with almost any other portion of the bird's body. Although, indeed, it pertains more strictly to the mental characters, and so is in a way outside the province of this volume, yet its application to physical adaptations is so evident that its omission would leave incomplete a most interesting phase of the possibilities of the adaptation of bird structure.

Although among perching birds the bill is the important organ for procuring food, yet such birds as the Chewink, the White-throated Sparrow, and the jays, in search of small insects use their feet to scratch away dead leaves and rubbish, kicking backward with both feet at once.

There are many curious things about toes to which we have not yet found the key. Who can tell why the Horned Lark, Pipit, and some other birds have such elongated claws on their rear toes? Perhaps the fact that these birds live almost entirely on the ground may have something to do with this peculiarity. Any one who has kept a cage full of small birds will soon have learned the fact that the claws of birds are continually growing. In a remarkably short time their claws become long and curved, and in a neglected aviary I have seen birds which were prisoners on their perch, unable to untwist their claws from it. When wild, birds wear down these structures by constant rubbing, and if given plenty of rough bark and wood in their cages, their claws will remain of usual length.

Although the tarsus, or that portion of the foot which we usually call the leg, is, in almost all birds, covered with

horny scales, yet these vary considerably in different groups. In many the scales are small, six-sided or oblong, as in plovers. In some of the higher song-birds these scales have become joined together until, as in our robin, the front of the leg is covered with a long "boot" of horn. The cause of this coalescence yet remains to be discovered.

FIG. 289.—Foot of American Pipit.

A considerable degeneration of the legs and feet is found among goatsuckers, humming-birds, and chimney swifts; but, small as are the feet of the latter birds, they make frequent use of them to break off the short twigs which are used in the construction of their nests. One may take a young swift and place it against the vertical surface of an ordinary brick (Fig. 326), and the bird will hold fast without slipping a fraction of an inch. The slender nails fasten in the slightest irregularity of the surface and hold the bird safely.

Some species of swifts have all four toes pointing

forward, forming a four-tined grapple by which they hang themselves up in their hollow nesting-trees. Whippoorwills and some other birds have a curious comb, or pecten, along the edge of the middle claw, which is perhaps of use in cleaning the long bristles about their mouths, or in arranging their very delicate, soft plumage. Kingfishers and several related groups of birds make so little use of their feet, except in motionless perching, that

Fig. 290.—Comb on toe of Chuck-will's-widow.

not only are the toes small and weak, but two of the front ones have grown together for over half their length.

Perhaps the most interesting condition of toe structure is found among the woodpeckers, parrots, cuckoos, and owls. In these groups we find a similar plan of general arrangement: two toes in front and two behind. With few exceptions it is the great, or first, toe and the fourth, or outer, toe which are reversed. This arrangement of toes is known as yoke-toed, or *zygodactyl*.

We have seen that in perching birds the arrangement is three toes in front and one behind; and now turning to the woodpeckers we are struck with the excellent toe arrangement of these climbing birds,—their claws spreading so that they point almost to the four points of the compass, thus forming an admirable grapple or vise, which makes a vertical position as safe for a woodpecker as a horizontal one for a percher.

Woodpeckers, the world over, have feet and toes which are remarkably alike; but in Canada and the most northern parts of our own country, and in certain portions of the Old World, there are several woodpeckers which are unique among the birds of this Order in possessing but three toes. For some unknown reason their first, or great, toe, which in all other woodpeckers points backward, has disappeared, leaving but a vestigial trace beneath the skin, while the outer toe is reversed to take its place. We may see one of these hardy three-toed fellows sliding and hitching up a pine-tree, pounding and hammering vigorously, the loss of an entire toe evidently not handicapping him in the least. In such fashion does Nature occasionally upset our hard-worked-out theories, leaving us confused and baffled before her inexplicable surprises.

Is it not rather disconcerting to find that this same arrangement of two toes in front and two behind also holds good for the other Orders of birds mentioned above, the parrots, cuckoos, and owls,—their toes all arranged in pairs, fore-and-aft? This is an excellent example of what is called parallelism, or the independent development of similar structures.

Parrots use their feet for more different purposes than do any other birds: they are the monkeys of the feathered

FIG. 291.—Cockatoo perching with one foot and holding food with the other.

world. They climb wires or branches one step after the other, their beaks taking the place of a third foot in this style of locomotion. They pick up food, such as a banana

or a nut, and, holding it in the foot while eating, turn
it from side to side as we revolve an apple in our hand.
With their claws they preen their plumage, and push each
other aside when too closely crowded. In fact the functions
of the feet and toes of parrots approach nearer to those
of a human hand than the limb of any other Order of birds.

FIG. 292.—Foot of Cuckoo, perching, and with toes outstretched.

Cuckoos are perching birds, and when we see the skilful way in which they creep through a dense thicket, never
missing their hold, we wonder why all perching birds do
not have this arrangement of two toes in front and two
behind. So completely are our theories set at naught
that we should hardly be surprised to see a bird with
one toe in front and three behind cheerfully hopping
from branch to branch! In the deserts of the south-

western part of the United States much of the vegetation consists of prickly cacti and thorny mesquite, most unpleasant to perch upon, and here we find the Road-runner, a kind of ground cuckoo, who has the fore-and-aft toe arrangement of his arboreal relations, but whose terrestrial life has developed remarkable powers of running and leaping. One of these birds can outstrip a horse for a hundred yards or more and, almost without effort, can leap upward ten or twelve feet, to all appearances unaided by its wings.

The owls can move their outer toes backward or forward at will, thus being able to assume the arrangement of toes both of a crow and of a parrot. However the yoke, or two-and-two, plan is the one most commonly seen among these birds. With such an automatic vise-trap ready to descend silently and with deadly swiftness upon him, the little mouse in the grass has indeed need to be ever on the alert. The talons of owls are curved and under the control of tendons of great strength. Their chief use is to capture living prey and then to hold it firmly while it is torn to pieces by the beak.

The deserts and plains where the Road-runner dwells are also the home of the Burrowing Owl, Fig. 351, which finds in its sharp little talons admirable picks and shovels, certainly a novel use for yoked toes. The feet and toes of birds are, in zero weather, their most vulnerable points (except their eyes), and they are most liable to be frozen. In the black wastes of the frozen boreal regions, the Arctic Owl is able to defy the intense cold, by means of a furry covering of hair-like feathers, which extends to the very claws, and even the soles of the feet are thickly covered, so that the skin of the bird is never in contact with the snow and ice on which it roosts.

The osprey, or fish-hawk, can, like the owls, reverse its outer toe, but all typical hawks and eagles have the

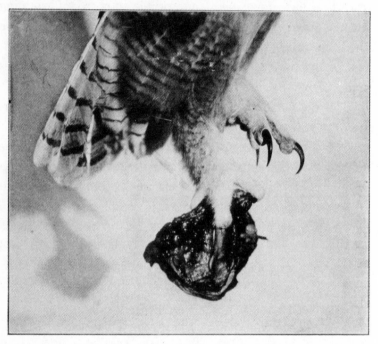

FIG. 293.—Owl gripping a piece of meat.

perching-bird arrangement. The talons of the osprey are immensely strong, and the scales on the soles of its feet and toes are hardened and roughened to such a degree that they are almost spike-like. A more efficient fish-trap cannot be imagined. The Golden Eagle has a splendid foot, with great curved talons, which, when they have

once clasped an object, never let go. It required two
men and two pairs of the thickest buckskin gloves to
obtain Fig. 295, and even then the foot could be held
still for only a moment. As the photograph shows, the

FIG. 294.—Foot of Snowy Owl.

leg is feathered all the way down to the toes in this eagle,
for some unexplained reason, while in almost all its relatives, as in the Bald Eagle, the legs are covered with
scales. The feet and toes of the Harpy Eagle, Fig. 204,
are probably the most terrible of their kind in the world:

certainly they are the strongest. When once they have closed on an object, and remain clutched, nothing short of severing the bird's leg will avail to loosen the fearful

Fig. 295.—Foot of Golden Eagle.

grip. Besides capturing their food, birds of prey carry the sticks for their nests in their talons.

When, instead of killing its prey, a species of bird feeds upon carrion, the change in its habits is reflected clearly in the appearance of its feet. Compare the feet of a vulture (Fig. 296) with those of one of the true birds of prey (Fig. 295). The muscles are weaker and the claws are shorter, more blunt, and, as a result, the toes have lost their clasping power, while the hind toe is higher and so

FIG. 296.—Feet of Vulture. (E. R. Sanborn, photographer.)

small that it is of no use even in perching. Such is the condition in the condor of South America.

When in captivity an eagle is given a piece of meat, it seizes the food in its talons and flies to some favourite spot to devour it, but a condor transports its meal in its beak, then holding it down firmly with one of its feet, it pulls upward and so tears the meat.

So exactly correlated are these changes of habit and of feet that in the Caracara, a Mexican bird of mixed habits, partly rapacious and partly vulturine, the toes and claws are correspondingly midway between the two groups of birds. This bird lacks sufficient grasping power to enable it to lift its prey from the ground after the manner of a true Hawk; but it will overcome this difficulty by carrying up the object in its beak, and then reaching forward with its feet, while in full flight, and taking a careful grip with its talons.

In South Africa is a bird known as the Secretary, which is really a terrestrial hawk, rarely flying, but spending most of its time stalking about in search of food. Any one who has seen an eagle progressing upon the ground by means of its awkward gallop, can realize the impossibility of such a short-legged bird preferring terrestrial life, but the legs of the Secretary are as long as those of a crane, although in other respects the bird would pass for a very long-tailed species of hawk; it is really a hawk on stilts. However, there are reasons for supposing that the Secretary Bird may be, not a more or less recent offshoot from the hawks, but a surviving type of old, old days when there were no hawks and cranes and herons, but instead, a few strange birds which combined the characteristics of all these groups.

The skilful way in which the Secretary Bird brings its feet into play in the capture of serpents, of which it is very fond, has been described as follows:

"When the snake strikes, the bird either evades the blow, by skipping to one side or the other, jumping backward, or springing into the air, or else, as frequently happens, he simply receives the venomous thrusts of his antagonist on the broad stiff feathers of the outer half

Fig. 297.—Secretary Bird.

of the long wing, with which he knocks the reptile down, following up the fall with a vigorous kick. His extreme agility enables him in a very short time to baffle and overcome a snake of four or five feet in length, whereupon he finally seizes it near the head with his bill, and holding the body down with one foot, proceeds to swallow it. In case a snake proves unusually hard to manage on the ground the dauntless bird watches his opportunity, seizes his adversary close to the head, and, flying aloft to a considerable height, lets it drop on the hard ground, which is usually sufficient to prepare it for the final ceremony of swallowing."

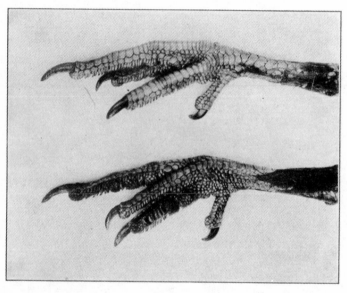

Fig. 298.—Feet of Ruffed Grouse, showing snowshoes of horn.

Quail, grouse, pheasants, turkeys, and all the fowl-like birds are scratchers, according to the old classification, and they well deserve the name; for scratching first with one foot and then the other among the leaves and soft dirt for insects is a very pronounced habit of them all. The arrangement of toes is the same as in the perching birds, but the claws are very different. These birds are true horny-handed sons of the soil: their claws are stubby, short, and blunt. Sharp edges would soon be dulled by scratching, and elongated ones would sliver and break. So, with his blunt claws, our chicken and his kind are well provided for.

The most interesting feet among these birds are those of the grouse. The ruffed drummer of our woods walks about, in summer, on slender toes over moss and logs, but, when soft deep snows come, his weight would make it difficult to keep from being buried at each step. So Nature provides him with snowshoes. From each side of each toe a broad, horny comb-like fringe grows out; not a web of skin which might soon freeze, but rows of horny projections, as of a myriad extra claws. This distributes his weight so that he trots merrily over snow through which a fox sinks deep and flounders awkwardly at every step.

But what of the ptarmigan, that snow-white grouse of the far North, whose home is amid those frigid barren regions? This bird is much more of a walker than the Snowy Owl, and its feet would surely freeze during the long winters if they were bare of feathers. So we find indeed that scarcely a claw is visible beyond the thick feathers which cover legs, toes, and soles. Such a provision against cold is evident and reasonable enough, but how are we to account for the feet and toes of the House Martin of Europe, which are densely feathered to the very claws? It breeds in Iceland and Lapland, but only in summer, when it would need no such protection against cold, and it is also true that it breeds upon the cliffs of Persia and southern India.

If we watch a duck as it settles itself for the night upon the snow, we will see it squat down, snuggle its beak deep among the feathers of the back, and finally draw up each foot from the frozen surface and tuck them up out of sight. Thus they are protected from freezing during the long, cold night.

The pugnacity of the males of the Order of game-birds has become proverbial; almost all are "fighting cocks" and yet their beaks are not fitted for defence or

Fig. 299.—Mallard asleep on the snow, with its feet drawn up to avoid freezing.

offence, nor can they clutch and tear with their claws. But we find spurs developed on the tarsus, or upper foot, in fowls, turkeys, pheasants, and peacocks, which are used with remarkable skill in their battles. In structure these outgrowths are identical with the horns of antelopes and cows, consisting of a bony projection over which grows a sheath of horn. The spurs of the peacock are long and sharp and are occasionally used with such effect that the results are fatal to each of the contestants. A diminutive relative of *Pavo*, the Peacock Pheasant of the East Indies, has two, three, or even four spurs of full size on the legs. The bird photographed on page 419 had two on the right leg and three on the left. Yet these birds are not as correspondingly pugnacious as we should imagine from their increased armature.

There is a small group of peculiar birds, known as Sand-grouse, which in many respects stand midway

FIG. 300.—Spur of Java Peacock.

between the true grouse and the pigeons. In certain of these the toes, to their very tips, are encased in the skin of the foot, the effect being of a mitten with only the claws free. The reason for this is yet to be found.

We now come to the water-loving birds, and we find that their varying associations with this element have wrought many interesting changes in their feet and legs. Those birds which are content to wade along the shallow margins of ponds and streams require long legs and long toes, the latter to distribute their weight as they walk over the soft muddy bottom, the former to lift their bodies above the surface of the water. Such, broadly speaking, are the plovers and sandpipers and herons. Let us see how the feet of these birds reflect their habits. With the exception of the tribe of plovers, almost all have four toes. The plovers have but three, and these are slender and not webbed, for although they usually feed on aquatic forms of life, yet their food is gleaned from the upper part of beaches, or from the sand-flats when the tide is out, and they therefore seldom have occasion to swim. The sandpipers venture into the shallows and are sometimes lifted from their feet by a small inrushing wave. But the majority even of these go through life unwebbed. One, the Semipalmated Sandpiper, shows a beginning of this in the half-webbed condition of the toes, but the group of phalaropes are actually sandpipers of the sea. I have seen them in flocks of thousands, resting upon the surface of the ocean, scores of miles from land. Yet when ashore they have need to be as active as other members of their Order in order to find sufficient food; so, instead of being hampered with a confining web, each toe has a series of broad scalloped lobes, serving admirably as water propellers, yet allowing the toes freedom of motion when the owner is scurrying over the sand.

I have observed Great Blue Herons almost hip-deep in the breakers along the Florida beaches, yet this is not a usual haunt for members of this group of birds. They usually prefer quiet inland waters, where they wade and watch—ever striving to satisfy their insatiable hunger.

So, in the case of herons, webs would be superfluous, length of limb being their only requirement.

The Wood Ibises (or more properly Storks), which are more active searchers after food than the herons, make use of their toes to stir up the bottom mud of shal-

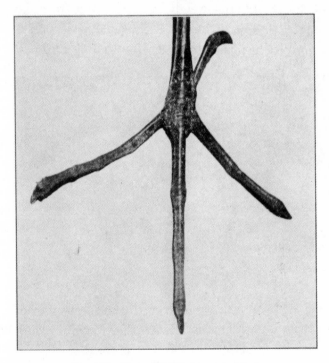

FIG. 301.—Toes of Gallinule outstretched.

low water, keeping the bill ready to snap up any small creatures thus disturbed.   When one sees a flock of gal-linules or jacanas feeding quietly in their haunts they appear to be walking *on* the water, and we find an in-teresting connection between the structure of their feet and toes and certain tropical plants.   Such are the great pads of water-lilies, which in places cover miles of water, over whose trembling surfaces the birds are able to run or walk. To enable them to do this without sinking, both the toes and claws are remarkably long and slender, so that in a bird which stands but ten or eleven inches in height the weight is distributed over an area of some fifty square inches. This makes it possible for them to feed in places too deep for wading birds and too

FIG. 302.- Gallinule holding food in its foot.

tangled with aquatic vegetation for swimmers readily to make their way. This is but another forceful example of the successful adaptive radiation of birds.

Gallinules have found that their long toes can be made useful in other ways besides locomotion, and we find that they are well-nigh as skilful as a parrot in grasping and holding. One of these birds perhaps spies a tuft of water-soaked reeds. He clasps it firmly, draws it up, and, holding it in the air near his bill, picks the small worms and snails from among the stems, finally discarding

it for another footful. We cannot imagine a heron performing such an action. Although the toes of gallinules
are so long and slender, yet, when the necessity arises,
they can swim quite rapidly for a short distance, working
their feet with such effort that the whole body bobs in
concert. Their cousins,
the coots, resemble the
phalaropes in having
broad lobes of skin
along each toe, so that,
although they and the
gallinules are often
seen feeding in the same
locality, yet the nata-
tory ability of the coot
allows it to venture
beyond the reserves of
the other species. The
toe-lobes also serve an-
other important func-
tion in permitting the
coots to feed upon soft
mud, thus keeping them
from sinking below the

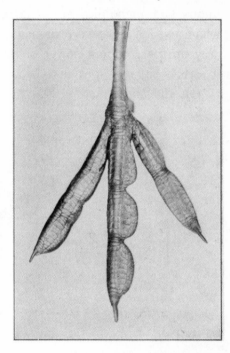

FIG. 303.—Foot of Coot.

surface, just as the horny "snowshoe" of the grouse supports it on the snow.

Herons are furnished with a comb-like edge to one of
the claws, similar to that on the claw of the whippoor-
will, but as yet we have no clue to its use. Although
differing so greatly from hawks in their method of feeding,

yet, when put upon the defensive, herons resort to much
the same tactics as do the birds of prey. When cornered
or wounded, so that escape by flight is impossible, the
bird throws itself upon its back and, with uplifted claws
and levelled beak, awaits the attack of its assailant. The
talons and mandibles of a hawk offer ten sharp points
which can all do severe damage; but the heron depends
only on the grasping power of its toes to hold fast, while
it strikes savage, spear-like blows with its beak.

On the borderland of the fully webbed aquatic birds

Fig. 304.—Comb on the toe of Heron.

we find the flamingo, combining characters of the herons
and ducks. Its haunts are the exposed coral-flats of
tropical keys, where at any time a high tide or a
severe storm may sweep all, old and young, from their
feet. Then it is lucky indeed that the youngsters have
webs between their toes in addition to their long legs.
It is a case of swim or be drowned.

In the great Orders of sea-birds, and in the ducks and
their allies, the three front toes are joined together by

a web of skin which, when swimming, offers a large area
of resistance to the water when the foot is pushed backward. The chick in the egg has a shadow-membrane
of his fish-like ancestors between his toes, and in these
water-birds the web of skin continues throughout life. In
the terns or sea-swallows, which swim· much less than
they fly, the web is excised, or scalloped out deeply, a
return to an almost semipalmated condition.

Fɪɢ. 305.—Rough-legged Hawk in position of defence.

A duck or swan out of sheer laziness will often hold
one foot up out of the water and propel itself with the
other, slightly altering the angle at which the web meets
the water, so as to maintain a perfectly direct course.
There is a little-known habit which I have frequently
observed in captive ducks and several times in wild ones,
of swimming thus with one foot when both eyes are shut
and the bird is apparently fast asleep. But, in such a

case, no attempt is made to proceed in a straight line. In a pool only thirty feet square I have seen a duck revolving thus for an hour or more at a time, impelled with slow, rhythmical (and apparently reflex) strokes. We

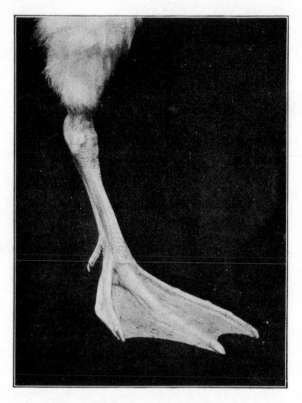

Fig. 306.—Foot of Black-necked Swan.

can imagine that such a habit would sometimes be of much advantage to a wild bird, enabling it to keep away from enemies on the shore and yet at the same time secure rest.

The name *Steganopodes* is applied to the gannets, pelicans, snake-birds, tropic-birds, and cormorants, because the toes of these birds are all bound together with a single web. The hind toe points almost in a forward direction when the foot is in action, and, to complete the adaptation for a perfect swimming foot, the outer toe is the longest, a rare condition among birds. If one will watch the snake-birds in a zoological park, as they swim about their glass tank, the extreme delicacy of the foot mechanism becomes apparent at once.

Not only is the flat side of the leg used as a cutwater, but the toes curl and uncurl with a slight oblique revolving motion like the blades of a propeller. When drawn forward through the water they are rolled up into a very small compass and then instantly spread out as widely as possible on the return stroke. To the eye it seems as if the bird was constantly grasping something tangible in the water and thrusting it behind.

This propeller motion may be observed even better in a captive grebe. If the bird's head is placed in a glass of water, its feet will move back and forth in the air with all the motion of swimming. The adaptation for swimming in these birds is so fundamental and thorough that even the claws are broadened and flattened until they resemble finger-nails. On land, grebes are absurdly awkward, although they can walk upright even up a slight incline. But they are powerless to rise from the ground, even with the aid of the wind,—needing the greater speed which a swimming take-off from the water will give them.

The most aquatic of all birds, the penguins, make much more use of their wings than of their feet in swimming and diving. The toes are webbed, however, and

are doubtless of considerable use when the bird is emerg-
ing from the water, which it generally does with a sudden
spurt of speed and a strong leap which lands it on its feet.

In landbirds which have either lost or are losing the
power of flight there is often an interesting correlation
to be observed between the lapsing of this mode of loco-

FIG. 307.—Feet of Penguin.

motion and an increased use and consequent greater development of the legs and feet. Of a South African bird,
about the size of our American Robin, known as the Rock-
jumper, it is said: "These curious birds are only to be
found on the rock-strewn slopes and summits of mountain-
ranges where they are able to hop from rock to rock for a

distance without having to cross level or open ground;
... at the slightest alarm they either drop into a crevice
or bound from rock to rock with extraordinary speed, looking more like india-rubber balls than birds, for there is no
perceptible interval between the end of one leap and the
beginning of the next, and the distance they can clear at a
single hop must be seen to be believed. Should they have
to cross a piece of level ground between two rocks which
they cannot clear with a single bound, they run across it with
great speed and usually with outspread wings. So feeble
are their powers of flight that they seldom attempt to
fly, and never when in a hurry or alarmed; at the most
they flutter feebly for a few hundred yards down hill.
I have occasionally amused myself by trying to drive
these birds across a piece of open ground, but I have never
succeeded in getting them to quit the shelter of the rocks,
where they easily avoid one by leaping over the stones
or hiding in the crevices. In spite of his loose, fluffy
plumage, which blows about in the slightest breeze and
gives him a rather untidy appearance, the cock is an exceedingly handsome bird." So we have here an isolated
case of direct relation between two organs, the balance
of power changing from wing to feet and affecting much
of the bird's structure, even the plumage losing its cohe-
siveness. The weak-flying Tinamou have unusually sturdy
legs, and many other instances might be mentioned.

For many reasons the most interesting of all birds'
feet are those of the ostriches and their allies, and among
them the most extreme examples of this same cause and
effect are to be found.

When one trains in college for a long-distance race, one rule to observe is, never touch your heels to the ground; run wholly on the ball of the foot. Untold centuries ago, wise old Nature whispered the very same direction to those of her children who had most need to run for their lives in life's great race, and down through the ages some of them have never broken training. When an animal acquires great speed in running or leaping, there is a tendency for one toe to become greatly enlarged at the expense of the others, as is seen in the case of the horse, the kangaroo, and the ostrich.

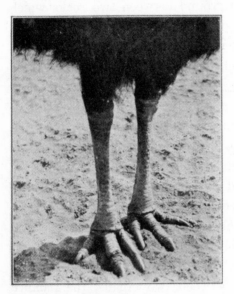

FIG. 308.—Feet and legs of Cassowary.

In the horse only the middle toe is functional, the second and fourth having degenerated into the small splint-bones at the side of the leg. The kangaroo progresses upon the fourth and fifth toes, the second and third being small and skin-bound. The ostrich has but two toes, one of which, the third, as in the case of the horse, is very large and armed with a thick claw, which, hoof-like, grows close to the toe. This toe supports most of the bird's weight, while the fourth or outer toe is only

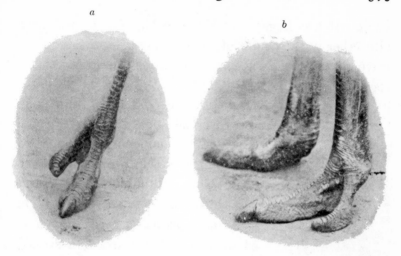

FIG. 309.—(a) Front and (b) side view of foot of Ostrich.

FIG. 310.—Feet of Donkey.   FIG. 311.—Feet of young Kangaroo.

one quarter as large; and indeed it bids fair to disappear
altogether in the course of time, and even now the diminutive nail which is often present is only as large as the
claw of a chicken.

The power of the ostrich to defend itself by kicking

is proverbial, but the claw on the
large toe is blunt and the ability to
inflict injury lies in the terrible force
of the blow. Its ally, the cassowary,
has three good-sized toes, and on
the innermost one a specially adapted weapon in the shape of a strong,
pointed, talon-like claw, four inches
in length.

The two photographs (Figs. 312
and 313) show how similar the
tracks which the modern cassowary
makes in walking over moist clay,
are to those made by the bipedal
reptilian *Dinosaurs* millions of years
ago, which have been found in the
Connecticut valley.

FIG. 312.—Tracks of Cassowary in soft clay.

Thus in our brief review we have
seen how the feet and legs of birds
serve them well in walking, hopping, running, perching, scratching, climbing, burrowing, swimming, diving,
in addition to the finding of their food, fighting,
preening their feathers, and in countless other ways.
The story of the bird's foot has not half been told,

but enough has been said to arouse our interest in this member and to put us on the watch for new facts.

Fig. 313.—Fossil Dinosaur tracks, found at Middletown, New York. (Courtesy of Prof. R. S. Lull.)

CHAPTER XV

`TAILS

E have found that almost every organ of a bird's body may be compared directly with the corresponding structure in the body of a lizard or of some reptile, and the tail is no exception: although a lizard with a fan-shaped group of feathers sprouting from the root of his tail would certainly be an anomaly; and even if we substitute scales for the feathers, the result would be ridiculous and unmeaning. But glance at the photograph of the tail of our ancient, original-bird acquaintance, the Archæopteryx, Fig. 315, which was taken expressly for this purpose.

Take twenty feathers and arrange them as in Fig. 314 a, representing the tail of Archæopteryx; then rearrange them as in 314 b, corresponding to the tail of modern birds, and the whole matter will be clear. Archæopteryx had twenty bones in its tail, all separate, long and slender, and arranged end to end, just as are the bones of a lizard's tail to-day. But in the case of the bird of olden time a pair of feathers grew out, one on each side of the tail-bone, making forty tail-feathers in all. As we have seen, this bird was rather weak-winged and probably more

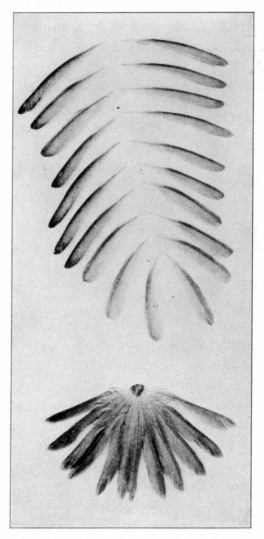

FIG. 314.—(a) Arrangement of 20 feathers, as in *Archæopteryx*; (b) tail-feathers of a Sparrow in place.

of a flutterer, or scaler, than a true flier, but as time went on, and birds became more and more expert on the wing, their wings grew stronger and their tails shorter and more compact. We can readily see the reason for this, if we imagine a ship which has been built with a rudder as long as its whole deck. What an awkward thing such a rudder would be! The waves would beat against it and great force would be necessary to turn it and to steer the ship. As long as a bird was content to climb a tree with its hands and feet, and then scale, like a flying squirrel, to the base of the next, a lizard-like tail would be all-sufficient. So conspicuous and so unbirdlike was the long appendage of the Archæopteryx that *Saururæ*—lizard-tailed—has been given as the name of the Sub-class which it occupies all to itself.

When we look at the bones of the tail of a modern bird, we find that many interesting changes have taken place since the days of the lizard-tailed ancestors. Thus in the common duck, for example, we find eight free bones followed by a large upturned bone, which, from its shape, is known as the ploughshare. It is this terminal bone which supports all the tail-feathers of modern birds, and in the duck it represents ten of the lizard-tail bones all telescoped and fused into one. Some of the feathers have been lost, as there are but sixteen in this bird's tail. This loss of tail-feathers is of no value in classification, as it may vary within narrow limits. For example, one species of cormorant has seven pairs of tail-feathers, while a closely related species has but six. Not only this, but the variation may be merely sexual, as in the

FIG. 315.—Tail of *Archæopteryx* in British Museum.

peacock, which has ten pairs, while the peahen has one pair less.

The fusing together of these bones has resulted in the drawing together of the feathers, so that, instead of the long, unwieldy, paired affair, they are arranged in fan shape, although still in pairs, and usually showing a slight graduation reminiscent of the old-style tail. Some birds have as few as four pairs of tail-feathers, while others

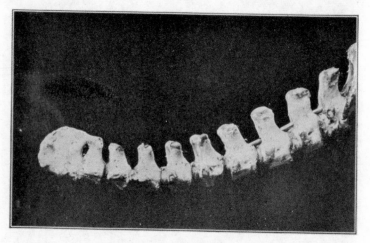

Fig. 316.—Tail-bones of Ostrich.

have as many as twelve. In the abnormal domestic breed of pigeons known as fantails, as many as forty tail-feathers are sometimes found. The cassowary and the emeu have none at all, while the ostrich seems to have an indefinite number; the tails of these two unrelated groups of birds seeming, like their wing-feathers, to have lost uniformity from little use. Besides these true tail-feathers there are others, usually smaller, which grow from above and below the tail, being known as upper and under tail-coverts. Mention is here made of these because of the important part they take in certain sham tails which will soon be described.

In the embryos of most birds of true flight the tail-tip of the back-bone is represented by six or ten separate pieces, which, before the chick hatches from the egg, fuse into the ploughshare bone. In the ostrich-like birds

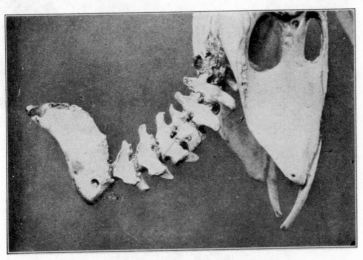

Fig. 317.—Tail-bones of Bald Eagle, showing greater fusion and more specialization than in Fig. 316.

these small bones never fuse, but remain separate throughout life—a reptilian character persistent in these strange birds (Fig.316). The ploughshare bone is seen splendidly developed in such a bird of strong flight as the Bald Eagle.

Now that we have explained the origin of the tail, let us consider what part it plays in the lives of the birds about us. So diverse are the modes of life, and so varied are the surroundings of this class of creatures, that we

FIG. 318.—Fan-tailed Pigeon, showing extreme development of tail.

FIG. 319.—Emeu, a tailless bird. (Courtesy of N. Y. Zoological Society.)

shall find many unexpected uses to which the tail is put,
and yet those which have been explained are a mere fraction of the problems which still await solution.

The principal use of the tail-feathers in birds is, of
course, to perform the function of a rudder, and we find
that the arrangement of the bones perfectly carries out
the simile of a tail to the rudder of a ship; namely, a
broad, expanded surface which is closely hinged to the

Fig. 320.   Fig. 321.

Tail of Barn Swallow, closed (320) and spread (321).

body by several movable joints. The real tail of a bird
is the small, fleshy protuberance which in our roast
chicken we call the "pope's nose"; but in common par-
lance the word tail has come to be applied to the large
feathers which sprout from this structure. Thus, although
not comparable to the appendages of mammals, the so-
called tail of a bird is superficially more like the corresponding organ of a whale than the tail-fin of a fish, since it is
expanded horizontally instead of vertically.

One interesting analogy to the fin of a fish is found in the tail of the Blue Duck of New Zealand. This bird lives in swift mountain streams and when swimming carries its long tail entirely submerged. By vigorous sidewise flicks of these tail-feathers it can turn around, as if on a pivot, without being carried down-stream, even when in the centre of a rapid, swirling current.

FIG. 322.—Murre showing tail. (Compare with Fig. 246.)

It is interesting to compare this use of the tail-feathers with the function of the tail in the flightless penguins. In the Black-footed species, at least, the tail-feathers are stiff and short, but the bones of the tail are unusually elongated and the flesh which covers them is flattened into a kind of vertical rudder. Strong muscles control this, and by it the extremely quick dives and turns are made possible. No feather would be stiff or rigid enough to offer to the water the resistance which these feathered seals require.

Exceptions to the rudder use in flying birds are found in the murres—sea-birds which share the cliffs of our northern coast with cormorants and gulls. The tail-feathers of a murre are so short as to be useless for steering purposes, so in flight the bird uses its webbed feet instead, stretching them out behind, opening, turning, and twisting them in harmony with the wings, with as satisfactory results as could be desired.

The shape of the tip of the tail varies greatly in birds. It may be square or rounded, or cuneate, or indented in the centre, or swallow-tailed, as we appropriately call the latter deeply forked condition. These conditions may be paralleled or duplicated in many different Families of birds. For example, the forked type is seen in our common Barn Swallow, in those dainty relatives of the gulls, the terns—"Swallows of the Sea,"—and again in the Forked-tailed Kite and the Scissor-tailed Flycatcher. By closely watching a swallow as it courses swiftly over a meadow, or shoots upward, buoying itself against the breeze, we can appreciate the delicate adjustment of the muscles which govern the tail-feathers. Each feather seems vital with life, now sliding one over the other until all are in a narrow line, then expanding, with less friction than ever a fan opened, into a wide-spreading, gently graduated fork. The quartet of forked-tailed birds mentioned above are splendid fliers, but we shall see that skill in flight depends but little upon the shape of the tip, when we consider certain birds with cuneate tails, or those in which the central feathers, soft and not rigid, are elongated, instead of the outer ones.

The Undulated Grass Parrakeet shows a condition almost the opposite of the swallow. The Mexican long-tailed jays, the magpies, and the tropic-birds are also all of this type, the latter being especially fine fliers and capable of remarkable aerial evolutions. Again, some

Fig. 323.—Tail of Grass Parrakeet.

of the flycatchers with moderate, rounded tails can execute most wonderful flight movements, steering in erratic darts through the air, or darting aside at right angles while at full speed, this being accomplished principally by means of the tail.

A tail serves also an important use as a brake. When a great pelican settles gradually toward the surface of the water, or a duck momentarily hovers before alighting, the tail, wide-spread and brought downward, gives efficient aid in retarding the impetus.

We notice that birds which have very short tails are unable to turn quickly and that their flight is very direct, or even where there is a long tail, if it is principally for ornament and not well muscled, it is of little use in helping its owner to change the direction of flight. The partridge-like tinamous of South America are good examples of the first-mentioned group. Their tails are small and useless, and when once the bird launches itself into

Fig. 324.—Tail of Pelican alighting.   Fig. 325.—Tail of Tern in flight.

the air, it can keep on only in a straight line and is at the mercy of every cross-current of air. A more familiar case, which any one may observe, is a Song Sparrow, or other small bird, which, from accident or from some irregularity of moult, has lost all or most of its tail-feathers. Instead of rising with the strong, darting flight with which such a bird is accustomed to make its escape from our path, its flight under such conditions is weak and direct, like the trial efforts of a young bird.

Reserving the mention of partly ornamental tails until the last, we may now consider the use of this member as a prop or support to the bird as it clings to or makes its way up vertical surfaces. Four groups of birds which are thus distinguished are the woodhewers—a tropical

FIG. 326.—Chimney Swift clinging to wall, resting upon tail.

family,—the creepers, woodpeckers, and swifts. These birds really sit upon their tails, the feathers of which are adapted for this special use, while retaining perfectly the rudder function in flight. The tail-feathers of the Chimney Swift are peculiar in having the ends, for a short dis-

tance, free of barbs, the tips being thus composed of a number of bare spines which are admirably adapted to catch
in the irregularities of hollow trees, or, as now in their
recently adopted homes, in the roughness of chimney-
bricks.   I one day caught a Chimney Swift and placed
it against a varnished wall composed of composition
bricks; and, smooth though the surface was, the bird's
tail and toes held it firmly, not slipping even a quarter
of an inch.   After photographing it, I watched it for
some minutes and saw the bird shift its position several
times, moving always with a certainty and surety of
grasp most inexplicable.

The tails of woodpeckers and creepers are not thus
denuded at the tip, but they are stiffened throughout
and are very elastic (Fig. 240).   When a woodpecker
brings up against a comparatively smooth tree-trunk, its
certainty of hold is a perfect bit of magic.   Then when
it braces itself and sets to work to hammer a hole into
the wood, or to excavate its nest, how the tail-feathers
bend and spread, buttressing themselves against every
roughness, the elasticity of the feather-tips allowing them
to slip into every crevice!

In many birds the tail is a perfect index of the emotions,
doing much to compensate for the lack of facial expression.
Especially is this true of the wrens, those feathered bundles
of tireless energy and curiosity, whose tails, upturned so
high that they fairly tilt forward over the back, twitch
and jerk with every passing mood.   Even the genetic
individuality of a species may be hinted at in the way
it carries its tail; quiet, soft-mannered birds holding it

low, beneath the wing-tips, while active, nervous species carry it more or less raised.

FIG. 327.—Tail of Chimney Swift.

In certain of the flycatchers the tail, which hangs demurely downward, reacts with a jerk to every note of the bird, as if connected with the bird's vocal apparatus, as in our common Least Flycatcher at every "Che-bec'!"

The jerking motion of the tail seems to have become a regular habit with many birds, and, curiously enough,

FIG. 328.—Tail of Flicker.

especially with those which spend their lives chiefly along

the borders of streams. We are all familiar with the tip-
ping of the tail in sandpipers, and, including the Green
Heron, we will see much the same motion in birds which
haunt the stream borders; even in the Water Thrush the
same habit prevailing, although, as we saw in the preceding chapter, this bird is closely related to the bright-
coloured warblers of our tree-tops. The wagtails have
received their name from this same habit, of which no
explanation has yet been offered.

The Road-runner, a ground cuckoo of the Western
plains, has a tail as long as its entire body, which is as
expressive as the gestures of a Frenchman. When sitting
quietly in the shade of a mesquite-bush in Mexico, I have
seen one of these birds dash into sight and drop, like an
arrow, upon a luckless lizard. At the moment of attack
all ten tail-feathers of the bird were wide-spread and
a-tremor, indicative of the extreme excitement attendant
upon the capture of the reptile. While eating what choice
parts were desired, the tail was folded and lifted out of
the way. Soon the bird spied some motion of mine, and
with the suspicion came the high extended neck, while the
tail turned up and forward, until almost touching the
bird's head. A second motion on my part, and the tail
manœuvred to a line and trailed limply after the bird,
as it half-flew, half-leaped to a high rock and on out of
sight.

The white under sides of the tails of the wild rabbit
and the white-tailed deer have been explained as warning
signals to others of the family or herd: white guides
which the less experienced members may follow and so

escape from danger. Again, the theory has been advanced that these white patches merge with the sky when the rabbit or deer makes the first high frantic leap to escape an assailant, the white spots thus tending to confuse the creature making the attack. We are, however, far from certain whether any such interpretations can be applied to those birds, such as the Junco, the Meadowlark, and the Vesper Sparrow, which have the lateral feathers of

the tail white; but in these cases the first theory seems at least more probable, as these birds live in flocks and in a more or less open environment, where such a signal would have the greatest chance for use. When a Junco is upon the ground, its black and gray plumage renders it very inconspicu-

FIG. 329.—Tail of Junco.

ous, but the instant it takes to wing, out flashes the white V in its tail.

We have seen that not a portion of the external parts of the bird has escaped, in one species or another, being utilized for ornament; generally, as well as we can tell, as some decoration to attract or charm the female. Tails bear even more than their share of adornment, which we cannot pass by without mention, although, as dealing with the psychological side of bird life, any discussion of this question is outside the province of this volume. Sometimes it is only some slight addition to the feathers of the tail proper, as the elongated middle feathers of the male Pintail Duck and the Sharp-tailed Grouse.

Turning to a few of the more decorative tails in the world of birds, we find a small Australian bird, known as the Emeu-wren, bearing aloft a half-dozen long feathers, so scantily clothed with barbs as to resemble somewhat the plumage of the Emeu itself. These skeleton plumes, for they are little else, while giving a striking appearance

FIG. 330.—Tail of Emeu-wren. (Cf. with Fig. 23.)

to the owner, must radically weaken its flight, as regards steering capacity; since the open-work mesh of the vanes can offer no resistance to the air. Indeed it is said of this bird that it is such a poor flier that it is seldom seen on the wing, but it runs rapidly and is able to leap into the lower branches of trees. The penalty of danger from weakened flight which the Emeu-wren must pay for his caudal decoration is paralleled by certain little whydah-finches of Africa, the males of which at the breeding season are decorated with several tail-feathers over five

times as long as their tiny bodies. When a heavy dew
falls during the night, drenching the plumage of these
birds, they become helpless and quite unable to fly. At
such times many are killed by their natural enemies;
and such indeed is their helplessness, brought about by

Fig. 331.—Male Paradise Whydah-bird showing tail.

this excess of nuptial dress, that a person can pick them
up in the hand without difficulty.

The beautiful tails of pheasants are in harmony with
the wealth of colour which many of these birds display
upon other parts of the body; the long graceful tail of the
Reeves being especially striking.

The folded, roof-shaped tail of the common rooster,

FIG. 332.—Japanese Long-tailed Fowls. (From a photograph provided by the American Museum of Natural History.)

and of his wild ancestors the Jungle-fowl, with the graceful overarching feathers, is a type of tail found elsewhere

Fig. 333.—Roof-like tail of Jungle-fowl.

only in certain pheasants. In the Boat-tailed Grackle the arrangement is reversed, the apex of the slope being

Fig. 334.—Decorative tail of Reeves Pheasant.

beneath instead of above. The possibilities of abnormal feather growth are well shown in the tails of the Japanese

Long-tailed Fowl—a breed of birds in which, by artificial stimulation, such perhaps as periodical pulling of the feathers or else retardation of moult, has produced, in the cocks, tails from twelve to twenty feet in length. This process dates back, in Corea at least, to A.D. 1000, and necessitates keeping the birds continually upon high perches, or else wrapping the feathers carefully in paper. The arrangement of feathers in this artificially induced character is duplicated in nature in the Paradise Why-dah-finch mentioned above.

In both the male and female Peacock Pheasant the tail is quite long and the feathers are decorated with beautiful iridescent " eyes." But in this bird usefulness exists as a corollary of beauty. When the young chicks are reared under a bantam hen, they invariably keep close be-hind their foster-mother, for

Fig. 335.—Useful tail of Peacock Pheasant.

no apparent reason; indeed this position often results in their death, a kick from the bird's foot generally being fatal. The reason for this strange instinctive act is at once clear when we see the chicks with their rightful mother. They spend much of their time hidden beneath the shelter of her long, sloping tail, coming out now and then to feed when she calls them, then hurrying back to their snug shelter. Thus when she walks from place to place, the tiny feet of the chicks may be seen scurrying along beneath the beautiful tail-feathers, all

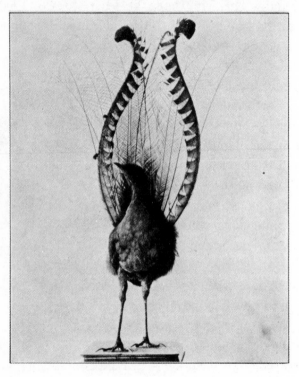

Fig. 336.—Tail of Lyre-bird.

but their legs concealed from view, giving a most remarkable appearance to the mother bird.

Among ornamental tails assumed for show during the breeding season, that of the Lyre-bird of Australia is unequalled. The name is well given, since the outer tail-feathers carry out the graceful, curving outline of the classic form of a lyre; while twelve of the central feathers, so scantily barbed that their stems are plainly visible, hold positions corresponding to the strings of that ancient instrument. The two elongated middle feathers cross each other and curve outward, adding still more to the decorative effect of this strangely beautiful member. Naturally we find that these birds are better runners than fliers. The females lack the ornamental tail.

If we judge from analogy with the human race, when an inordinate amount of ostentatious show is noticeable among birds, we occasionally find that it is, in a sense, a sham display; although the analogy ceases when we find that such a case among birds is no less interesting than where the phenomenon is really what it appears to be. Upon seeing a specimen of the beautiful trogon commonly called the Quezal, the involuntary ex-

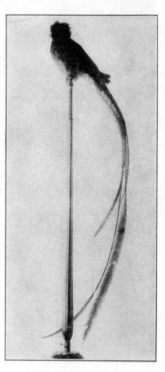

FIG. 337.—Tail-coverts of Quezal.

clamation is, "What a magnificent tail!" And no wonder; for, while the bird is only about the size of a small dove, behind it, for three and a half feet, there stream long, iridescent green plumes, soft as down, brilliant as emeralds. Yet the true tail is a short, squarish affair, completely hidden by the overhanging train of gorgeous plumes, which are in reality the upper tail-coverts.

The same thing is true of the peacock, whose real tail, while it has the power of spreading, consists solely of

Fig. 338.—Train of Peacock spread.

short, dull, brownish feathers, acting as a support to the glorious train of ocellated plumes which springs from the lower back. Indeed the tail-feathers of a turkey-cock are far more beautiful than the real tail of a peacock. This is especially evident when, after a peacock has moulted

his long train, he sometimes spreads the real, inconspicuous tail. Large and heavy as this decoration of
the peacock is, the birds fly with remarkable ease. In
such places as the New York Zoological Park, after roost-

Fig. 339.—Rear view of train of Peacock, showing real tail.

ing all night in the tallest trees, they sail down in the
early morning, the long train waving gracefully behind—a
sight which, once seen, is never forgotten.

We must leave unmentioned scores of beautiful and

interesting types of tail-feathers—those of hummingbirds, birds of paradise, and many others; but there is one which deserves especial mention. These birds, of which there are a number of species, are the motmots, abundant in many parts of Mexico and southward. The tail-feathers of the Mexican motmot, which are bluish green in colour,

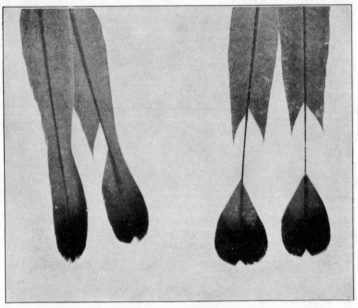

Fig. 340.—Tails of Motmot: (a) young male; (b) adult female.

have nothing peculiar about them, except the middle pair, which are two inches longer than the others. Of this extra length one inch is bare shaft, while at the tip the barbs are normal, forming a racket-shaped extremity. The fact which places this slight decoration above all other more elaborate examples in point of interest is that the *birds themselves voluntarily produce the racket condition.* Even the youngest birds, of both sexes, when the long central tail-feathers have grown beyond the others, instinctively begin to pick at the vane, soon denuding the shaft so symmetrically that the rackets are equal in size. The

Fig. 341.—Motmot swinging its tail.

photographs show this perfectly. Figure *a* is the tail of a young male where the operation of ornamental denudation has just begun; while *b* shows the condition in an adult female. The photograph of the entire living bird also shows the rackets, as well as the peculiar pendulum motion of the tail from side to side, although the motion is more abrupt than is the motion of a pendulum. The Mexican motmot is brilliantly coloured, yet in a densely foliaged tree, among the bright spots of sunlight, it becomes almost invisible. It is the motion of the tail which most often betrays the bird.

In the tail marked *a* in Fig. 340 it will be noticed that, where the barbs have not yet been picked off, the unmutilated vane is considerably narrowed—an interesting fact for the consideration of evolutionists, as it offers strong circumstantial evidence, but by no means absolute proof, of a case of the inheritance of acquired characters, a much-mooted question not many years ago among scientists. If we choose to accept the evidence thus, we may presume that if this habit is continued through a sufficient number of generations, the vane will, at the point of continued denudation, ultimately become naturally bare.

But, in any case, it is a fact which must hold the interest of the most superficial bird student that here is a bird which voluntarily tears away a portion of its plumage. To the best of our present knowledge this is solely to ornament itself, but the fact that both sexes equally possess this habit makes such an explanation the merest theory. The interest which this has for us here is not the ultimate psychological significance of the habit, but the fact that there is a bird which thus voluntarily mutilates its plumage. As in so many other cases, we must depend on future study of live birds in their natural haunts to clear up the difficulty. It is this very complexity of Nature's problems which makes a naturalist's life ever one of enthusiasm and zest.

CHAPTER XVI

THE EGGS OF BIRDS

PERHAPS the most fascinating phase of Nature is the way in which she cares for her children during the early part of their lives. The story of seeds and eggs has not been half told. Think of the tiny thistle-fluff which soars away, borne on the lightest breath of air; of the great cocoanuts in their husks, so hard that they will turn the edge of a knife; of the burrs which ever patiently reach out for some passing creature to carry them to a distant home; of the cones of the forest, whose seeds may be transported by birds, or dropped to the ground only to smother in the shadow of the parent tree.

In that "mother of life" the sea, the wonder of the first beginnings holds us spellbound. We see the tiny hydroids, those animal plants, flowering and budding on their waving stalks, and presently setting free their "seeds"—jelly-fish,—throbbing with life, drifting away on the ocean currents. Again observe these jellies scattering behind them an untold host of eggs, as a rocket marks its path with a myriad sparks. Think of the salmon seeking her spawning-grounds in the uppermost reaches of rivers, or the cod boldly playing for her offspring the chance in the lottery of life in the open ocean. Of her nine millions of eggs, will one survive?

How strange is the four-tendriled, purse-like cradle of the baby shark; how delicate the forms and patterns of butterflies' eggs! and was there ever a more model parent than that frog which holds its eggs in its mouth until the tadpoles grow up?

The white leathery eggs of turtles and lizards bring us to our subject. Leading all in beauty and interest are the eggs of birds. Precious stones have always exerted a great fascination over mankind, and in appearance birds' eggs may be compared with gems; indeed the shell itself is almost wholly composed of mineral matter. But, far from being an inanimate crystal, an egg shelters one of the marvels of the world—an embryo bird. The gaudy sea-shell cloaks a slimy snail, but from the beautiful egg of a bird emerges a greater beauty.

Reptiles lay white eggs whose shells are not brittle, but, when broken, curl up like a celluloid film. Some of these reptilian eggs are oblong in shape, but most are spherical and the great majority are deposited in the ground, or under bark, and are hatched by the heat of the decaying vegetation or by the direct rays of the sun. Thus we see that there is little need for variation in shape or colour. Among birds, however, we find very different conditions.

As we know that birds have evolved from reptiles, we have a right to suppose that the early forms of birds laid white, leathery eggs, perhaps in hollow trees; but the power of flight has taken birds entirely out of the

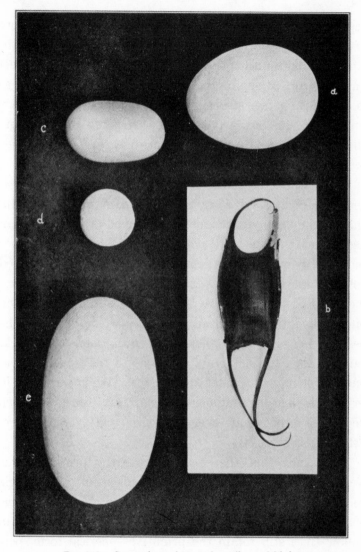

Fig. 342.—Comparison of eggs of reptiles and birds.
(a) Egg of Hen.   (b) Egg of Skate.   (c) Egg of Snake.   (d) Egg of Turtle.
(e) Egg of Alligator.

reptilian horizon, and greatly altered all the conditions of their life. The history of the egg of a bird, from the time it is laid until it hatches, has an all-important effect on its form, colour, and even upon the number of eggs laid. This is not strange when we consider that every minute of the bird's life is open to many dangers, and that the egg stage—that bridging over of generations—is a most precarious period.

That which adds the greatest interest to anything is the *why* of it, and a vast collection of eggs, beautiful though they are, yet, if ignorantly looked at, is worse than useless. Why one bird lays twenty eggs and another but two; why one bird's eggs are white, another's of varied colours, we will never learn from blown museum specimens. Not until we have the patience and skill to watch and to find the most deadly enemies which threaten the nests and eggs of birds, their number and modes of attack, can we hope for successful solutions to the thousand and one problems which offer themselves. What we know in respect to eggs is fragmentary and rests on so slight a degree of proof that every theory is attacked and re-attacked in turn.

Supposing that the eggs of the early forms of birds were round,—that being the most typical form of a single cell,—we find many variations in shape among the eggs of living species. Many of the eggs which are laid in hollow trees still retain the primitive spherical form, per-haps an advantage in keeping the eggs in a close group in the centre of the floor of the cavity.

So characteristic of the eggs of birds is the pear-shape

—one end blunt and narrowing to the other—that they have given to it its name: oval. In the eggs of certain sea-birds which breed on the narrow ledges of perpendicular cliffs this oval shape is carried to an extreme, and apparently for an excellent reason, mechanical, but of inestimable value to the birds. Eggs laid in such positions

Fig. 343.—Egg of Murre.

are of course especially exposed to danger from the wind or from some sudden movement of the birds, which generally nest very close together. Were it not that the eggs, on account of their peculiar shape, describe an arc of very small diameter when they roll, doubtless a far greater number would roll off and be dashed down upon the rocks below. Among the plovers, sandpipers, and phalaropes we again find a peculiarly pronounced pyriform shape of egg, serving in these instances a very apparent and useful end. These birds almost invariably lay four eggs, which are of large size in comparison with the birds, and their shape allows them to be fitted closely together, each forming one of the four segments, their points all but meeting in the centre. Thus the little body of the

Fig. 344.—Eggs of Killdeer.

parent is large enough to cover them all, which would be impossible were the eggs arranged at random. The eggs of grebes are peculiar in having both ends alike.

The number of eggs which a bird lays has been found to bear a definite relation to the amount of danger to which the species is exposed—a fact which holds good in the young of many, if not all, other Phyla of animals, and which is one of the most interesting provisions brought about by the slow but sure working of evolution. We may instance the few eggs of the voracious and masterful sharks and the millions of spawn necessary to enable the halibut and the cod to continue in existence.

Mr. Ernest Ingersoll has so admirably summed up the matter of this relation of the number of eggs to the corresponding danger that I cannot do better than to follow his argument, quoting his words with a slight change here and there. This phase of the study of eggs being so clearly understood, it is well worth a little detail as an illustration of how interesting all the other problems will become when we once get on the right road to their solution.

Among the majority of birds the average number of eggs in a nest is from three to six; we may take five as a typical average. "Any considerable departure from this normal number in a species or Family must then be accounted for by some specific or tribal peculiarity in circumstances.

"Beginning with the ostrichlike group at the bottom of the list, we find ourselves face to face with an interesting state of things, to which the number of eggs is an index. Ostriches, rheas, and emeus incubate large clutches—a dozen or more,—those inhabiting the continents of Africa and South America, however, producing twice as many eggs annually as their relatives of Australia and the neighbouring smaller islands.

"Immediately following and contrasting with them are

the three groups characterized by the curious elephant-footed, often gigantic moas, and similar birds of Madagascar, Mauritius, New Zealand, and the Papuan region, which have become extinct within the historic period, except the kiwis, to be spoken of later. All of these, so far as we know, laid only one egg at a time, which, plainly enough, was sufficient to keep the race going in the limited space afforded to each species by its island, but which did not suffice to prevent an almost immediate extinction of these species as soon as mankind discovered that the birds and their eggs were serviceable. But Providence, or Nature, or natural selection, or whatever has been the ruling influence in determining means and limits for animal life, seems never to have taken man into account.

"Turning now to the sea-birds—penguins, gannets, murres, puffins, auks, petrels, guillemots, tropic-birds, and the like,—we find that none of them is in the habit of laying more than one egg, as all breed on such remote and inaccessible rocks, often in holes, that harm can rarely happen to their young, and therefore a very high percentage comes to maturity. Many of these breed in companies, and are so unacquainted with danger that they make no attempt to hide their eggs or to leave the nest when the place is visited by some wandering naturalist or egging party.

"The habit of the King Penguin deserves a note to itself. This big Antarctic bird guards its one white egg from harm by carrying it somewhat as a marsupial does its young, in a pouch formed by a fold of the skin of the

FIG. 345.—Nest and eggs of Junco.

body between the thighs. Both sexes are provided with this contrivance during the breeding season, and relieve each other of the burden at intervals.

"The gull tribe, however, are far more exposed to accident and to enemies, both in adult life and as to their eggs and young, than are the penguins, petrels, and others mentioned above; and here the rule is from two (skuas) to four (gulls and terns) eggs in a nest. When we come

FIG. 346.—Eggs of Ostrich, Cassowary, Hummingbird, and Hen, showing comparative size.

to the shore- and marsh-birds—the plovers, snipe, sandpipers, jacanas, all of which nestle on the ground, usually near the shore of the sea or lakes—we judge them to be exposed to about the average of dangers, since their nest complement is from four to six. The northern, tundraloving cranes need raise few young, and hatch only two eggs; but when we come to the water-birds—the rails, gallinules, ducks, and geese—we find an extensive group

whose nests average a dozen eggs in each set. Explanations are ready for this: the birds themselves are exposed
to unusual peril, from weather as well as from active
enemies, since they mostly emigrate to the extreme North
and nest in the edges of marshes, where the sitting birds,

Fig. 347.—Nest of Laughing Gull.

eggs, and young are all subjected to freezings, floods,
and countless marauders that depend largely upon them
for food during the Arctic summer, so that a heavy annual
recruiting must be made to repair losses. Few birds are
liable to so many misfortunes and mishaps as the water-

fowl, except perhaps the big and pugnacious swans, who can take better care of themselves, and lay only five eggs or fewer. The long-legged wading birds also, such as the storks, ibises, herons, and the like, are fairly safe in the breeding season, because they nest in trees, as a rule, (Fig. 356,) and consequently we here find only two

FIG. 348.—Nest and eggs of California Partridge.

to four young in the annual brood; so with the snake-birds.

"This brings us to the game-birds—the world-wide tribes of partridges, pheasants, grouse, turkeys, jungle fowls, peacocks, and the like—which are of large size, run about on the ground, and are of interest to sportsmen and epicures. With few exceptions, these must put forth a

FIG. 349.—Nest and eggs of Mourning Dove.

large complement of eggs (eight to twenty) in order to bring to maturity enough young to replace the yearly mortality, for the ground-built homes and huddling chicks encounter a multitude of dangers to which birds in trees, or even the small-sized ground-nesters, are not exposed. One exception here singularly favours the rule. The Thibetan Peacock Pheasant inhabits the heights of the Himalayas, where it has to contend with only three or four nest-robbers, instead of the countless foes that infest the lower jungles; hence its ample breast warms but two eggs.

"The doves and pigeons lay only two eggs, and a few lay but one; but this seems to be due to the fact that their extraordinary powers of flight render them, as adults, unusual immunity from capture and famine, rather than to any special safety pertaining to their method of nidification.

"Hawks and owls in general have four or five eggs, and as this is about the average number of the small birds on which they largely prey, it seems evident that their chances of life and the difficulty of sustaining it are, on the whole, no less than are met with by their victims. The owls, however, vary much among themselves in this respect; the Snowy Owls, whose home is in the snowy north, where a nest in the tundra moss is accessible to every marauder, and the Burrowing Owls, whose underground homes are constantly robbed, being obliged to lay twice as many eggs as the remainder of the family in order to overcome the high percentage of casualties due to these unfortunate situations.

"An odd feature in the nidification of some of the

Arctic-breeding owls, where the nesting must take place at an unreasonably early and cold date in order to give the fledglings time to reach mature strength before the succeeding winter assails them, is that these birds deposit their eggs at intervals of a week or ten days. In this way the mother can envelop in her plumage and keep thoroughly warm one egg and a callow fledgling at a

Fig. 350.—Eggs of Screech Owl.

time, and is assisted, in respect to the later eggs and fledglings, by the warmth of the older young in the nest.

"The parrots are a wide-spread and numerous tribe, and none of the larger species need lay more than two or three eggs, for they protect them in deep holes in the earth or in trees, and are able to defend them; but some of the smaller parrakeets lay as many as twelve eggs, reflecting the greater dangers with which they have to contend. Toucans are able to get along with a pair of eggs; while a hornbill, by sealing its mate up in its little arboreal cavern during nidification, is so adequately protected that one to three eggs in each family suffice to keep the race going, since practically every young

Fig. 351.—Burrowing Owl at nesting hole.

bird is brought to maturity. Of the host of smaller and weaker birds nesting in cavities, two to five eggs are the usual quota. This brings us to the tribes of little singing birds with which we started, whose average is about five; but a few interesting exceptions may be noted. Our whippoorwills and night-hawks, for instance, lay only two eggs. These are placed on the ground in the woods, surrounded by no nest, and are so precisely the colour of the dead leaves that nothing but the merest accident would lead to their discovery by the eye alone. The same is eminently true of the bird itself. None of the almost uncatchable hummingbirds needs to lay more than two eggs in order to recruit the ranks of its

FIG. 352.—Nest and eggs of the Anna Hummingbird.

species to the full quota permitted it in the numerical adjustment of bird life.

"I have gone into this matter somewhat at length, though by no means exhaustively, because I am not aware that the matter has ever been exploited, and because it embodies a general law or principle. Thus we see that the nest complement of eggs of any bird is in exact proportion to the average danger to which that species is exposed. I believe that this factor is fairly constant for species or tribes of similar habits, and that exceptions indicate peculiarities of circumstances which in many cases we can easily perceive, because I believe that Nature is strictly economical of energy, allowing no more eggs to be laid, and consequently young to be produced, than the conditions justify in each case. Thus the uniformity of avine population—the balance of bird-life—is maintained."

When a bird's nest and eggs are destroyed, she will often lay another setting, and some birds raise two and even three broods in a season under normal conditions. If the eggs of a bird are removed as fast as they are laid, the bird will sometimes continue to lay, one of the most remarkable instances of this in an uncaged bird being a Flicker which laid seventy-one eggs during the space of three-and-seventy days. A tiny African Waxbill in captivity has been known to rear fifty-four young in the course of a year, during the same period laying an additional sixty-seven eggs! The domestic hen has become a veritable egg-laying machine, thanks to careful breeding in the past, since the wild Red Jungle Fowl from which all varieties of poultry are descended, lays only one nestful of seven to twelve eggs once a year.

Many birds still hold to the old style of nesting in hollow trees and such concealed places. Whether they hunt around until they find a cavity ready-made by the elements, or whether, like the woodpeckers, they proceed to excavate a home in a dead branch, or, kingfisher-like, to tunnel deep into a sand-bank, their eggs are almost invariably white. Many indeed have such glossy, highly polished shells that, were they laid in exposed situations, their shining surface would be a sure guide to hungry

Fig. 353.—White eggs of Hairy Woodpecker in hollow tree.
(Bowdish, photographer.)

egg-eaters. Among such birds may be mentioned the owls, woodpeckers and parrots, trogons, motmots, kingfishers and puffins, besides many others which hide their eggs in domed nests. On the other hand we find a number of birds laying spotted eggs in concealed nests, and white eggs in open places; so that no universal law can be framed to account for the varied colouring. This is not surprising when we think of the great difference of conditions under which each species lives. Take for example the two species of marsh wrens which live so happily among the reeds of the marshes of our Eastern States. Both birds build globular mouse-like nests, both hide their treasures deep in the interior, but the eggs of the Long-billed species are dark chocolate-brown, while the Short-bill's eggs are like pearls. We do not know why this difference exists, but that need not deter us from accepting the facts to which the majority of eggs seem to point: that eggs which are concealed, having no need for colouring, are white like those of reptiles. If, as many writers have suggested, the colours of eggs are only meaningless by-products, there is no reason why these hues should not run riot upon each egg or nestful of eggs, as is the case in one or two interesting isolated cases to be mentioned shortly.

Perhaps the most marked exceptions to the theory of the protective coloration of eggs is to be found in doves and pigeons, which lay white eggs in open nests (Fig. 349); with the exception, curiously enough, of the Rock Dove, the wild progenitor of our domestic birds, which places its nest in inaccessible caverns in the face of cliffs. The almost total extermination of the Passenger Pigeon has been instanced as an example of a "mistake" of Nature in allotting to it white eggs; the absurdity of which statement is apparent when we consider that the havoc was wrought upon the *adult birds* and by *man*!

Wallace has suggested that the nests of doves are so loosely and so flimsily built—being in reality mere platforms of sticks—that, looking up at them, the eggs simulated the colour of the sky beyond and so became inconspicuous; but unfortunately that argument is so decidedly

Fig. 354.—Nest and eggs of Mallard Duck.

suggestive of human presence that it loses much of its value when we remember that egg-hunters among the mammals and birds do not stand on the ground to take observations, but either climb the trees in search of nests or fly low above the branches.

The eggs of ducks and grouse are white or very light-coloured, and are laid in open nests upon the ground. The mother duck's plumage is the very essence of the mottled lights and shadows among the reeds, and when she leaves her eggs she backs carefully away, drawing over them, at the same time, a coverlet of beautiful down, the protective colouring of which is ample to shield the eggs. Ordinarily this coverlet is rolled up at the edge of the nest. It is to such a habit that the eider-down hunters owe their supply. A grouse does not pluck the down from her breast, but in devotion and ability to remain close upon her eggs she has few equals. It is rare indeed to find the nest of a grouse unguarded, and the mother bird will all but wait until your hand is upon her before leaving her eggs exposed.

The many species of hummingbirds lay the whitest of eggs, but here it is the nest which is protected,—fashioned of dull-hued plant-down, with beams and rafters of cobweb, covered outside in our Eastern species with lichens exactly like those which are growing upon the limb to which the tiny air-castle is attached. The nests of vireos, also, are much like their surroundings.

Herons and egrets, pelicans, cormorants, storks, swans and geese, all lay white or whitish eggs in open nests; but obviously these birds require little protection, all being able to defend themselves with beak or wing. Some of them nest, too, in large colonies, adding the advantage of numbers. The constant need of vigilance in protecting eggs thus exposed is at once evident when mankind —that disturber of Nature for whose intrusion she seems never prepared—comes upon the scene. If we make our way into the heart of a Florida rookery of herons, ibises, or cormorants, many of the birds will be frightened from their nests and the Fish Crows take instant advantage,

FIG. 355.—Nest and eggs of Ruby-throated Hummingbird.

449

swooping down one after another upon the nests and each impaling an egg upon its beak and flying off with it. They would never dare such open villainy were the herons undisturbed.

Fig. 356.—Colony of Great Blue Herons.

Many of the more isolated cases of exposed white eggs are to be explained, I think, by the fact that the habits of birds often change rapidly, while their structural adaptation follows more slowly. For example, let us take the group of owls. The majority of these birds nest in hollow trees, but even these occasionally make use of an open hollow or a very shallow one, and individual, radical departures from the conventional owl-habitation are doubtless not uncommon. But these exposed eggs are soon destroyed; for no crow, jay, or squirrel could ever resist any opportunity to avenge himself for the wrongs inflicted by his ancestral enemy, the owl. But when, urged on by that impulse which ever tends to make birds vary their habits in all directions, some owl, such as the Short-eared, finds good feeding on marshes and open, treeless plains, it naturally takes to nesting on the ground, in nests but partly concealed by the overhanging grasses.

Three things might now happen. If sufficient variation occurred and the conditions demanded it, natural selection might bring about a protective colour on the shells of the eggs; if enemies were few and easily over-awed, the eggs might remain white; while, on the other hand, the enterprising race might be wiped out of existence for no more reason than the colour of the egg-shells. The second result seems to be the good fortune of the Short-eared Owls. All of these fates have undoubtedly overtaken birds again and again, and it is by the inter-action of such condition , combined with an ever-changing environment, that many phenomena are brought about.

It was by reason of the general similarity in colour which the eggs of related groups of birds tend to show to each other that oölogy, or the science of egg-shells, was able to initiate an important scientific discovery.

At one time the sandpipers and plovers were classed as wading birds, and the gulls and terns in an Order placed at a remote distance in the scheme of classification from the former birds; no one suspecting that the two groups were in any way related. The striking resemblance which their eggs showed, however, suggested an affinity

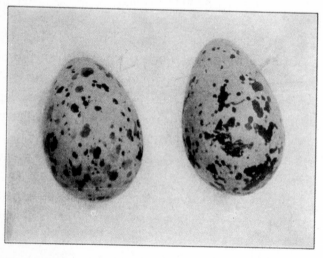

Fig. 357.—(a) Egg of common Tern compared with (b) egg of Black-necked Stilt

which was later perfectly confirmed by anatomists and embryologists.

The few thousands of years during which our race has risen to inheritance of the earth is all too short a time, geologically speaking, for us to flatter ourselves that any of the protective colours of animals were developed on our account; but in many instances we, sharing the same five senses of animals, may put ourselves in their position. Imagining ourselves egg-hunting

FIG. 358.—Eggs of Cassowary.

FIG. 359.—Eggs of Ostrich.

animals, let us consider some of the more patent cases where eggs are coloured for protection — where they mimic their surroundings so perfectly that only the most careful search reveals their whereabouts. Ostriches and Cassowaries are two interesting examples, the former bird laying its white eggs upon the white sands of the desert; while the cassowary, in the depths of its jungle home, incubates a nestful of eggs of the most exquisite emerald hue, matching perfectly the green moss upon which they rest. I knew of one of these birds confined in a small paddock of green grass, whose splendid eggs, measuring three by six inches, once remained undiscovered for weeks, although laid openly upon the ground. Special search was necessary to find even these great eggs.

If we walk in the woods in June and happen to flush a night-hawk from the ground, the most careful scrutiny of the place where the bird rose will often fail to reveal to our sight what at last our fingers detect—two eggs, their shells imbued with the colours of the forest floor. I have led persons to a spot on a beach of shells and sand, told them that there were twenty-one good-sized eggs within a radius of fifteen feet, and seen them utterly baffled. The olive-gray, blotched shell of a tern's egg rests among dark pebbles, or more often upon a wisp of seaweed, into whose irregularities the hues of the eggs melt and mingle perfectly. The Black Skimmer, that most interesting bird of our coast, lays its eggs upon the bare sand among, or sometimes *in*, the large clam-shells which the storms throw up in windrows. Against man's systematic search their wonderful assimilative colouring is of course often useless,

but sharp as is the eye of passing crow or beach-patrolling
bear, the eggs to them would appear but bits of sand and
shadow.

And thus we might go on with many other examples
of protection derived from the pigment on the shells—
protection which in a hundred instances might prove

Fig. 360.—Eggs of Night-hawk.

futile, but which in the great summing up and balancing
of Nature's profit and loss is of inestimable value to the
race.

We find an unusual condition in the colouring of the
eggs of sea-birds,—of certain of those species which nest
on inaccessible cliffs. If pigment was developed in the

eggs of the ancestors of these birds for the sake of protection, all need for it is now lacking, and as an apparent result the various hues seem to have run riot. One may place a hundred murres' eggs side by side and find no two alike, while the extremes would never be recognized as belonging to the same species of bird.

Fig. 361.—Nests of Tern and Skimmer.

Another instance of extreme variability in the colour of eggs and an instance of intensely interesting import is found in the English Cuckoo, which may be taken as an example of species which are parasitical,—in the sense that the females make no nest of their own, but deposit their eggs in the nests of other birds, the young being thus

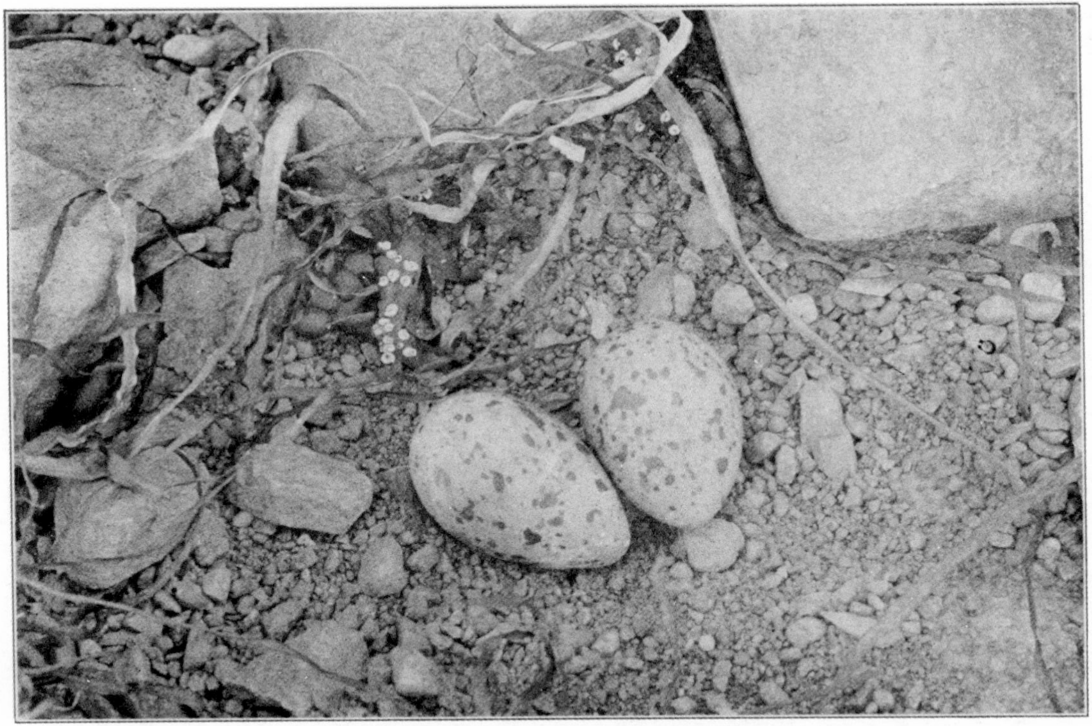

Fig. 362.—Nest and eggs of Common Tern.

hatched and reared by foster-parents. Such an unusual, almost unique habit has brought about a considerable modification of the eggs. Anything which would tend to deceive the greatest number of intended victims would, of course, greatly redound to the advantage of parasitical birds.

The remarkable similarity of the English Cuckoo's egg to those in the nest in which it is laid has been explained as due to each individual bird being accustomed to lay its egg in the nest of the same species favoured by its parents and its more distant ancestors; its eggs in course of time, by natural selection, thus coming to resemble the eggs of that particular species. Other adaptations are the extremely small size of the egg in comparison with the parent bird, and also the unusual strength and weight of the shell. This last is doubtless of great value; for, strange as it may seem, the bird first deposits its egg upon the ground and then picks it up in its beak and places it in the nest selected. Thus a strong shell is a very necessary requirement.

The colours of eggs have been carefully examined with the spectroscope and are found to consist, chemically, of seven pigments: a brownish red, two delicate blues, two clear yellows, a peculiar brown hue, while the seventh is a rather indefinite shade, known as lichenixanthine—most interesting of all as being identical with a colour substance common in plants and especially in lichens and fungi. These substances somewhat resemble those found in the blood and the bile. They are deposited on the shell while the egg is passing down the oviduct, and it is to the circular or erratic motion of the egg that the curious scrawls and blotches upon some eggs are due. The shell is deposited in successive layers, and from the dim, clouded appearance of many colours we judge that the pigment is often partly concealed by the outermost layers of the shell.

FIG. 363.—Nest and eggs of Skimmer, showing the remarkable variation in colour of the eggs in a single nest, heightening their resemblance to pebbles or sea-shells.

Occasionally, in the eggs of birds which number only two in a nest, one egg will be almost white and the other coated with an abnormal density of pigment. In certain species of small birds which lay four or five eggs, one egg always differs remarkably from the rest. Can we not account for this latter condition on the hypothesis that an actual change—an increase—is slowly taking place in the number of eggs of this species, the abnormal shell reflecting the as yet only partial readjustment of the pigment-gland to meet the extra demand?

The carbonate of lime, of which the shell is chiefly composed, varies in its composition, being sometimes so fine that the surface has a high gloss, the eggs of woodpeckers being a good example, or again loose and chalky, as in cormorants. In tinamous the glossiness is carried to an extreme, their eggs resembling ovals of highly burnished metal, green and purple in colour.

The shells of ducks' eggs are impregnated with an oily substance, which must be of great use in resisting the dampness and moisture of their surroundings.

The eggs of some entire Families of birds are easily recognized by the resemblance of the grain of the shell; while, on the other hand, this microscopic appearance in the eggs of individual species may differ considerably, as in the case of the eggs of the Mute and Whooping Swans. The eggs of the North African Ostrich have a surface smooth as ivory, while the eggs laid by the South African birds are deeply pitted. The beautiful eggs of the cassowary show an extreme condition, the light green surface of the egg being covered with raised irregularities of a darker green colour.

The thickness of the shells of ostrich eggs is remarkable, and their strength permits their use as water-bottles—an invaluable boon to the Arabs of the desert.

With the relative size of the egg and the bird which

lays it we will not here concern ourselves, except to remark that the largest egg in proportion to the size of the bird is that of the apteryx. If we imagine a rather smallish hen laying an egg 3×5 inches in size, we will get a vivid idea of this bird's ability, and it lays two at a setting! The smallest of all eggs is that of the hummingbird, while the largest is the egg of the extinct giant *Æpyornis* of Madagascar, the shell of which measures 9×13 inches. In some cases the fossil egg is all that is left to us to hint of the existence of these great feathered creatures. Many of these shells have been found buried with some old native chief, the whole egg placed beside him to furnish food for the long journey after death.

Whether we look at eggs from the standpoint of an artist's delight in harmonious and delicate colouring, or from the wonder of their scientific composition, or even from the point of view of a hungry man sitting down to breakfast, we must admit that they deserve all the appreciation which their beauty and their utility demand.

CHAPTER XVII

THE BIRD IN THE EGG

THE embryology, or life of the bird in the egg, is the most mysterious and wonderful part of the entire physical aspect. Many of the lesser details of growth are very difficult to study without the use of microscopic sections and wax models; but a little knowledge of the subject is more interesting and simple than one would imagine.

The very best way to begin our study of the life in the egg will be to go to the nearest pond or marsh, if it is springtime, and bring home a pailful of freshly laid frog's eggs —those queer, gelatinous masses filled with black dots. Place them in a flat, white basin, and into a smaller saucer near by break a fresh hen's egg, being careful not to injure the yolk. Separate one of the frog's eggs with a spoon and put it beside that of the fowl. Now examine them carefully with a good dissecting-microscope or even with a hand-lens.

We see a large, round, yellow yolk in the case of one egg, and a tiny speck of black and white in the other,— both apparently inanimate bits of matter, but which, merely by the application of heat in the one instance

and the presence of water in the other, will slowly take
on the semblance of living creatures; the one eventually
to swim forth, live the life of a fish for a time, then to
leap upon the land and croak among the reeds. The
other yolk would have evolved into a downy, yellow chick.
We cannot hope to solve the mystery of life, but there
is a fascination in seeing how near its beginnings we can
approach.

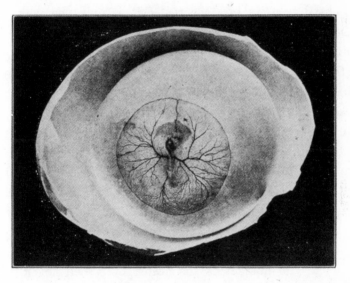

Fig. 364.—Egg of Hen, opened to show a 3-day embryo in position on the yolk.
(Slightly enlarged.)

If we have ever watched under the microscope the strange
little creatures which live in the mud at the bottom of
ponds, we will have realized the wonderful possibilities of a
single drop of living matter,—a single cell,—from the
amœba with its ever-changing shape to the swiftly moving
slipper paramecium and the beautiful animal vases,—the

vorticella, on their queer little corkscrew stems. All these are made up of but a single cell, and in the beginning all seeds of plants and all eggs of animals likewise consist of one cell.

If we examine a chicken while it is being dressed for the table, we can easily find the ovary, a mass of hundreds of tiny golden spheres,—eggs which would have been laid during the coming years. So we realize that the most essential part, in fact the real egg, is only the yolk; all else being merely protective. The shell protects the yolk while the chick is developing during incubation, and although formed of crystals of lime, yet it is so porous that oxygen can enter and carbonic acid gas escape. The viscid white, or albumen, is nutritious as well as protective, while the yolk itself is the real food of the embryo and also acts as a support to the developing chick. If we look carefully, we will see two whitish, twisted strands which extend from the yolk through the white. These two strands have whitish opaque knots strung along them, and from a fancied resemblance to hailstones they are called *chalazœ*. These act as pads to protect the yolk from sudden jars, but they do not act as suspensories. A hen never turns her eggs, as many people imagine, to warm the different sides equally, for the germ-dot—the position of the future embryo (of which we will speak presently)—is always on the lightest side of the yolk, and whichever way the egg is turned it always swings uppermost, nearest the heat from the body of the sitting hen. The turning, however, may be of advantage in allowing moisture to act upon a greater surface of shell.

Now let us examine closely the egg of the frog. It, too, has a protective gelatinous outer coating. Before the egg was laid it was enveloped with several very delicate membranes, which were sponge-like in their property of absorbing water, and when deposited in a pond they immediately swelled up to the present gelatinous consistency. If the egg has been deposited but an hour or two, it will show a perfectly smooth surface under the lens, but look at it intermittently for a half-hour, or even longer, and you will be well repaid. Slowly but surely, as the shadow of an eclipse darkens the face of the sun, a tiny furrow ploughs its way over the surface of the dark end of the egg. It lengthens and deepens and soon divides the egg into two equal halves.

Let us stop a minute and realize what we have seen. It is all but the beginning of life, the first hint of a higher order of things than those one-celled creatures which we dredged from the mud,—than the life which, untold ages ago, was all that the earth boasted. The original cell of the egg has, before our eyes, divided into two! But while we have been lost in wonder and awe,—for the lover of Nature must indeed be stolid if the first sight of such a happening does not stir his deepest emotions,—the life has ceased its progress never an instant. A new furrow appears, crossing the first at right angles, dividing the egg into quarters; then other furrows dividing it into eighths, then cross-furrows, and the count is lost; the multitude of cells repeating themselves hour after hour, day and night, arranging themselves, each in its right position, obeying some inscrutable law, until at the end of about 300 hours the tadpole wriggles his way through the cloudy mass of gelatine and swims into the water.

The first steps of this dividing or cleaving of the original single cell is similar in all eggs. The deep significance of the equality of the first two cells may be better appreciated when we know that if one of these be destroyed by a touch from a red-hot needle, a perfect *half* tadpole will develop from the other unharmed twin cell. If we observe the cleavage of the whiter portion of the frog's egg, we will notice that the furrows, though ultimately extending all the way around, yet grow very slowly in that portion. This is because much of the white part consists of yolk, or true food-matter, the more active formative material being confined to the black portion.

If we follow this segmentation of the cells for some time, the egg of the frog will come to look like a diminutive blackberry—a single layer of cells thickly covering its entire surface, like the rounded protuberances of the berry. Now a curious thing happens. A tiny nick appears in one side, which gradually deepens and widens until it extends deep into the egg, pressing two rows of cells into close proximity to each other. This will be perfectly clear if we take a small rubber ball and squeeze it until one hollow hemisphere is pressed into the other. This stage of embryological life is called the gastrula, and is of the greatest significance, as we shall soon see.

Without further comment at present, let us now leave the frog's egg and consider that of the fowl. When the yolk or egg has but just left the ovary a tiny dot is visible on one side,—the germinal vesicle, which after fertilization

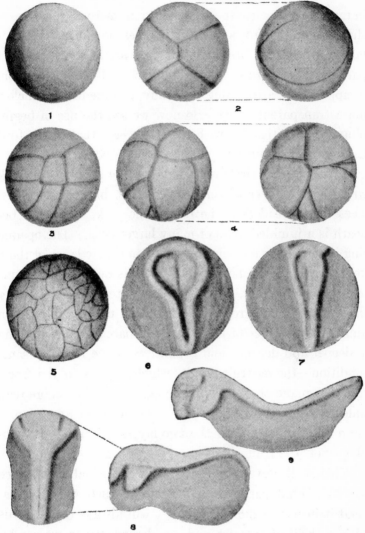

Fig. 365.—Stages in the development of frog's egg, from first division into two cells up to well-formed larval tadpole. (From original drawings by the author.)

467

immediately begins to divide into numerous cells, as in the case of the frog's egg. This goes on until the egg is laid, and when we break the shell, we see at the uppermost part of the sphere of yellow yolk a well-defined portion, in appearance a tiny ring of cloudy, opaque matter enclosing a transparent circle. So now we see the use of beginning our investigation with the frog's egg, that of the fowl having reached quite an advanced stage before it is laid.

The ring and circle of the embryonic spot on the yolk consists of a layer of small, even cells, like cobblestones. These are spread over the top of the yolk, while just beneath is a jumbled mass of many larger cells. The opaque ring is caused by a thicker, denser concentric layer of these lower cells. When heat is applied, this outer layer begins to segment rapidly, the new cells spreading down over the surface of the great ball of yolk; a curving depression dimples the surface of the little transparent circle, pushing in deeper and deeper; and behold! we have the very same condition—the gastrula stage—which we saw in the frog's egg. To make this stage in the egg of the hen more real, squeeze the rubber ball into a hemisphere and clap it upon an orange so that the two layers of rubber fit, cap-like, upon the fruit.

This is all very wonderful, but what special significance has it? What particular point upon which we may suspend it in our memory, so that it will always return to us with a thrill of interest and wonder whenever we see an egg? Just this. When we first examined the frog's egg, and when the egg of the chick was still attached to the ovary, they were comparable to the one-celled creatures

living in the mud of the pond, which are the most lowly
organized beings in the world. The gastrula stage—the
double-walled cup, into which the real egg-part of each

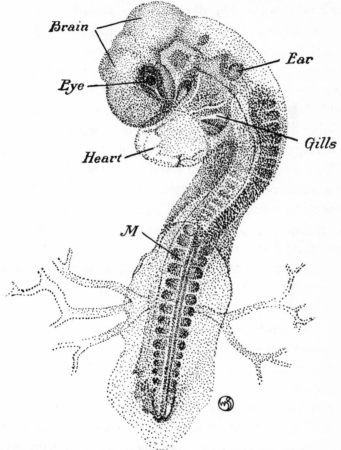

Brain

Ear

Eye

Heart

Gills

M

FIG. 366.—Third-day stage of embryo chick. (See Fig. 364.) Greatly enlarged·
M, Muscle-plates (false vertebræ).

yolk forms itself, is comparable with the next higher class
of living creatures, the sponges. For the simplest of
these are nothing more than a cup of cells, two layers deep

(these layers being known as the ectoderm and endoderm, or outer skin and inner skin). The name gastrula, or little stomach, is certainly most applicable, for an animal of this kind consists of hardly more than stomach and mouth.

But the embryo of the frog's egg does not long remain in this sponge-like condition; for almost immediately a third layer, the mesoderm, or middle skin, appears between the other two. From these three layers of cells all the parts of the body of the future chick arise, by the continued dividing of the cells. The details are far too involved to be followed without going into technicalities.

Suffice it to say that in the development of the embryo chick we have one of the surest proofs of the truth of the theory of evolution,—of the gradual evolving of each of the higher groups of animals from some lower, more generalized form, until all are originally derived from an organism consisting of a single cell, with its tiny germ-spot. The dividing of this ge m-spot in the dawn of creation was the beginning of that wonderful unrolling of life which to-day culminates in birds and the higher mammals,—even in man himself.

It would be too much to expect that the growing embryo chick distinctly reflects in its successive stages of growth, during a short three weeks, the embryonic states of all its unnumbered generations of ancestors. The record, like that of palæontology, is imperfect. Many important phases are slurred over or apparently entirely omitted; in order, evidently, to give freer play to the development of organs which will be of vital importance in the future active life of the bird. Now and then, however, a gleam—

a spark of life reflected from the far-distant past shines forth so vividly as to hold us spellbound, almost instantly to fade out forever, having no part in the actual life of the chick. Like the finding of the Archæopteryx, these dim reflections seem to have been preserved by some kind Providence, especially to aid our groping efforts to find the truth of ages that are past. Were it not for these we should never dare to voice such an incredible theory as the story of evolution would be, were it not supported by unanswerable proofs. The question which interests scientists to-day is not whether evolution is true, but *how* its processes and changes have been brought about.

The difficulty of seizing upon these evanescent bits of realism of the past will be appreciated when we know that while, in the case of the hen's egg, three weeks are required before the chick is ready to break the shell, yet when incubation has proceeded but eighteen hours, a tiny rod of cells shows where the notochord will be formed— that gelatinous foreshadowing of the back-bone. Thus a character, found first in living organisms as high in the scale of life as fish and primitive fish-like creatures, makes its appearance in a few hours, giving but the scantest opportunity for the passing in review of embryonic features of the great group of invertebrates, or those animals, like starfishes, crabs, worms, and insects, which lack a back-bone.

The simplest way to study the growing embryo is to put a number of eggs in an incubator, or under a hen, and examine one on each successive day. If the egg is held firmly, by pressing it down into a box of loose sand, the upper part of the shell may be carefully picked away with a pin and the little embryo exposed to view.

When thirty-six hours old it measures almost one quarter of an inch in length and shows many interesting things. The embryo is set off from the rest of the yolk, much as one's hand is if placed under a piece of cloth, the latter then being tucked in beneath the palm in all directions, until the gathered portion is closely constricted. We are able with a good lens to make out which is the head and which the tail end of the future chick, the former being broader and showing the beginning of the two tiny swellings—the future eyes. Behind these, four faintly outlined enlargements along the central line show the *anlagen* of the various parts of the brain. These take up about one third of the entire length of the embryo, showing the importance of the organs of the head. Still farther back are two rows of little segments strung along the centre line—the false back-bone, hinting of the worm-like series of muscles, of which we have already spoken (page 69).

A heart is even now hinted at, but is seen better in a later stage. An interesting thing about it, however, is that, at this stage, it is really *in* the head region, vividly recalling the condition existing in fishes, where it is very far forward in the body, in fact only just behind the gills. At this period in the chick embryo the heart, instead of being a complicated organ, divided into four complete cavities, is very similar to that organ in our old friend Amphioxus, that lowliest of all fishes, where it is nothing but a slightly enlarged, contractile blood-vessel. In this latter creature there have been found as many as a hundred and eighty pairs of gill-clefts, such a remarkable number aerating the blood with but little necessary propulsion, but when in the higher fishes the number of gills in many species is reduced to four, we realize at once the need for a stronger engine to force the blood through the lessened number, this accounting for the increased complexity of the heart.

Up to about the twelfth day the tiny foreshadowings of bones are cartilaginous, like those of the shark, but at this time real osseous, or bony, tissue begins to be deposited in spots which spread rapidly. In the various portions of the skull these bony centres spread until the bones are separated only by narrow sutures, and in the adult bird even these are obliterated, unlike the condition in the skull of a cat or a dog.

The bones of the adult bird are so neatly joined together, and are so mutually dependent, that we might easily imagine that they were formed in the order of size or importance, or in a regular series, following their connection with one another; but this is not true. The ribs, for example, are formed between the segments of the primitive sheets of muscle, independently of the back-bone, and only later become attached to it. There is no trace of the great keel-bone, or even of the sternum of the adult fowl, until after the ends of the ribs have met in the middle line of the body, when they grow together and give rise to the sternum—a structure not found in fishes. We have learned that the repetition of similar structures (as the ribs) is a sign of a low degree of organization, and the truth of this is emphasized in the development of the embryo, during which process a number of additional ribs disappear. The abortive ribs of the neck-bones are especially noticeable during the egg-life of the bird, so that in some species we can make out traces of as many as fifteen ribs all told.

On page 97 a short account was given of the origin of

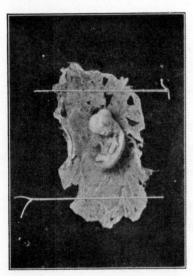

the wings and feet, in the case of the chick—from a primitive fin-fold in some generalized aquatic ancestor. About the fourth day of incubation, sections of our embryo chick will show a low, rounded ridge, extending the whole length from the neck to the tail. While we can never be absolutely certain that perfect homology exists between the two, yet it is very significant that soon after its development it dwindles away, leaving four conical, isolated

FIG. 367.—Early embryo of Canada Goose, showing fin-like limbs.

buds—the beginnings of the limbs of the bird. Within two or three days after the appearance of the limbs, faint streaks become visible upon the tips of the extremities, and these hints of the bones of fingers and toes, for such they are, soon push out beyond the edge, still bound together by their transparent membrane, and for some time they present the appearance of webbed paws or radiate fins. But as early as the tenth day, except for the absence of feathers and claws, the limbs are, in appearance, very perfect wings and feet. The most interesting fact in connection with the limbs is that their development begins superficially and works inward, not, as would be thought, starting at the shoulder and ending at the digits.

Even the deep-seated shoulder- and thigh-girdles of bone (pp. 85 and 89) are not derived from the axial skeleton. The former, in the long ago, was gradually pushed inward from the surface by the deep-reaching rays of the fin-like fore limbs, and it is believed that the pelvic girdle had its origin in the spliced scales of some fish-like ancestor of old, which had scales like those of some of the fossil ganoids. These probably covered over the cartilage girdle and then sunk in.

An example of one out of many reptilian structures which appear for a time and then vanish, is found in the procoracoid bone which has apparently much to do with the development of the typical coracoids, but which is absent or reduced to a mere process in the adult bird.* Strangely enough, in the embryo of the common chick the coracoid and scapula fuse together at an early stage, being then in a condition comparable only to that found in the full-grown ostrich. Later this inexplicable fusion is dissolved and the bones complete their development as they began,—two wholly independent structures.

Again, in the embryo of a tern, faint vestiges of teeth

---

* This process is quite pronounced in the case of the Ostrich.

have been observed, instantly bringing to mind that somewhat gull-like, toothed bird of old—*Icthyornis*.

The origin and subsequent changes, in the embryo chick, of the vascular system, including the heart, nerves, and arteries, are more intricate than the development of any other system of organs, and for an excellent reason. We know that the frog's egg hatches as a tadpole, which breathes by means of gills and lives, for a considerable time, in the water. We learned in Chapter IV that important parts of the head and sense-organs of birds are derived from metamorphosed gills; so the inference is that all the changes in the blood-channels, which in the tadpole and frog take place during several months, are in the embryo chick gone through with in a period of a few days.

The blood in the heart of a fish is sent from the single ventricle to the gills, and from there it is distributed all over the body. In the gills it passes through the paired series of red fringes and is oxygenated by the water. Now in the chick there are six pairs of these gills, or paired blood-vessels (although not more than three or four are found at one time). The chick breathes by means of a membranous sheet of blood-vessels spread out just beneath the shell, and even the lungs are not brought into use until just before the bird hatches. But strange to say, although there is no water to supply the gill-channels with life-giving oxygen, yet blood actually flows through them, in obedience to the long-forgotten ancestral life-habits—useless these many millions of years.

Of all the gill-channels, but three remain in the adult bird. The great aorta, which springs from the heart and

FIG. 368.—Pineal eye in Lizard.

turns to the right (in ourselves, the left-side gill-channel forms this aortic arch), is what is left of the fourth pair of aortic gill-arches, while the two arteries which, in all higher animals, leads to the right and left lungs. are the self-same channels which in the creatures of olden time encircled the sixth pair of gill-bars.

Although the eye of the bird is far superior to that of a fish in seeing ability, yet in actual structure there is not very much difference, except that the bird has gained eyelids, tear-glands, and a few other structures. Fishes, frogs, lizards, birds, and mammals, through all the ages, have depended on these two eyes and have found them all-sufficient; but there are hints that once,

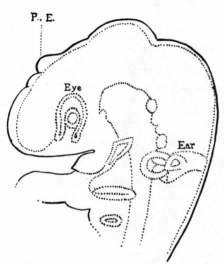

FIG. 369.—Pineal eye in Chick (P. E.).

long ago, the ancestors of all the higher animals had a sense-organ, probably of sight, situated, like that of the mythical Polyphemus, in the centre of the head. In lizards this vestigial organ is sometimes quite well developed, having a nerve which leads up from the centre of the brain to a kind of translucent, lens-like scale which lies among the other scales of the skin, upon the centre of the forehead. In the long-extinct Ichthyosaurs this median eye was probably functional. In an embryo chick of even the third day this organ is remarkably prominent; but although traces of it always remain, yet it fades away to a vestige.

Look with a hand-lens at the head of a polywog, and see the whitish dot between the eyes; or when you touch

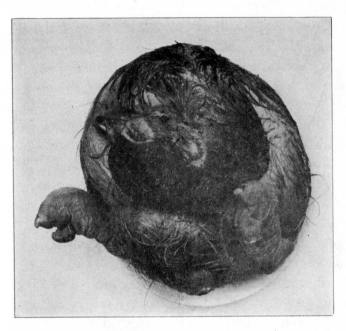

Fig. 370.—Forty-day embryo Ostrich, showing position in the shell.

the "soft spot" on the head of a human baby, let it recall the strange third eye which is its cause.

And so we might continue to tell of the wonder of embryo life: how up to the sixth day the little being might be mistaken for the embryo of a reptile or a mammal, but from this day onward the bird characteristics become more and more noticeable. On the ninth day feathers begin to be seen, looking, however, more like tiny cones than anything else (Fig. 11). The muscles and the cartilage skeleton are well defined on the fourteenth day, and about this time the tiny beak with its white egg-tooth is pressed against the membrane of the air-chamber at the large end of the egg. Reptiles also show this tiny bit of sharp lime upon the head, which drops off soon after its function is completed. Not until almost the last day is the membrane pierced and the first gasp of air breathed into the little lungs. By an instinctive moving of the head back and forth the shell is filed through and cracked, and the chick rolls out into the world, weak and helpless and for a while absolutely dependent upon warmth and the care of its mother, before it is fit for its future life. (Figs. 18 and 19.)

Thus do all wild birds begin life, passing through similar phases within the egg; and although we so often admire a nest full of eggs, yet how seldom do we give thought to the tiny creatures within,—their hearts even at that very minute, perhaps, giving their first fluttering beat!

The instant that its eyes have cleared and its shaky legs have gained strength to support its body, the chick begins to use its senses and to store up experiences, taking note of this sound and that taste, learning to fear or to ignore, to flee or to pursue, to call or to remain silent. And thus does the brain of the chick and of all wild nestlings begin to act and its psychological life commences, with intermingled perceptions, instincts, and gleams of intelligence. Here belong the making of nests and journeys,

FIG. 371.—Ostrich chicks hatching   (Cawston, photographer.)

481

courtship and songs, the rearing of young birds, the avoiding of enemies, the selection of food and suitable haunts, and, lastly, the encountering and overcoming of dangers,—new and wide-spread,—which are now affecting the environment of every creature of this world. Of greater importance than ever before is this adaptation to new conditions; since man and his traps and his guns have come upon the scene, upsetting all the world-old order of Nature and slowly, surely, claiming the whole earth for himself.

May the naturalists of to-day realize their opportunity and do their best to preserve to us and to posterity what is left to us of wild life! If not, let us pity the Nature-lover of two hundred years hence!

APPENDIX

A FEW EXCELLENT BOOKS RELATING DIRECTLY OR INDIRECTLY TO ORNITHOLOGY

EVOLUTION

ORIGIN OF SPECIES.
    Charles Darwin. Appleton & Co., New York.
FROM THE GREEKS TO DARWIN.
    Henry Fairfield Osborn. Macmillan Co., New York.
ORGANIC EVOLUTION.
    M. M. Metcalf. Macmillan Co., New York.
VARIATION IN ANIMALS AND PLANTS.
    H. M. Vernon. Henry Holt & Co., New York.

BOOKS FOR THE IDENTIFICATION OF NORTH AMERICAN BIRDS

GUIDE TO THE BIRDS OF NEW ENGLAND AND EASTERN NEW YORK.
    Ralph Hoffmann. Houghton, Mifflin & Co., Boston.
HANDBOOK OF BIRDS OF EASTERN NORTH AMERICA.
    F. M. Chapman. Appleton & Co., New York.
HANDBOOK OF BIRDS OF THE WESTERN UNITED STATES.
    Florence M. Bailey. Houghton, Mifflin & Co., Boston.
KEY TO NORTH AMERICAN BIRDS (2 vols.).
    Elliot Coues. Dana Estes & Co., Boston.
BIRDS OF NORTH AND MIDDLE AMERICA (3 parts; others to follow).
    Robert Ridgway. Bulletin of the United States National Museum, No. 50, Washington, D. C.
HISTORY OF NORTH AMERICAN LAND BIRDS (3 vols.).
    Baird, Brewer, and Ridgway. Little, Brown & Co., Boston.

BIRDS IN GENERAL

Dictionary of Birds.
>Alfred Newton.   A. & C. Black, London.

Riverside Natural History, Vol. IV. Birds.
>L. Stejneger.   Houghton, Mifflin & Co., New York.

MISCELLANEOUS

Birds of Essex County, Massachusetts.
>C. W. Townsend.   Memoir of Nuttall Ornithological Club, No. III.
>Cambridge, Mass.   (A type of a local bird-study)

The Woodpeckers.
>Fannie H. Eckstorm.   Houghton, Mifflin & Co., Boston.   (A popu-
>lar study of a single group of birds.)

INDEX

Figures in heavy-faced type indicate illustrations.

A

Abdominal ribs, 79
Adaptation of feet, 361, 362
Adaptative Radiation, 15-18; in warblers, 361-367
Adjutant, head of, 273, **276**; hair from neck of, **276**
Æpyornis, com. size of egg of, 461
Aftershaft, 36
Aggressive coloration, use of, 308; in Arctic fox, 309; in Cuckoo, 311; in Gyrfalcon, 309, **312**; in Ivory Gull, 309, **311**; in Penguin, 309, **310**; in pickerel, **310**; in Snowy Owl, 309, **313**
Air-sacs, cf. with respiratory system of insects, 173: extent of, 173; function of, 174, 177; in Prairie Hen, 177
Albatross, wing of, 320, 321, **325**, 332
Albinism, 314
Alligator, egg of, **429**; foot of, **354**; nictitating membrane of, 215; relation to birds, 9; skull of, **105**
Altricial nestling, **30**
Amœba, 185, **186** 463
Amphioxus, 66; gill-clefts in, 473; notochord of, 66; segments of, 78; trachea of, 169; breathing motions in, 180
Anaximander, 12
Ancestors of birds, 1-18
Aorta, 476
Apoplexy in birds, 202
Apteryx, ody-feathers of, 289; eyes in, 254, **255**, 256; sense of touch in, 219
Archæopteryx, as parallel branch, 10; as ancestral type, 10; foot of, 353; general description of, 7; in Berlin Museum, **11**; in British Museum, 8; probable habits of, 12-13; restoration of, **14**; tail of, 398, **399**, **400**, **401**
Aristotle, cf. with Darwin, 12

Artery, 182
Arteries, course of vertebral, 79
Atlas of Jabiru, **72**
Auk, wing of Great, 339, **340**; wing of razor-billed, 339, **340**
Avocet, bill of, 237, **239**
Axis of Jabiru, **72**

B

Back-bone, of Amphioxus, 66; evolution of, 64-70; of shark, 68
Barbs, of Condor's feather, **32**
Barbicels, 32, 34
Barbules, 32, 34
Bats, keel of, 83-84; used as food, 158
Beak, see Bill
Beaks and Bills, 223-251
Bear, feet of, **102**
Bellbird, wattles of, 273
Bill,
  function of, 223, 224, 250, 251
  of Avocet, 237, **239**; Archæopteryx, 226; Cormorant, **227**, 228; Crossbill 24, **249**, 245; Crow, 226; Shoveller Duck, **233**, 235; Purple Finch, **249**; Golden Eagle, **242**; Flamingo, **128**, 234, **235**, 236; Gannet, **227**, 228; Boat-billed Heron, 237, **238**; Great Blue Heron, **237**; Night Heron, 237; Huiabird, 248, **249**, **250**; Hummingbirds, 244, 245, **246**, **247**, **248**; Ibis, 237, **239**; Shell Ibis, 240; Merganser, **233**, 234; Nuthatch, 245; Owls, 242; Oyster-catcher, 238, **240**; Parrots, 242; Pelican, 228, **229**, **230**; Crook-billed Plover, 240, 241; American Raven, **225**; Black Skimmer, **231**, **232**, 236; Snakebird, 228, **229**; Dowitcher Snipe, 241; Spoonbill, 220, 236, **239**; Stilt, 237; Chimney Swift, 244, **246**, 245; Tailor-bird, 245; Tern, **231**, **232**; Toucans, **243**, 244; Triceratops,

CATALOGUE OF DOVER BOOKS

Books Explaining Science and Mathematics

WHAT IS SCIENCE?, N. Campbell. The role of experiment and measurement, the function of mathematics, the nature of scientific laws, the difference between laws and theories, the limitations of science, and many similarly provocative topics are treated clearly and without technicalities by an eminent scientist. "Still an excellent introduction to scientific philosophy," H. Margenau in PHYSICS TODAY. "A first-rate primer . . . deserves a wide audience," SCIENTIFIC AMERICAN. 192pp. 5⅜ x 8.   S43 Paperbound **$1.25**

THE NATURE OF PHYSICAL THEORY, P. W. Bridgman. A Nobel Laureate's clear, non-technical lectures on difficulties and paradoxes connected with frontier research on the physical sciences. Concerned with such central concepts as thought, logic, mathematics, relativity, probability, wave mechanics, etc. he analyzes the contributions of such men as Newton, Einstein, Bohr, Heisenberg, and many others. "Lucid and entertaining . . . recommended to anyone who wants to get some insight into current philosophies of science," THE NEW PHILOSOPHY. Index. xi + 138pp. 5⅜ x 8.   S33 Paperbound **$1.25**

EXPERIMENT AND THEORY IN PHYSICS, Max Born. A Nobel Laureate examines the nature of experiment and theory in theoretical physics and analyzes the advances made by the great physicists of our day: Heisenberg, Einstein, Bohr, Planck, Dirac, and others. The actual process of creation is detailed step-by-step by one who participated. A fine examination of the scientific method at work. 44pp. 5⅜ x 8.   S308 Paperbound **75¢**

THE PSYCHOLOGY OF INVENTION IN THE MATHEMATICAL FIELD, J. Hadamard. The reports of such men as Descartes, Pascal, Einstein, Poincaré, and others are considered in this investigation of the method of idea-creation in mathematics and other sciences and the thinking process in general. How do ideas originate? What is the role of the unconscious? What is Poincaré's forgetting hypothesis? are some of the fascinating questions treated. A penetrating analysis of Einstein's thought processes concludes the book. xiii + 145pp. 5⅜ x 8.   T107 Paperbound **$1.25**

THE NATURE OF LIGHT AND COLOUR IN THE OPEN AIR, M. Minnaert. Why are shadows sometimes blue, sometimes green, or other colors depending on the light and surroundings? What causes mirages? Why do multiple suns and moons appear in the sky? Professor Minnaert explains these unusual phenomena and hundreds of others in simple, easy-to-understand terms based on optical laws and the properties of light and color. No mathematics is required but artists, scientists, students, and everyone fascinated by these "tricks" of nature will find thousands of useful and amazing pieces of information. Hundreds of observational experiments are suggested which require no special equipment. 200 illustrations; 42 photos. xvi + 362pp. 5⅜ x 8.   T196 Paperbound **$2.00**

THE UNIVERSE OF LIGHT, W. Bragg. Sir William Bragg, Nobel Laureate and great modern physicist, is also well known for his powers of clear exposition. Here he analyzes all aspects of light for the layman: lenses, reflection, refraction, the optics of vision, x-rays, the photoelectric effect, etc. He tells you what causes the color of spectra, rainbows, and soap bubbles, how magic mirrors work, and much more. Dozens of simple experiments are described. Preface. Index. 199 line drawings and photographs, including 2 full-page color plates. x + 283pp. 5⅜ x 8.   T538 Paperbound **$1.85**

SOAP-BUBBLES: THEIR COLOURS AND THE FORCES THAT MOULD THEM, C. V. Boys. For continuing popularity and validity as scientific primer, few books can match this volume of easily-followed experiments, explanations. Lucid exposition of complexities of liquid films, surface tension and related phenomena, bubbles' reaction to heat, motion, music, magnetic fields. Experiments with capillary attraction, soap bubbles on frames, composite bubbles, liquid cylinders and jets, bubbles other than soap, etc. Wonderful introduction to scientific method, natural laws that have many ramifications in areas of modern physics. Only complete edition in print. New Introduction by S. Z. Lewin, New York University. 83 illustrations; 1 full-page color plate. xii + 190pp. 5⅜ x 8½.   T542 Paperbound **95¢**

CATALOGUE OF DOVER BOOKS

THE STORY OF X-RAYS FROM RONTGEN TO ISOTOPES, A. R. Bleich, M.D. This book, by a member of the American College of Radiology, gives the scientific explanation of x-rays, their applications in medicine, industry and art, and their danger (and that of atmospheric radiation) to the individual and the species. You learn how radiation therapy is applied against cancer, how x-rays diagnose heart disease and other ailments, how they are used to examine mummies for information on diseases of early societies, and industrial materials for hidden weaknesses. 54 illustrations show x-rays of flowers, bones, stomach, gears with flaws, etc. 1st publication. Index. xix + 186pp. 5⅜ x 8.   **T622 Paperbound $1.35**

SPINNING TOPS AND GYROSCOPIC MOTION, John Perry. A classic elementary text of the dynamics of rotation — the behavior and use of rotating bodies such as gyroscopes and tops. In simple, everyday English you are shown how quasi-rigidity is induced in discs of paper, smoke rings, chains, etc., by rapid motions; why a gyrostat falls and why a top rises; precession; how the earth's motion affects climate; and many other phenomena. Appendix on practical use of gyroscopes. 62 figures. 128pp. 5⅜ x 8.   **T416 Paperbound $1.00**

SNOW CRYSTALS, W. A. Bentley, M. J. Humphreys. For almost 50 years W. A. Bentley photographed snow flakes in his laboratory in Jericho, Vermont; in 1931 the American Meteorological Society gathered together the best of his work, some 2400 photographs of snow flakes, plus a few ice flowers, windowpane frosts, dew, frozen rain, and other ice formations. Pictures were selected for beauty and scientific value. A very valuable work to anyone in meteorology, cryology; most interesting to layman; extremely useful for artist who wants beautiful, crystalline designs. All copyright free. Unabridged reprint of 1931 edition. 2453 illustrations. 227pp. 8 x 10½.   **T287 Paperbound $3.00**

A DOVER SCIENCE SAMPLER, edited by George Barkin. A collection of brief, non-technical passages from 44 Dover Books Explaining Science for the enjoyment of the science-minded browser. Includes work of Bertrand Russell, Poincaré, Laplace, Max Born, Galileo, Newton; material on physics, mathematics, metallurgy, anatomy, astronomy, chemistry, etc. You will be fascinated by Martin Gardner's analysis of the sincere pseudo-scientist, Moritz's account of Newton's absentmindedness, Bernard's examples of human vivisection, etc. Illustrations from the Diderot Pictorial Encyclopedia and De Re Metallica. 64 pages.   **FREE**

THE STORY OF ATOMIC THEORY AND ATOMIC ENERGY, J. G. Feinberg. A broader approach to subject of nuclear energy and its cultural implications than any other similar source. Very readable, informal, completely non-technical text. Begins with first atomic theory, 600 B.C. and carries you through the work of Mendelejeff, Röntgen, Madame Curie, to Einstein's equation and the A-bomb. New chapter goes through thermonuclear fission, binding energy, other events up to 1959. Radioactive decay and radiation hazards, future benefits, work of Bohr, moderns, hundreds more topics. "Deserves special mention . . . not only authoritative but thoroughly popular in the best sense of the word," Saturday Review. Formerly, "The Atom Story." Expanded with new chapter. Three appendixes. Index. 34 illustrations. vii + 243pp. 5⅜ x 8.   **T625 Paperbound $1.60**

THE STRANGE STORY OF THE QUANTUM, AN ACCOUNT FOR THE GENERAL READER OF THE GROWTH OF IDEAS UNDERLYING OUR PRESENT ATOMIC KNOWLEDGE, B. Hoffmann. Presents lucidly and expertly, with barest amount of mathematics, the problems and theories which led to modern quantum physics. Dr. Hoffmann begins with the closing years of the 19th century, when certain trifling discrepancies were noticed, and with illuminating analogies and examples takes you through the brilliant concepts of Planck, Einstein, Pauli, Broglie, Bohr, Schroedinger, Heisenberg, Dirac, Sommerfeld, Feynman, etc. This edition includes a new, long postscript carrying the story through 1958. "Of the books attempting an account of the history and contents of our modern atomic physics which have come to my attention, this is the best," H. Margenau, Yale University, in "American Journal of Physics." 32 tables and line illustrations. Index. 275pp. 5⅜ x 8.   **T518 Paperbound $1.50**

SPACE AND TIME, E. Borel. Written by a versatile mathematician of world renown with his customary lucidity and precision, this introduction to relativity for the layman presents scores of examples, analogies, and illustrations that open up new ways of thinking about space and time. It covers abstract geometry and geographical maps, continuity and topology, the propagation of light, the special theory of relativity, the general theory of relativity, theoretical researches, and much more. Mathematical notes. 2 Indexes. 4 Appendices. 15 figures. xvi + 243pp. 5⅜ x 8.   **T592 Paperbound $1.45**

FROM EUCLID TO EDDINGTON: A STUDY OF THE CONCEPTIONS OF THE EXTERNAL WORLD, Sir Edmund Whittaker. A foremost British scientist traces the development of theories of natural philosophy from the western rediscovery of Euclid to Eddington, Einstein, Dirac, etc. The inadequacy of classical physics is contrasted with present day attempts to understand the physical world through relativity, non-Euclidean geometry, space curvature, wave mechanics, etc. 5 major divisions of examination: Space; Time and Movement; the Concepts of Classical Physics; the Concepts of Quantum Mechanics; the Eddington Universe. 212pp. 5⅜ x 8.   **T491 Paperbound $1.35**

Nature, Biology

NATURE RECREATION: Group Guidance for the Out-of-doors, William Gould Vinal. Intended for both the uninitiated nature instructor and the education student on the college level, this complete "how-to" program surveys the entire area of nature education for the young. Philosophy of nature recreation; requirements, responsibilities, important information for group leaders; nature games; suggested group projects; conducting meetings and getting discussions started; etc. Scores of immediately applicable teaching aids, plus completely updated sources of information, pamphlets, field guides, recordings, etc. Bibliography. 74 photographs. + 310pp. 5⅜ x 8½. T1015 Paperbound **$1.75**

HOW TO KNOW THE WILD FLOWERS, Mrs. William Starr Dana. Classic nature book that has introduced thousands to wonders of American wild flowers. Color-season principle of organization is easy to use, even by those with no botanical training, and the genial, refreshing discussions of history, folklore, uses of over 1,000 native and escape flowers, foliage plants are informative as well as fun to read. Over 170 full-page plates, collected from several editions, may be colored in to make permanent records of finds. Revised to conform with 1950 edition of Gray's Manual of Botany. xlii + 438pp. 5⅜ x 8½. T332 Paperbound **$2.00**

HOW TO KNOW THE FERNS, F. T. Parsons. Ferns, among our most lovely native plants, are all too little known. This classic of nature lore will enable the layman to identify almost any American fern he may come across. After an introduction on the structure and life of ferns, the 57 most important ferns are fully pictured and described (arranged upon a simple identification key). Index of Latin and English names. 61 illustrations and 42 full-page plates. xiv + 215pp. 5⅜ x 8. T740 Paperbound **$1.35**

MANUAL OF THE TREES OF NORTH AMERICA, Charles Sprague Sargent. Still unsurpassed as most comprehensive, reliable study of North American tree characteristics, precise locations and distribution. By dean of American dendrologists. Every tree native to U.S., Canada, Alaska, 185 genera, 717 species, described in detail—leaves, flowers, fruit, winterbuds, bark, wood, growth habits etc. plus discussion of varieties and local variants, immaturity variations. Over 100 keys, including unusual 11-page analytical key to genera, aid in identification. 783 clear illustrations of flowers, fruit, leaves. An unmatched permanent reference work for all nature lovers. Second enlarged (1926) edition. Synopsis of families. Analytical key to genera. Glossary of technical terms. Index. 783 illustrations, 1 map. Two volumes. Total of 982pp. 5⅜ x 8. T277 Vol. I Paperbound **$2.25**
T278 Vol. II Paperbound **$2.25**
The set **$4.50**

TREES OF THE EASTERN AND CENTRAL UNITED STATES AND CANADA, W. M. Harlow. A revised edition of a standard middle-level guide to native trees and important escapes. More than 140 trees are described in detail, and illustrated with more than 600 drawings and photographs. Supplementary keys will enable the careful reader to identify almost any tree he might encounter. xiii + 288pp. 5⅜ x 8. T395 Paperbound **$1.35**

GUIDE TO SOUTHERN TREES, Ellwood S. Harrar and J. George Harrar. All the essential information about trees indigenous to the South, in an extremely handy format. Introductory essay on methods of tree classification and study, nomenclature, chief divisions of Southern trees, etc. Approximately 100 keys and synopses allow for swift, accurate identification of trees. Numerous excellent illustrations, non-technical text make this a useful book for teachers of biology or natural science, nature lovers, amateur naturalists. Revised 1962 edition. Index. Bibliography. Glossary of technical terms. 920 illustrations; 201 full-page plates. ix + 709pp. 4⅝ x 6⅜. T945 Paperbound **$2.35**

FRUIT KEY AND TWIG KEY TO TREES AND SHRUBS, W. M. Harlow. Bound together in one volume for the first time, these handy and accurate keys to fruit and twig identification are the only guides of their sort with photographs (up to 3 times natural size). "Fruit Key": Key to over 120 different deciduous and evergreen fruits. 139 photographs and 11 line drawings. Synoptic summary of fruit types. Bibliography. 2 Indexes (common and scientific names). "Twig Key": Key to over 160 different twigs and buds. 173 photographs. Glossary of technical terms. Bibliography. 2 Indexes (common and scientific names). Two volumes bound as one. Total of xvii + 126pp. 5⅝ x 8⅜. T511 Paperbound **$1.25**

INSECT LIFE AND INSECT NATURAL HISTORY, S. W. Frost. A work emphasizing habits, social life, and ecological relations of insects, rather than more academic aspects of classification and morphology. Prof. Frost's enthusiasm and knowledge are everywhere evident as he discusses insect associations and specialized habits like leaf-rolling, leaf-mining, and case-making, the gall insects, the boring insects, aquatic insects, etc. He examines all sorts of matters not usually covered in general works, such as: insects as human food, insect music and musicians, insect response to electric and radio waves, use of insects in art and literature. The admirably executed purpose of this book, which covers the middle ground between elementary treatment and scholarly monographs, is to excite the reader to observe for himself. Over 700 illustrations. Extensive bibliography. x + 524pp. 5⅜ x 8. T517 Paperbound **$2.45**

COMMON SPIDERS OF THE UNITED STATES, J. H. Emerton. Here is a nature hobby you can pursue right in your own cellar! Only non-technical, but thorough, reliable guide to spiders for the layman. Over 200 spiders from all parts of the country, arranged by scientific classification, are identified by shape and color, number of eyes, habitat and range, habits, etc. Full text, 501 line drawings and photographs, and valuable introduction explain webs, poisons, threads, capturing and preserving spiders, etc. Index. New synoptic key by S. W. Frost. xxiv + 225pp. 5⅜ x 8.   T223 Paperbound **$1.45**

THE LIFE STORY OF THE FISH: HIS MANNERS AND MORALS, Brian Curtis. A comprehensive, non-technical survey of just about everything worth knowing about fish. Written for the aquarist, the angler, and the layman with an inquisitive mind, the text covers such topics as evolution, external covering and protective coloration, physics and physiology of vision, maintenance of equilibrium, function of the lateral line canal for auditory and temperature senses, nervous system, function of the air bladder, reproductive system and methods—courtship, mating, spawning, care of young—and many more. Also sections on game fish, the problems of conservation and a fascinating chapter on fish curiosities. "Clear, simple language . . . excellent judgment in choice of subjects . . . delightful sense of humor," New York Times. Revised (1949) edition. Index. Bibliography of 72 items. 6 full-page photographic plates. xii + 284pp. 5⅜ x 8.   T929 Paperbound **$1.65**

BATS, Glover Morrill Allen. The most comprehensive study of bats as a life-form by the world's foremost authority. A thorough summary of just about everything known about this fascinating and mysterious flying mammal, including its unique location sense, hibernation and cycles, its habitats and distribution, its wing structure and flying habits, and its relationship to man in the long history of folklore and superstition. Written on a middle-level, the book can be profitably studied by a trained zoologist and thoroughly enjoyed by the layman. "An absorbing text with excellent illustrations. Bats should have more friends and fewer thoughtless detractors as a result of the publication of this volume," William Beebe, Books. Extensive bibliography. 57 photographs and illustrations. x + 368pp. 5⅜ x 8½.
T984 Paperbound **$2.00**

BIRDS AND THEIR ATTRIBUTES, Glover Morrill Allen. A fine general introduction to birds as living organisms, especially valuable because of emphasis on structure, physiology, habits, behavior. Discusses relationship of bird to man, early attempts at scientific ornithology, feathers and coloration, skeletal structure including bills, legs and feet, wings. Also food habits, evolution and present distribution, feeding and nest-building, still unsolved questions of migrations and location sense, many more similar topics. Final chapter on classification, nomenclature. A good popular-level summary for the biologist; a first-rate introduction for the layman. Reprint of 1925 edition. References and index. 51 illustrations. viii + 338pp. 5⅜ x 8½.   T957 Paperbound **$1.85**

LIFE HISTORIES OF NORTH AMERICAN BIRDS, Arthur Cleveland Bent. Bent's monumental series of books on North American birds, prepared and published under auspices of Smithsonian Institute, is the definitive coverage of the subject, the most-used single source of information. Now the entire set is to be made available by Dover in inexpensive editions. This encyclopedic collection of detailed, specific observations utilizes reports of hundreds of contemporary observers, writings of such naturalists as Audubon, Burroughs, William Brewster, as well as author's own extensive investigations. Contains literally everything known about life history of each bird considered: nesting, eggs, plumage, distribution and migration, voice, enemies, courtship, etc. These not over-technical works are musts for ornithologists, conservationists, amateur naturalists, anyone seriously interested in American birds.

BIRDS OF PREY. More than 100 subspecies of hawks, falcons, eagles, buzzards, condors and owls, from the common barn owl to the extinct caracara of Guadaloupe Island. 400 photographs. Two volume set. Index for each volume. Bibliographies of 403, 520 items. 197 full-page plates. Total of 907pp. 5⅜ x 8½.   Vol. I   T931 Paperbound **$2.50**
                                                                Vol. II T932 Paperbound **$2.50**

WILD FOWL. Ducks, geese, swans, and tree ducks—73 different subspecies. Two volume set. Index for each volume. Bibliographies of 124, 144 items. 106 full-page plates. Total of 685pp. 5⅜ x 8½.   Vol. I   T285 Paperbound **$2.50**
                                                                Vol. II T286 Paperbound **$2.50**

SHORE BIRDS. 81 varieties (sandpipers, woodcocks, plovers, snipes, phalaropes, curlews, oyster catchers, etc.). More than 200 photographs of eggs, nesting sites, adult and young of important species. Two volume set. Index for each volume. Bibliographies of 261, 188 items. 121 full-page plates. Total of 860pp. 5⅜ x 8½.   Vol. I   T933 Paperbound **$2.35**
                                                                Vol. II T934 Paperbound **$2.35**

THE LIFE OF PASTEUR, R. Vallery-Radot. 13th edition of this definitive biography, cited in Encyclopaedia Britannica. Authoritative, scholarly, well-documented with contemporary quotes, observations; gives complete picture of Pasteur's personal life; especially thorough presentation of scientific activities with silkworms, fermentation, hydrophobia, inoculation, etc. Introduction by Sir William Osler. Index. 505pp. 5⅜ x 8.   T632 Paperbound **$2.00**

Puzzles, Mathematical Recreations

SYMBOLIC LOGIC and THE GAME OF LOGIC, Lewis Carroll. "Symbolic Logic" is not concerned with modern symbolic logic, but is instead a collection of over 380 problems posed with charm and imagination, using the syllogism, and a fascinating diagrammatic method of drawing conclusions. In "The Game of Logic" Carroll's whimsical imagination devises a logical game played with 2 diagrams and counters (included) to manipulate hundreds of tricky syllogisms. The final section, "Hit or Miss" is a lagniappe of 101 additional puzzles in the delightful Carroll manner. Until this reprint edition, both of these books were rarities costing up to $15 each. Symbolic Logic: Index. xxxi + 199pp. The Game of Logic: 96pp. 2 vols. bound as one. 5⅜ x 8.   T492 Paperbound **$1.50**

PILLOW PROBLEMS and A TANGLED TALE, Lewis Carroll. One of the rarest of all Carroll's works, "Pillow Problems" contains 72 original math puzzles, all typically ingenious. Particularly fascinating are Carroll's answers which remain exactly as he thought them out, reflecting his actual mental process. The problems in "A Tangled Tale" are in story form, originally appearing as a monthly magazine serial. Carroll not only gives the solutions, but uses answers sent in by readers to discuss wrong approaches and misleading paths, and grades them for insight. Both of these books were rarities until this edition, "Pillow Problems" costing up to $25, and "A Tangled Tale" $15. Pillow Problems: Preface and Introduction by Lewis Carroll. xx + 109pp. A Tangled Tale: 6 illustrations. 152pp. Two vols. bound as one. 5⅜ x 8.   T493 Paperbound **$1.50**

AMUSEMENTS IN MATHEMATICS, Henry Ernest Dudeney. The foremost British originator of mathematical puzzles is always intriguing, witty, and paradoxical in this classic, one of the largest collections of mathematical amusements. More than 430 puzzles, problems, and paradoxes. Mazes and games, problems on number manipulation, unicursal and other route problems, puzzles on measuring, weighing, packing, age, kinship, chessboards, joiners', crossing river, plane figure dissection, and many others. Solutions. More than 450 illustrations. vii + 258pp. 5⅜ x 8.   T473 Paperbound **$1.25**

THE CANTERBURY PUZZLES, Henry Dudeney. Chaucer's pilgrims set one another problems in story form. Also Adventures of the Puzzle Club, the Strange Escape of the King's Jester, the Monks of Riddlewell, the Squire's Christmas Puzzle Party, and others. All puzzles are original, based on dissecting plane figures, arithmetic, algebra, elementary calculus and other branches of mathematics, and purely logical ingenuity. "The limit of ingenuity and intricacy," The Observer. Over 110 puzzles. Full Solutions. 150 illustrations. vii + 225pp. 5⅜ x 8.
T474 Paperbound **$1.25**

MATHEMATICAL EXCURSIONS, H. A. Merrill. Even if you hardly remember your high school math, you'll enjoy the 90 stimulating problems contained in this book and you will come to understand a great many mathematical principles with surprisingly little effort. Many useful shortcuts and diversions not generally known are included: division by inspection, Russian peasant multiplication, memory systems for pi, building odd and even magic squares, square roots by geometry, dyadic systems, and many more. Solutions to difficult problems. 50 illustrations. 145pp. 5⅜ x 8.   T350 Paperbound **$1.00**

MAGIC SQUARES AND CUBES, W. S. Andrews. Only book-length treatment in English, a thorough non-technical description and analysis. Here are nasik, overlapping, pandiagonal, serrated squares; magic circles, cubes, spheres, rhombuses. Try your hand at 4-dimensional magical figures! Much unusual folklore and tradition included. High school algebra is sufficient. 754 diagrams and illustrations. viii + 419pp. 5⅜ x 8.   T658 Paperbound **$1.85**

CALIBAN'S PROBLEM BOOK: MATHEMATICAL, INFERENTIAL AND CRYPTOGRAPHIC PUZZLES, H. Phillips (Caliban), S. T. Shovelton, G. S. Marshall. 105 ingenious problems by the greatest living creator of puzzles based on logic and inference. Rigorous, modern, piquant; reflecting their author's unusual personality, these intermediate and advanced puzzles all involve the ability to reason clearly through complex situations; some call for mathematical knowledge, ranging from algebra to number theory. Solutions. xi + 180pp. 5⅜ x 8.
T736 Paperbound **$1.25**

MATHEMATICAL PUZZLES FOR BEGINNERS AND ENTHUSIASTS, G. Mott-Smith. 188 mathematical puzzles based on algebra, dissection of plane figures, permutations, and probability, that will test and improve your powers of inference and interpretation. The Odic Force, The Spider's Cousin, Ellipse Drawing, theory and strategy of card and board games like tit-tat-toe, go moku, salvo, and many others. 100 pages of detailed mathematical explanations. Appendix of primes, square roots, etc. 135 illustrations. 2nd revised edition. 248pp. 5⅜ x 8.
T198 Paperbound **$1.00**

MATHEMAGIC, MAGIC PUZZLES, AND GAMES WITH NUMBERS, R. V. Heath. More than 60 new puzzles and stunts based on the properties of numbers. Easy techniques for multiplying large numbers mentally, revealing hidden numbers magically, finding the date of any day in any year, and dozens more. Over 30 pages devoted to magic squares, triangles, cubes, circles, etc. Edited by J. S. Meyer. 76 illustrations. 128pp. 5⅜ x 8.   T110 Paperbound **$1.00**

CATALOGUE OF DOVER BOOKS

THE BOOK OF MODERN PUZZLES, G. L. Kaufman. A completely new series of puzzles as fascinating as crossword and deduction puzzles but based upon different principles and techniques. Simple 2-minute teasers, word labyrinths, design and pattern puzzles, logic and observation puzzles — over 150 braincrackers. Answers to all problems. 116 illustrations. 192pp. 5⅜ x 8.
T143 Paperbound **$1.00**

NEW WORD PUZZLES, G. L. Kaufman. 100 ENTIRELY NEW puzzles based on words and their combinations that will delight crossword puzzle, Scrabble and Jotto fans. Chess words, based on the moves of the chess king; design-onyms, symmetrical designs made of synonyms; rhymed double-crostics; syllable sentences; addle letter anagrams; alphagrams; linkograms; and many others all brand new. Full solutions. Space to work problems. 196 figures. vi + 122pp. 5⅜ x 8.
T344 Paperbound **$1.00**

MAZES AND LABYRINTHS: A BOOK OF PUZZLES, W. Shepherd. Mazes, formerly associated with mystery and ritual, are still among the most intriguing of intellectual puzzles. This is a novel and different collection of 50 amusements that embody the principle of the maze: mazes in the classical tradition; 3-dimensional, ribbon, and Möbius-strip mazes; hidden messages; spatial arrangements; etc.—almost all built on amusing story situations. 84 illustrations. Essay on maze psychology. Solutions. xv + 122pp. 5⅜ x 8.
T731 Paperbound **$1.00**

MAGIC TRICKS & CARD TRICKS, W. Jonson. Two books bound as one. 52 tricks with cards, 37 tricks with coins, bills, eggs, smoke, ribbons, slates, etc. Details on presentation, misdirection, and routining will help you master such famous tricks as the Changing Card, Card in the Pocket, Four Aces, Coin Through the Hand, Bill in the Egg, Afghan Bands, and over 75 others. If you follow the lucid exposition and key diagrams carefully, you will finish these two books with an astonishing mastery of magic. 106 figures. 224pp. 5⅜ x 8. T909 Paperbound **$1.00**

PANORAMA OF MAGIC, Milbourne Christopher. A profusely illustrated history of stage magic, a unique selection of prints and engravings from the author's private collection of magic memorabilia, the largest of its kind. Apparatus, stage settings and costumes; ingenious ads distributed by the performers and satiric broadsides passed around in the streets ridiculing pompous showmen; programs; decorative souvenirs. The lively text, by one of America's foremost professional magicians, is full of anecdotes about almost legendary wizards: Dede, the Egyptian; Philadelphia, the wonder-worker; Robert-Houdin, "the father of modern magic;" Harry Houdini; scores more. Altogether a pleasure package for anyone interested in magic, stage setting and design, ethnology, psychology, or simply in unusual people. A Dover original. 295 illustrations; 8 in full color. Index. viii + 216pp. 8⅜ x 11¼.
T774 Paperbound **$2.25**

HOUDINI ON MAGIC, Harry Houdini. One of the greatest magicians of modern times explains his most prized secrets. How locks are picked, with illustrated picks and skeleton keys; how a girl is sawed into twins; how to walk through a brick wall — Houdini's explanations of 44 stage tricks with many diagrams. Also included is a fascinating discussion of great magicians of the past and the story of his fight against fraudulent mediums and spiritualists. Edited by W.B. Gibson and M.N. Young. Bibliography. 155 figures, photos. xv + 280pp. 5⅜ x 8.
T384 Paperbound **$1.35**

MATHEMATICS, MAGIC AND MYSTERY, Martin Gardner. Why do card tricks work? How do magicians perform astonishing mathematical feats? How is stage mind-reading possible? This is the first book length study explaining the application of probability, set theory, theory of numbers, topology, etc., to achieve many startling tricks. Non-technical, accurate, detailed! 115 sections discuss tricks with cards, dice, coins, knots, geometrical vanishing illusions, how a Curry square "demonstrates" that the sum of the parts may be greater than the whole, and dozens of others. No sleight of hand necessary! 135 illustrations. xii + 174pp. 5⅜ x 8.
T335 Paperbound **$1.00**

EASY-TO-DO ENTERTAINMENTS AND DIVERSIONS WITH COINS, CARDS, STRING, PAPER AND MATCHES, R. M. Abraham. Over 300 tricks, games and puzzles will provide young readers with absorbing fun. Sections on card games; paper-folding; tricks with coins, matches and pieces of string; games for the agile; toy-making from common household objects; mathematical recreations; and 50 miscellaneous pastimes. Anyone in charge of groups of youngsters, including hard-pressed parents, and in need of suggestions on how to keep children sensibly amused and quietly content will find this book indispensable. Clear, simple text, copious number of delightful line drawings and illustrative diagrams. Originally titled "Winter Nights Entertainments." Introduction by Lord Baden Powell. 329 illustrations. v + 186pp. 5⅜ x 8½.
T921 Paperbound **$1.00**

STRING FIGURES AND HOW TO MAKE THEM, Caroline Furness Jayne. 107 string figures plus variations selected from the best primitive and modern examples developed by Navajo, Apache, pygmies of Africa, Eskimo, in Europe, Australia, China, etc. The most readily understandable, easy-to-follow book in English on perennially popular recreation. Crystal-clear exposition; step-by-step diagrams. Everyone from kindergarten children to adults looking for unusual diversion will be endlessly amused. Index. Bibliography. Introduction by A. C. Haddon. 17 full-page plates. 960 illustrations. xxiii + 401pp. 5⅜ x 8½.
T152 Paperbound **$2.00**

Entertainments, Humor

ODDITIES AND CURIOSITIES OF WORDS AND LITERATURE, C. Bombaugh, edited by M. Gardner. The largest collection of idiosyncratic prose and poetry techniques in English, a legendary work in the curious and amusing bypaths of literary recreations and the play technique in literature—so important in modern works. Contains alphabetic poetry, acrostics, palindromes, scissors verse, centos, emblematic poetry, famous literary puns, hoaxes, notorious slips of the press, hilarious mistranslations, and much more. Revised and enlarged with modern material by Martin Gardner. 368pp. 5⅜ x 8. T759 Paperbound **$1.50**

A NONSENSE ANTHOLOGY, collected by Carolyn Wells. 245 of the best nonsense verses ever written, including nonsense puns, absurd arguments, mock epics and sagas, nonsense ballads, odes, "sick" verses, dog-Latin verses, French nonsense verses, songs. By Edward Lear, Lewis Carroll, Gelett Burgess, W. S. Gilbert, Hilaire Belloc, Peter Newell, Oliver Herford, etc., 83 writers in all plus over four score anonymous nonsense verses. A special section of limericks, plus famous nonsense such as Carroll's "Jabberwocky" and Lear's "The Jumblies" and much excellent verse virtually impossible to locate elsewhere. For 50 years considered the best anthology available. Index of first lines specially prepared for this edition. Introduction by Carolyn Wells. 3 indexes: Title, Author, First lines. xxxiii + 279pp. T499 Paperbound **$1.35**

THE BAD CHILD'S BOOK OF BEASTS, MORE BEASTS FOR WORSE CHILDREN, and A MORAL ALPHABET, H. Belloc. Hardly an anthology of humorous verse has appeared in the last 50 years without at least a couple of these famous nonsense verses. But one must see the entire volumes—with all the delightful original illustrations by Sir Basil Blackwood—to appreciate fully Belloc's charming and witty verses that play so subacidly on the platitudes of life and morals that beset his day—and ours. A great humor classic. Three books in one. Total of 157pp. 5⅜ x 8. T749 Paperbound **$1.00**

THE DEVIL'S DICTIONARY, Ambrose Bierce. Sardonic and irreverent barbs puncturing the pomposities and absurdities of American politics, business, religion, literature, and arts, by the country's greatest satirist in the classic tradition. Epigrammatic as Shaw, piercing as Swift, American as Mark Twain, Will Rogers, and Fred Allen, Bierce will always remain the favorite of a small coterie of enthusiasts, and of writers and speakers whom he supplies with "some of the most gorgeous witticisms of the English language" (H. L. Mencken). Over 1000 entries in alphabetical order. 144pp. 5⅜ x 8. T487 Paperbound **$1.00**

THE PURPLE COW AND OTHER NONSENSE, Gelett Burgess. The best of Burgess's early nonsense, selected from the first edition of the "Burgess Nonsense Book." Contains many of his most unusual and truly awe-inspiring pieces: 36 nonsense quatrains, the Poems of Patagonia, Alphabet of Famous Goops, and the other hilarious (and rare) adult nonsense that place him in the forefront of American humorists. All pieces are accompanied by the original Burgess illustrations. 123 illustrations. xiii + 113pp. 5⅜ x 8. T772 Paperbound **$1.00**

MY PIOUS FRIENDS AND DRUNKEN COMPANIONS and MORE PIOUS FRIENDS AND DRUNKEN COMPANIONS, Frank Shay. Folksingers, amateur and professional, and everyone who loves singing: here, available for the first time in 30 years, is this valued collection of 132 ballads, blues, vaudeville numbers, drinking songs, sea chanties, comedy songs. Songs of pre-Beatnik Bohemia; songs from all over America, England, France, Australia; the great songs of the Naughty Nineties and early twentieth-century America. Over a third with music. Woodcuts by John Held, Jr. convey perfectly the brash insouciance of an era of rollicking unabashed song. 12 illustrations by John Held, Jr. Two indexes (Titles and First lines and Choruses). Introductions by the author. Two volumes bound as one. Total of xvi + 235pp. 5⅜ x 8½. T946 Paperbound **$1.25**

HOW TO TELL THE BIRDS FROM THE FLOWERS, R. W. Wood. How not to confuse a carrot with a parrot, a grape with an ape, a puffin with nuffin. Delightful drawings, clever puns, absurd little poems point out far-fetched resemblances in nature. The author was a leading physicist. Introduction by Margaret Wood White. 106 illus. 60pp. 5⅜ x 8. T523 Paperbound **75¢**

PECK'S BAD BOY AND HIS PA, George W. Peck. The complete edition, containing both volumes, of one of the most widely read American humor books. The endless ingenious pranks played by bad boy "Hennery" on his pa and the grocery man, the outraged pomposity of Pa, the perpetual ridiculing of middle class institutions, are as entertaining today as they were in 1883. No pale sophistications or subtleties, but rather humor vigorous, raw, earthy, imaginative, and, as folk humor often is, sadistic. This peculiarly fascinating book is also valuable to historians and students of American culture as a portrait of an age. 100 original illustrations by True Williams. Introduction by E. F. Bleiler. 347pp. 5⅜ x 8. T497 Paperbound **$1.35**

CATALOGUE OF DOVER BOOKS

THE HUMOROUS VERSE OF LEWIS CARROLL. Almost every poem Carroll ever wrote, the largest collection ever published, including much never published elsewhere: 150 parodies, burlesques, riddles, ballads, acrostics, etc., with 130 original illustrations by Tenniel, Carroll, and others. "Addicts will be grateful . . . there is nothing for the faithful to do but sit down and fall to the banquet," N. Y. Times. Index to first lines. xiv + 446pp. 5⅜ x 8.
T654 Paperbound **$2.00**

DIVERSIONS AND DIGRESSIONS OF LEWIS CARROLL. A major new treasure for Carroll fans! Rare privately published humor, fantasy, puzzles, and games by Carroll at his whimsical best, with a new vein of frank satire. Includes many new mathematical amusements and recreations, among them the fragmentary Part III of "Curiosa Mathematica." Contains "The Rectory Umbrella," "The New Belfry," "The Vision of the Three T's," and much more. New 32-page supplement of rare photographs taken by Carroll. x + 375pp. 5⅜ x 8.
T732 Paperbound **$1.65**

THE COMPLETE NONSENSE OF EDWARD LEAR. This is the only complete edition of this master of gentle madness available at a popular price. A BOOK OF NONSENSE, NONSENSE SONGS, MORE NONSENSE SONGS AND STORIES in their entirety with all the old favorites that have delighted children and adults for years. The Dong With A Luminous Nose, The Jumblies, The Owl and the Pussycat, and hundreds of other bits of wonderful nonsense. 214 limericks, 3 sets of Nonsense Botany, 5 Nonsense Alphabets, 546 drawings by Lear himself, and much more. 320pp. 5⅜ x 8.
T167 Paperbound **$1.00**

THE MELANCHOLY LUTE, The Humorous Verse of Franklin P. Adams ("FPA"). The author's own selection of light verse, drawn from thirty years of FPA's column, "The Conning Tower," syndicated all over the English-speaking world. Witty, perceptive, literate, these ninety-six poems range from parodies of other poets, Millay, Longfellow, Edgar Guest, Kipling, Masefield, etc., and free and hilarious translations of Horace and other Latin poets, to satiric comments on fabled American institutions—the New York Subways, preposterous ads, suburbanites, sensational journalism, etc. They reveal with vigor and clarity the humor, integrity and restraint of a wise and gentle American satirist. Introduction by Robert Hutchinson. vi + 122pp. 5⅜ x 8½.
T108 Paperbound **$1.00**

SINGULAR TRAVELS, CAMPAIGNS, AND ADVENTURES OF BARON MUNCHAUSEN, R. E. Raspe, with 90 illustrations by Gustave Doré. The first edition in over 150 years to reestablish the deeds of the Prince of Liars exactly as Raspe first recorded them in 1785—the genuine Baron Munchausen, one of the most popular personalities in English literature. Included also are the best of the many sequels, written by other hands. Introduction on Raspe by J. Carswell. Bibliography of early editions. xliv + 192pp. 5⅜ x 8.
T698 Paperbound **$1.00**

THE WIT AND HUMOR OF OSCAR WILDE, ed. by Alvin Redman. Wilde at his most brilliant, in 1000 epigrams exposing weaknesses and hypocrisies of "civilized" society. Divided into 49 categories—sin, wealth, women, America, etc.—to aid writers, speakers. Includes excerpts from his trials, books, plays, criticism. Formerly "The Epigrams of Oscar Wilde." Introduction by Vyvyan Holland, Wilde's only living son. Introductory essay by editor. 260pp. 5⅜ x 8.
T602 Paperbound **$1.00**

MAX AND MORITZ, Wilhelm Busch. Busch is one of the great humorists of all time, as well as the father of the modern comic strip. This volume, translated by H. A. Klein and other hands, contains the perennial favorite "Max and Moritz" (translated by C. T. Brooks), Plisch and Plum, Das Rabennest, Eispeter, and seven other whimsical, sardonic, jovial, diabolical cartoon and verse stories. Lively English translations parallel the original German. This work has delighted millions, since it first appeared in the 19th century, and is guaranteed to please almost anyone. Edited by H. A. Klein, with an afterword. x + 205pp. 5⅝ x 8½.
T181 Paperbound **$1.15**

HYPOCRITICAL HELENA, Wilhelm Busch. A companion volume to "Max and Moritz," with the title piece (Die Fromme Helena) and 10 other highly amusing cartoon and verse stories, all newly translated by H. A. Klein and M. C. Klein: Adventure on New Year's Eve (Abenteuer in der Neujahrsnacht), Hangover on the Morning after New Year's Eve (Der Katzenjammer am Neujahrsmorgen), etc. English and German in parallel columns. Hours of pleasure, also a fine language aid. x + 205pp. 5⅝ x 8½.
T184 Paperbound **$1.00**

THE BEAR THAT WASN'T, Frank Tashlin. What does it mean? Is it simply delightful wry humor, or a charming story of a bear who wakes up in the midst of a factory, or a satire on Big Business, or an existential cartoon-story of the human condition, or a symbolization of the struggle between conformity and the individual? New York Herald Tribune said of the first edition: ". . . a fable for grownups that will be fun for children. Sit down with the book and get your own bearings." Long an underground favorite with readers of all ages and opinions. v + 51pp. Illustrated. 5⅜ x 8½.
T939 Paperbound **75¢**

RUTHLESS RHYMES FOR HEARTLESS HOMES and MORE RUTHLESS RHYMES FOR HEARTLESS HOMES, Harry Graham ("Col. D. Streamer"). Two volumes of Little Willy and 48 other poetic disasters. A bright, new reprint of oft-quoted, never forgotten, devastating humor by a precursor of today's "sick" joke school. For connoisseurs of wicked, wacky humor and all who delight in the comedy of manners. Original drawings are a perfect complement. 61 illustrations. Index. vi + 69pp. Two vols. bound as one. 5⅜ x 8½.
T930 Paperbound **75¢**

Say It language phrase books

These handy phrase books (128 to 196 pages each) make grammatical drills unnecessary for an elementary knowledge of a spoken foreign language. Covering most matters of travel and everyday life each volume contains:

> Over 1000 phrases and sentences in immediately useful forms — foreign language plus English.
>
> Modern usage designed for Americans. Specific phrases like, "Give me small change," and "Please call a taxi."
>
> Simplified phonetic transcription you will be able to read at sight.
>
> The only completely indexed phrase books on the market.
>
> Covers scores of important situations: — Greetings, restaurants, sightseeing, useful expressions, etc.

These books are prepared by native linguists who are professors at Columbia, N.Y.U., Fordham and other great universities. Use them independently or with any other book or record course. They provide a supplementary living element that most other courses lack. Individual volumes in:

Russian 75¢	Italian 75¢	Spanish 75¢	German 75¢
Hebrew 75¢	Danish 75¢	Japanese 75¢	Swedish 75¢
Dutch 75¢	Esperanto 75¢	Modern Greek 75¢	Portuguese 75¢
Norwegian 75¢	Polish 75¢	French 75¢	Yiddish 75¢
Turkish 75¢		English for German-speaking people 75¢	
English for Italian-speaking people 75¢		English for Spanish-speaking people 75¢	

Large clear type. 128-196 pages each. 3½ x 5¼. Sturdy paper binding.

Listen and Learn language records

LISTEN & LEARN is the only language record course designed especially to meet your travel and everyday needs. It is available in separate sets for FRENCH, SPANISH, GERMAN, JAPANESE, RUSSIAN, MODERN GREEK, PORTUGUESE, ITALIAN and HEBREW, and each set contains three 33⅓ rpm long-playing records—1½ hours of recorded speech by eminent native speakers who are professors at Columbia, New York University, Queens College.

Check the following special features found only in LISTEN & LEARN:

- **Dual-language recording.** 812 selected phrases and sentences, over 3200 words, spoken first in English, then in their foreign language equivalents. A suitable pause follows each foreign phrase, allowing you time to repeat the expression. You learn by unconscious assimilation.
- **128 to 206-page manual** contains everything on the records, plus a simple phonetic pronunciation guide.
- **Indexed for convenience. The only set on the market** that is completely indexed. No more puzzling over where to find the phrase you need. Just look in the rear of the manual.
- **Practical.** No time wasted on material you can find in any grammar. LISTEN & LEARN covers central core material with phrase approach. Ideal for the person with limited learning time.
- **Living, modern expressions,** not found in other courses. Hygienic products, modern equipment, shopping—expressions used every day, like "nylon" and "air-conditioned."
- **Limited objective.** Everything you learn, no matter where you stop, is immediately useful. You have to finish other courses, wade through grammar and vocabulary drill, before they help you.
- **High-fidelity recording.** LISTEN & LEARN records equal in clarity and surface-silence any record on the market costing up to $6.

"Excellent . . . the spoken records . . . impress me as being among the very best on the market," **Prof. Mario Pei,** Dept. of Romance Languages, Columbia University. "Inexpensive and well-done . . . it would make an ideal present," CHICAGO SUNDAY TRIBUNE. "More genuinely helpful than anything of its kind which I have previously encountered," **Sidney Clark,** well-known author of "ALL THE BEST" travel books.

UNCONDITIONAL GUARANTEE. Try LISTEN & LEARN, then return it within 10 days for full refund if you are not satisfied.

Each set contains three twelve-inch 33⅓ records, manual, and album.

SPANISH	the set $5.95	GERMAN	the set $5.95
FRENCH	the set $5.95	ITALIAN	the set $5.95
RUSSIAN	the set $5.95	JAPANESE	the set $5.95
PORTUGUESE	the set $5.95	MODERN GREEK	the set $5.95
MODERN HEBREW	the set $5.95		

Americana

THE EYES OF DISCOVERY, J. Bakeless. A vivid reconstruction of how unspoiled America appeared to the first white men. Authentic and enlightening accounts of Hudson's landing in New York, Coronado's trek through the Southwest; scores of explorers, settlers, trappers, soldiers. America's pristine flora, fauna, and Indians in every region and state in fresh and unusual new aspects. "A fascinating view of what the land was like before the first highway went through," Time. 68 contemporary illustrations, 39 newly added in this edition. Index. Bibliography. x + 500pp. 5⅜ x 8. **T761 Paperbound $2.00**

AUDUBON AND HIS JOURNALS, J. J. Audubon. A collection of fascinating accounts of Europe and America in the early 1800's through Audubon's own eyes. Includes the Missouri River Journals —an eventful trip through America's untouched heartland, the Labrador Journals, the European Journals, the famous "Episodes", and other rare Audubon material, including the descriptive chapters from the original letterpress edition of the "Ornithological Studies", omitted in all later editions. Indispensable for ornithologists, naturalists, and all lovers of Americana and adventure. 70-page biography by Audubon's granddaughter. 38 illustrations. Index. Total of 1106pp. 5⅜ x 8.
T675 Vol I Paperbound $2.25
T676 Vol II Paperbound $2.25
The set $4.50

TRAVELS OF WILLIAM BARTRAM, edited by Mark Van Doren. The first inexpensive illustrated edition of one of the 18th century's most delightful books is an excellent source of first-hand material on American geography, anthropology, and natural history. Many descriptions of early Indian tribes are our only source of information on them prior to the infiltration of the white man. "The mind of a scientist with the soul of a poet," John Livingston Lowes. 13 original illustrations and maps. Edited with an introduction by Mark Van Doren. 448pp. 5⅜ x 8. **T13 Paperbound $2.00**

GARRETS AND PRETENDERS: A HISTORY OF BOHEMIANISM IN AMERICA, A. Parry. The colorful and fantastic history of American Bohemianism from Poe to Kerouac. This is the only complete record of hoboes, cranks, starving poets, and suicides. Here are Pfaff, Whitman, Crane, Bierce, Pound, and many others. New chapters by the author and by H. T. Moore bring this thorough and well-documented history down to the Beatniks. "An excellent account," N. Y. Times. Scores of cartoons, drawings, and caricatures. Bibliography. Index. xxviii + 421pp. 5⅝ x 8⅜. **T708 Paperbound $1.95**

THE EXPLORATION OF THE COLORADO RIVER AND ITS CANYONS, J. W. Powell. The thrilling first-hand account of the expedition that filled in the last white space on the map of the United States. Rapids, famine, hostile Indians, and mutiny are among the perils encountered as the unknown Colorado Valley reveals its secrets. This is the only uncut version of Major Powell's classic of exploration that has been printed in the last 60 years. Includes later reflections and subsequent expedition. 250 illustrations, new map. 400pp. 5⅝ x 8⅜. **T94 Paperbound $2.25**

THE JOURNAL OF HENRY D. THOREAU, Edited by Bradford Torrey and Francis H. Allen. Henry Thoreau is not only one of the most important figures in American literature and social thought; his voluminous journals (from which his books emerged as selections and crystallizations) constitute both the longest, most sensitive record of personal internal development and a most penetrating description of a historical moment in American culture. This present set, which was first issued in fourteen volumes, contains Thoreau's entire journals from 1837 to 1862, with the exception of the lost years which were found only recently. We are reissuing it, complete and unabridged, with a new introduction by Walter Harding, Secretary of the Thoreau Society. Fourteen volumes reissued in two volumes. Foreword by Henry Seidel Canby. Total of 1888pp. 8⅜ x 12¼. **T312-3 Two volume set, Clothbound $20.00**

GAMES AND SONGS OF AMERICAN CHILDREN, collected by William Wells Newell. A remarkable collection of 190 games with songs that accompany many of them; cross references to show similarities, differences among them; variations; musical notation for 38 songs. Textual discussions show relations with folk-drama and other aspects of folk tradition. Grouped into categories for ready comparative study: Love-games, histories, playing at work, human life, bird and beast, mythology, guessing-games, etc. New introduction covers relations of songs and dances to timeless heritage of folklore, biographical sketch of Newell, other pertinent data. A good source of inspiration for those in charge of groups of children and a valuable reference for anthropologists, sociologists, psychiatrists. Introduction by Carl Withers. New indexes of first lines, games. 5⅜ x 8½. xii + 242pp. **T354 Paperbound $1.75**

Art, History of Art, Antiques, Graphic Arts, Handcrafts

ART STUDENTS' ANATOMY, E. J. Farris. Outstanding art anatomy that uses chiefly living objects for its illustrations. 71 photos of undraped men, women, children are accompanied by carefully labeled matching sketches to illustrate the skeletal system, articulations and movements, bony landmarks, the muscular system, skin, fasciae, fat, etc. 9 x-ray photos show movement of joints. Undraped models are shown in such actions as serving in tennis, drawing a bow in archery, playing football, dancing, preparing to spring and to dive. Also discussed and illustrated are proportions, age and sex differences, the anatomy of the smile, etc. 8 plates by the great early 18th century anatomic illustrator Siegfried Albinus are also included. Glossary. 158 figures, 7 in color. x + 159pp. 5⅝ x 8⅜. T744 Paperbound **$1.50**

AN ATLAS OF ANATOMY FOR ARTISTS, F Schider. A new 3rd edition of this standard text enlarged by 52 new illustrations of hands, anatomical studies by Cloquet, and expressive life studies of the body by Barcsay. 189 clear, detailed plates offer you precise information of impeccable accuracy. 29 plates show all aspects of the skeleton, with closeups of special areas, while 54 full-page plates, mostly in two colors, give human musculature as seen from four different points of view, with cutaways for important portions of the body. 14 full-page plates provide photographs of hand forms, eyelids, female breasts, and indicate the location of muscles upon models. 59 additional plates show how great artists of the past utilized human anatomy. They reproduce sketches and finished work by such artists as Michelangelo, Leonardo da Vinci, Goya, and 15 others. This is a lifetime reference work which will be one of the most important books in any artist's library. "The standard reference tool," AMERICAN LIBRARY ASSOCIATION. "Excellent," AMERICAN ARTIST. Third enlarged edition. 189 plates, 647 illustrations. xxvi + 192pp. 7⅞ x 10⅝. T241 Clothbound **$6.00**

AN ATLAS OF ANIMAL ANATOMY FOR ARTISTS, W. Ellenberger, H. Baum, H. Dittrich. The largest, richest animal anatomy for artists available in English. 99 detailed anatomical plates of such animals as the horse, dog, cat, lion, deer, seal, kangaroo, flying squirrel, cow, bull, goat, monkey, hare, and bat. Surface features are clearly indicated, while progressive beneath-the-skin pictures show musculature, tendons, and bone structure. Rest and action are exhibited in terms of musculature and skeletal structure and detailed cross-sections are given for heads and important features. The animals chosen are representative of specific families so that a study of these anatomies will provide knowledge of hundreds of related species. "Highly recommended as one of the very few books on the subject worthy of being used as an authoritative guide," DESIGN. "Gives a fundamental knowledge," AMERICAN ARTIST. Second revised, enlarged edition with new plates from Cuvier, Stubbs, etc. 288 illustrations. 153pp. 11⅜ x 9. T82 Clothbound **$6.00**

THE HUMAN FIGURE IN MOTION, Eadweard Muybridge. The largest selection in print of Muybridge's famous high-speed action photos of the human figure in motion. 4789 photographs illustrate 162 different actions: men, women, children—mostly undraped—are shown walking, running, carrying various objects, sitting, lying down, climbing, throwing, arising, and performing over 150 other actions. Some actions are shown in as many as 150 photographs each. All in all there are more than 500 action strips in this enormous volume, series shots taken at shutter speeds of as high as 1/6000th of a second! These are not posed shots, but true stopped motion. They show bone and muscle in situations that the human eye is not fast enough to capture. Earlier, smaller editions of these prints have brought $40 and more on the out-of-print market. "A must for artists," ART IN FOCUS. "An unparalleled dictionary of action for all artists," AMERICAN ARTIST. 390 full-page plates, with 4789 photographs. Printed on heavy glossy stock. Reinforced binding with headbands. xxi + 390pp. 7⅞ x 10⅝. T204 Clothbound **$10.00**

ANIMALS IN MOTION, Eadweard Muybridge. This is the largest collection of animal action photos in print. 34 different animals (horses, mules, oxen, goats, camels, pigs, cats, guanacos, lions, gnus, deer, monkeys, eagles—and 21 others) in 132 characteristic actions. The horse alone is shown in more than 40 different actions. All 3919 photographs are taken in series at speeds up to 1/6000th of a second. The secrets of leg motion, spinal patterns, head movements, strains and contortions shown nowhere else are captured. You will see exactly how a lion sets his foot down; how an elephant's knees are like a human's—and how they differ; the position of a kangaroo's legs in mid-leap; how an ostrich's head bobs; details of the flight of birds—and thousands of facets of motion only the fastest cameras can catch. Photographed from domestic animals and animals in the Philadelphia zoo, it contains neither semiposed artificial shots nor distorted telephoto shots taken under adverse conditions. Artists, biologists, decorators, cartoonists, will find this book indispensable for understanding animals in motion. "A really marvelous series of plates," NATURE (London). "The dry plate's most spectacular early use was by Eadweard Muybridge," LIFE. 3919 photographs; 380 full pages of plates. 440pp. Printed on heavy glossy paper. Deluxe binding with headbands. 7⅞ x 10⅝. T203 Clothbound **$10.00**

THE AUTOBIOGRAPHY OF AN IDEA, Louis Sullivan. The pioneer architect whom Frank Lloyd Wright called "the master" reveals an acute sensitivity to social forces and values in this passionately honest account. He records the crystallization of his opinions and theories, the growth of his organic theory of architecture that still influences American designers and architects, contemporary ideas, etc. This volume contains the first appearance of 34 full-page plates of his finest architecture. Unabridged reissue of 1924 edition. New introduction by R. M. Line. Index. xiv + 335pp. 5⅜ x 8. **T281 Paperbound $2.00**

THE DRAWINGS OF HEINRICH KLEY. The first uncut republication of both of Kley's devastating sketchbooks, which first appeared in pre-World War I Germany. One of the greatest cartoonists and social satirists of modern times, his exuberant and iconoclastic fantasy and his extra-ordinary technique place him in the great tradition of Bosch, Breughel, and Goya, while his subject matter has all the immediacy and tension of our century. 200 drawings. viii + 128pp. 7¾ x 10¾. **T24 Paperbound $1.85**

MORE DRAWINGS BY HEINRICH KLEY. All the sketches from Leut' Und Viecher (1912) and Sammel-Album (1923) not included in the previous Dover edition of Drawings. More of the bizarre, mercilessly iconoclastic sketches that shocked and amused on their original publication. Nothing was too sacred, no one too eminent for satirization by this imaginative, individual and accomplished master cartoonist. A total of 158 illustrations. Iv + 104pp. 7¾ x 10¾. **T41 Paperbound $1.85**

PINE FURNITURE OF EARLY NEW ENGLAND, R. H. Kettell. A rich understanding of one of America's most original arts that collectors of antiques, interior decorators, craftsmen, woodworkers, and everyone interested in American history and art will find fascinating and immensely useful. 413 illustrations of more than 300 chairs, benches, racks, beds, cupboards, mirrors, shelves, tables, and other furniture will show all the simple beauty and character of early New England furniture. 55 detailed drawings carefully analyze outstanding pieces. "With its rich store of illustrations, this book emphasizes the individuality and varied design of early American pine furniture. It should be welcomed," ANTIQUES. 413 illustrations and 55 working drawings. 475. 8 x 10¾. **T145 Clothbound $10.00**

THE HUMAN FIGURE, J. H. Vanderpoel. Every important artistic element of the human figure is pointed out in minutely detailed word descriptions in this classic text and illustrated as well in 430 pencil and charcoal drawings. Thus the text of this book directs your attention to all the characteristic features and subtle differences of the male and female (adults, children, and aged persons), as though a master artist were telling you what to look for at each stage. 2nd edition, revised and enlarged by George Bridgman. Foreword. 430 illustrations. 143pp. 6⅛ x 9¼. **T432 Paperbound $1.50**

LETTERING AND ALPHABETS, J. A. Cavanagh. This unabridged reissue of LETTERING offers a full discussion, analysis, illustration of 89 basic hand lettering styles — styles derived from Caslons, Bodonis, Garamonds, Gothic, Black Letter, Oriental, and many others. Upper and lower cases, numerals and common signs pictured. Hundreds of technical hints on make-up, construction, artistic validity, strokes, pens, brushes, white areas, etc. May be reproduced without permission! 89 complete alphabets; 72 lettered specimens. 121pp. 9¾ x 8. **T53 Paperbound $1.35**

STICKS AND STONES, Lewis Mumford. A survey of the forces that have conditioned American architecture and altered its forms. The author discusses the medieval tradition in early New England villages; the Renaissance influence which developed with the rise of the merchant class; the classical influence of Jefferson's time; the "Mechanicsvilles" of Poe's generation; the Brown Decades; the philosophy of the Imperial facade; and finally the modern machine age. "A truly remarkable book," SAT. REV. OF LITERATURE. 2nd revised edition. 21 illustrations. xvii + 228pp. 5⅜ x 8. **T202 Paperbound $1.65**

THE STANDARD BOOK OF QUILT MAKING AND COLLECTING, Marguerite Ickis. A complete easy-to-follow guide with all the information you need to make beautiful, useful quilts. How to plan, design, cut, sew, appliqué, avoid sewing problems, use rag bag, make borders, tuft, every other aspect. Over 100 traditional quilts shown, including over 40 full-size patterns. At-home hobby for fun, profit. Index. 483 illus. 1 color plate. 287pp. 6¾ x 9½. **T582 Paperbound $2.00**

THE BOOK OF SIGNS, Rudolf Koch. Formerly $20 to $25 on the out-of-print market, now only $1.00 in this unabridged new edition! 493 symbols from ancient manuscripts, medieval cathedrals, coins, catacombs, pottery, etc. Crosses, monograms of Roman emperors, astrological, chemical, botanical, runes, housemarks, and 7 other categories. Invaluable for handicraft workers, illustrators, scholars, etc., this material may be reproduced without permission. 493 illustrations by Fritz Kredel. 104pp. 6½ x 9¼. **T162 Paperbound $1.00**

PRIMITIVE ART, Franz Boas. This authoritative and exhaustive work by a great American anthropologist covers the entire gamut of primitive art. Pottery, leatherwork, metal work, stone work, wood, basketry, are treated in detail. Theories of primitive art, historical depth in art history, technical virtuosity, unconscious levels of patterning, symbolism, styles, literature, music, dance, etc. A must book for the interested layman, the anthropologist, artist, handicrafter (hundreds of unusual motifs), and the historian. Over 900 illustrations (50 ceramic vessels, 12 totem poles, etc.). 376pp. 5⅜ x 8. **T25 Paperbound $2.00**

CATALOGUE OF DOVER BOOKS

Fiction

THE LAND THAT TIME FORGOT and THE MOON MAID, Edgar Rice Burroughs. In the opinion of many, Burroughs' best work. The first concerns a strange island where evolution is individual rather than phylogenetic. Speechless anthropoids develop into intelligent human beings within a single generation. The second projects the reader far into the future and describes the first voyage to the Moon (in the year 2025), the conquest of the Earth by the Moon, and years of violence and adventure as the enslaved Earthmen try to regain possession of their planet. "An imaginative tour de force that keeps the reader keyed up and expectant," NEW YORK TIMES. Complete, unabridged text of the original two novels (three parts in each). 5 illustrations by J. Allen St. John. vi + 552pp. 5⅜ x 8½.
T1020 Clothbound **$3.75**
T358 Paperbound **$2.00**

AT THE EARTH'S CORE, PELLUCIDAR, TANAR OF PELLUCIDAR: THREE SCIENCE FICTION NOVELS BY EDGAR RICE BURROUGHS. Complete, unabridged texts of the first three Pellucidar novels. Tales of derring-do by the famous master of science fiction. The locale for these three related stories is the inner surface of the hollow Earth where we discover the world of Pellucidar, complete with all types of bizarre, menacing creatures, strange peoples, and alluring maidens—guaranteed to delight all Burroughs fans and a wide circle of adventure lovers. Illustrated by J. Allen St. John and P. F. Berdanier. vi + 433pp. 5⅜ x 8½.
T1051 Paperbound **$2.00**

THREE MARTIAN NOVELS, Edgar Rice Burroughs. Contains: Thuvia, Maid of Mars; The Chessmen of Mars; and The Master Mind of Mars. High adventure set in an imaginative and intricate conception of the Red Planet. Mars is peopled with an intelligent, heroic human race which lives in densely populated cities and with fierce barbarians who inhabit dead sea bottoms. Other exciting creatures abound amidst an inventive framework of Martian history and geography. Complete unabridged reprintings of the first edition. 16 illustrations by J. Allen St. John. vi + 499pp. 5⅜ x 8½.
T39 Paperbound **$1.85**

TO THE SUN? and OFF ON A COMET!, Jules Verne. Complete texts of two of the most imaginative flights into fancy in world literature display the high adventure that have kept Verne's novels read for nearly a century. Only unabridged edition of the best translation, by Edward Roth. Large, easily readable type. 50 illustrations selected from first editions. 462pp. 5⅜ x 8.
T634 Paperbound **$1.75**

FROM THE EARTH TO THE MOON and ALL AROUND THE MOON, Jules Verne. Complete editions of two of Verne's most successful novels, in finest Edward Roth translations, now available after many years out of print. Verne's visions of submarines, airplanes, television, rockets, interplanetary travel; of scientific and not-so-scientific beliefs; of peculiarities of Americans; all delight and engross us today as much as when they first appeared. Large, easily readable type. 42 illus. from first French edition. 476pp. 5⅜ x 8.
T633 Paperbound **$1.75**

THREE PROPHETIC NOVELS BY H. G. WELLS, edited by E. F. Bleiler. Complete texts of "When the Sleeper Wakes" (1st book printing in 50 years), "A Story of the Days to Come," "The Time Machine" (1st complete printing in book form). Exciting adventures in the future are as enjoyable today as 50 years ago when first printed. Predict TV, movies, intercontinental airplanes, prefabricated houses, air-conditioned cities, etc. First important author to foresee problems of mind control, technological dictatorships. "Absolute best of imaginative fiction," N. Y. Times. Introduction. 335pp. 5⅜ x 8.
T605 Paperbound **$1.50**

SEVEN SCIENCE FICTION NOVELS, H. G. Wells. Full unabridged texts of 7 science-fiction novels of the master. Ranging from biology, physics, chemistry, astronomy to sociology and other studies, Mr. Wells extrapolates whole worlds of strange and intriguing character. "One will have to go far to match this for entertainment, excitement, and sheer pleasure . . . ," NEW YORK TIMES. Contents: The Time Machine, The Island of Dr. Moreau, First Men in the Moon, The Invisible Man, The War of the Worlds, The Food of the Gods, In the Days of the Comet. 1015pp. 5⅜ x 8.
T264 Clothbound **$4.50**

28 SCIENCE FICTION STORIES OF H. G. WELLS. Two full unabridged novels, MEN LIKE GODS and STAR BEGOTTEN, plus 26 short stories by the master science-fiction writer of all time. Stories of space, time, invention, exploration, future adventure—an indispensable part of the library of everyone interested in science and adventure. PARTIAL CONTENTS: Men Like Gods, The Country of the Blind, In the Abyss, The Crystal Egg, The Man Who Could Work Miracles, A Story of the Days to Come, The Valley of Spiders, and 21 more! 928pp. 5⅜ x 8.
T265 Clothbound **$4.50**

THE WAR IN THE AIR, IN THE DAYS OF THE COMET, THE FOOD OF THE GODS: THREE SCIENCE FICTION NOVELS BY H. G. WELLS. Three exciting Wells offerings bearing on vital social and philosophical issues of his and our own day. Here are tales of air power, strategic bombing, East vs. West, the potential miracles of science, the potential disasters from outer space, the relationship between scientific advancement and moral progress, etc. First reprinting of "War in the Air" in almost 50 years. An excellent sampling of Wells at his storytelling best. Complete, unabridged reprintings. 16 illustrations. 645pp. 5⅜ x 8½.
T1135 Paperbound **$2.00**

Music

A GENERAL HISTORY OF MUSIC, Charles Burney. A detailed coverage of music from the Greeks up to 1789, with full information on all types of music: sacred and secular, vocal and instrumental, operatic and symphonic. Theory, notation, forms, instruments, innovators, composers, performers, typical and important works, and much more in an easy, entertaining style. Burney covered much of Europe and spoke with hundreds of authorities and composers so that this work is more than a compilation of records . . . it is a living work of careful and first-hand scholarship. Its account of thoroughbass (18th century) Italian music is probably still the best introduction on the subject. A recent NEW YORK TIMES review said, "Surprisingly few of Burney's statements have been invalidated by modern research . . . still of great value." Edited and corrected by Frank Mercer. 35 figures. Indices. 1915pp. 5⅜ x 8. 2 volumes.   T36 The Set, Clothbound **$12.50**

A DICTIONARY OF HYMNOLOGY, John Julian. This exhaustive and scholarly work has become known as an invaluable source of hundreds of thousands of important and often difficult to obtain facts on the history and use of hymns in the western world. Everyone interested in hymns will be fascinated by the accounts of famous hymns and hymn writers and amazed by the amount of practical information he will find. More than 30,000 entries on individual hymns, giving authorship, date and circumstances of composition, publication, textual variations, translations, denominational and ritual usage, etc. Biographies of more than 9,000 hymn writers, and essays on important topics such as Christmas carols and children's hymns, and much other unusual and valuable information. A 200 page double-columned index of first lines — the largest in print. Total of 1786 pages in two reinforced clothbound volumes. 6¼ x 9¼.
                                                          The set, T333 Clothbound **$17.50**

MUSIC IN MEDIEVAL BRITAIN, F. Ll. Harrison. The most thorough, up-to-date, and accurate treatment of the subject ever published, beautifully illustrated. Complete account of institutions and choirs; carols, masses, and motets; liturgy and plainsong; and polyphonic music from the Norman Conquest to the Reformation. Discusses the various schools of music and their reciprocal influences; the origin and development of new ritual forms; development and use of instruments; and new evidence on many problems of the period. Reproductions of scores, over 200 excerpts from medieval melodies. Rules of harmony and dissonance; influence of Continental styles; great composers (Dunstable, Cornysh, Fairfax, etc.); and much more. Register and index of more than 400 musicians. Index of titles. General Index. 225-item bibliography. 6 Appendices. xix + 491pp. 5⅝ x 8¾.   T705 Clothbound **$10.00**

THE MUSIC OF SPAIN, Gilbert Chase. Only book in English to give concise, comprehensive account of Iberian music; new Chapter covers music since 1941. Victoria, Albéniz, Cabezón, Pedrell, Turina, hundreds of other composers; popular and folk music; the Gypsies; the guitar; dance, theatre, opera, with only extensive discussion in English of the Zarzuela; virtuosi such as Casals; much more. "Distinguished . . . readable," Saturday Review. 400-item bibliography. Index. 27 photos. 383pp. 5⅜ x 8.   T549 Paperbound **$2.00**

ON STUDYING SINGING, Sergius Kagen. An intelligent method of voice-training, which leads you around pitfalls that waste your time, money, and effort. Exposes rigid, mechanical systems, baseless theories, deleterious exercises. "Logical, clear, convincing . . . dead right," Virgil Thomson, N.Y. Herald Tribune. "I recommend this volume highly," Maggie Teyte, Saturday Review. 119pp. 5⅜ x 8.   T622 Paperbound **$1.25**

Prices subject to change without notice.

Dover publishes books on art, music, philosophy, literature, languages, history, social sciences, psychology, handcrafts, orientalia, puzzles and entertainments, chess, pets and gardens, books explaining science, intermediate and higher mathematics, mathematical physics, engineering, biological sciences, earth sciences, classics of science, etc. Write to:

Dept. catrr.
Dover Publications, Inc.
180 Varick Street, N.Y. 14, N.Y.